an A. ATKINSON
Dip. EE., C. Eng., M.I.E.E.

OCTOBER 1986.

HANDBOOK OF ELECTRICAL INSTALLATION PRACTICE

Volume 2
Equipment

Editor
E. A. Reeves, DFH(Hons), CEng, MIEE

Technical Adviser
A. G. Howell, CEng, FIEE

GRANADA
London Toronto Sydney New York

Granada Technical Books
Granada Publishing Ltd
8 Grafton Street, London W1X 3LA

First published in Great Britain by Granada Publishing Ltd 1983
Reprinted 1984

Copyright © 1983 by E. A. Reeves

British Library Cataloguing in Publication Data
Handbook of electrical installation practice.
   1. Electric wiring, Interior   2. Buildings—
Electric equipment
I. Reeves, E. A.
621.319'24   TK3271
   ISBN 0–246–11949–7 (two-volume set)
   ISBN 0–246–11744–3 v. 1
   ISBN 0–246–11747–8 v. 2

Printed and bound in Great Britain by
William Clowes Limited, Beccles and London

Contents

Acknowledgements

Extracts from British Standards are reproduced by permission of the British Standards Institution, 2 Park Street, London, W1A 2BS from whom complete copies can be obtained.

Chapter 11

Distribution Transformers

G. P. Harvey, CEng, MIEE
Technical Director
Parsons Peebles Distribution Transformers

Power distribution throughout most of the world, before the final
consumer voltage, is at voltages usually between 10 and 13.8 kV and
although some old systems of 5.0, 5.5 and 6.6 kV still remain these
are rapidly being replaced with a higher voltage on economic grounds.

Distribution transformers for domestic and industrial applications
are usually rated at 1600 kVA and below although 2500 kVA is not
uncommon. This simplifies the subject because it restricts the scope
of this chapter to naturally cooled transformers. In general, forced
cooling is applied to larger units where the increase in capacity
justifies the cost of the forced cooling equipment. It is not often
that this cost can be justified on naturally cooled liquid immersed
transformers below 5000 kVA although successful applications of forced
air cooling have been made on special dry-type transformers.

TYPES OF TRANSFORMERS
All transformers covered in this chapter should comply with the
requirements of BS 171 or IEC 76 as regards design and performance.
The British Standard defines a transformer as a static piece of
apparatus which by electromagnetic induction transforms alternating
voltage and current between two or more windings at the same frequency
and usually at different values of voltage and current.

There are two basic types of distribution transformers in common
use today. One in which the core and windings are enclosed in a
liquid-filled tank which provides cooling and insulation and the other
where the core and windings are cooled directly by air. Liquid-filled
transformers can again be sub-divided into units using flammable

substance (mineral oil) and those using various types of fire-resistant liquid (askarel, silicone liquid or synthetic hydrocarbon).

Dry-type transformers are also available in two distinct types:
those with the insulated turns of the winding directly in contact with
the cooling air and those with the complete windings encapsulated
within a moisture-resistant cladding of epoxy resin.   Preferred
ratings are listed in table 11.1.

Table 11.1   *Preferred values of rated*
power for three-phase
transformers (BS 171)

kVA	kVA	kVA
5.0	31.5	200
6.3	40	250
8	50	315
10	63	400
12.5	80	500
16	100	630
20	125	800
25	160	1000 etc.

The heart of the conventional three-phase distribution transformer
is a laminated electrical sheet steel core of three limbs.   Each limb
carries two concentrically wound coils; the secondary (low voltage)
inside nearest the core and the primary (high voltage) on the outside,
the whole being contained within an enclosure of steel.   In the case
of the liquid-filled transformer the enclosure consists of a leakproof
tank while the dry-type transformer merely requires a ventilated
casing to enclose the live parts.

Tappings are usually included on the h.v. windings of distribution
transformers to alter the turns ratio between the high and low voltage
windings and thereby to compensate for variations in primary supply
voltage in order to maintain the consumer voltage within the statutory
limits.   On distribution transformers taps are selected by means of an
off-circuit device; the transformer must be disconnected from the
supply before the taps can be changed.

Winding conductors are more commonly copper.   However, under
certain modern manufacturing techniques thin, wide strip, aluminium
conductors have found increasing use.

Mineral-oil-filled transformers

This is the most common type of distribution transformer. It can be found on electrical supply systems in every country of the world. Although the insulating oil is a flammable liquid, the reliability of the oil-immersed transformer has been proven over many years on supply systems where security of supply is of the utmost importance. However, mineral oil is flammable and although most fault conditions that occur within the windings of a transformer result in no more than a discharge of oil it is possible, particularly when an electrical arc occurs just below the surface of the oil, for it to be ignited. For this reason oil-immersed distribution transformers are usually positioned outside buildings within a suitable fence enclosure or in separate brick-built buildings away from personnel.

Where mineral-oil-filled transformers are sited within an occupied area it is usual to find some form of automatic fire extinguishing system.

The integrity of the insulation system of an oil-immersed transformer relies partly on the condition of the oil. It has been common practice on most established supply networks in the world to let transformers breath naturally as the insulating liquid expands and contracts with load. However, it has also been recognised that some form of protection system that prevents the contamination of the liquid by air-borne pollutants has the advantage of a longer insulation life, particularly when load factors are high.

The simplest form of oil protection system, which is perfectly adequate for most installations of distribution transformers below 500 kVA installed in the temperate zones of the world, is a silica-gel dehydrating breather. Here, the air drawn into the transformer tank during reduced load conditions is passed through an oil bath, to reduce solid contaminants, and then through the dehydrating crystals of silica-gel to remove the moisture. It is essential, however, that the silica-gel crystals are maintained dry and replaced as soon as the colour changes from blue to pink.

Probably the most common form of oil protection system is found with the conservator or expansion vessel; this has a sump which traps most air-borne pollutants, fig. 11.1.

3

*Figure 11.1   A 500 kVA 11 kV/380 V mineral-oil-filled transformer
with conservator (Bonar Long Ltd)*

The most obvious method of eliminating oil contamination is to
seal the tank from the outside air and design it to tolerate the
pressures developed by the expanding liquid coolant, fig. 11.2.

Because of gas solubility in oil these pressures are never very
high and rarely exceed 0.43 kg/cm^2 under steady load conditions.

The development of special machinery which automatically folds
and welds the steel plate into deep corrugations to form the transformer tank side, has allowed the corrugated tank to become more cost
effective.   The steel plate is usually between 1.2 and 1.5 mm thick.

4

The finished tank is light and compact and has the advantage of flexing under internal pressures.

Plate widths up to 1.8 m wide and corrugations as deep as 400 mm allow transformers up to 5 MVA to be cooled by this method. The strength of the tank is obtained by the deep closely spaced corrugations.

Figure 11.2 A sealed oil-filled transformer rated at 1600 kVA for use in a cement works (Parsons Peebles Distribution Transformers)

Askarel-filled transformers

Askarel-filled transformers were introduced about 30 years ago when the demand arose for a fire-resistant liquid to replace the mineral oil in units that were to be installed in occupied buildings. The increasing concern for the safety of people should a fire occur in a mineral-oil-filled transformer placed pressure on manufacturers to find an alternative coolant.

Askarels appeared on the market under a variety of names such as Pyroclor, Inerteen, Aroclor and Pyranol. They comprise a mixture of polychlorinated biphenyl (pcb) and trichlorobenzene (tcb), the latter being used to reduce the viscosity of the pcb. Basically, apart from a few synthetic resin products, the design of the transformer remained unaltered from the mineral-oil-filled unit but the use of this liquid has introduced hazards not appreciated at the time.

During the last few years it has become widely realised that pcbs are toxic and are also resistant to biological and chemical degradation. Research has shown that if ingested they can persist in the fatty tissues and cause damage to organs of the body.

Many of the transformers that were filled with pcbs have been in service for more than 15 years. Some of the older ones have developed slight leaks, usually at gasketted joints, and are easily repaired. There have been reports of welds leaking after 15 to 20 years of service and although there is no substantive evidence to show that pcbs attack metal it is of concern that so many tanks have started to leak. To guard against the danger of spillage due to leaks and internal faults some transformer users are having the pcbs removed and replaced by an alternative fire-resistant liquid. Special techniques have been adopted to carry out this replacement, the operation being termed retrofilling, fig. 11.3. Because this is a specialist function requiring a high degree of expertise it must be performed only by organisations trained and equipped to do it.

Once removed the pcb has to be taken to an incinerator for destruction and again this is a specialist operation requiring skills and plant available from only a few organisations. The toxicity of pcbs and their handling are described in the UK Department of Environment publication 'Waste Management Paper No. 6'.

Another school of thought insists that the pcbs cannot be completely removed by any retrofilling process and that the only sure way of removing pcbs from the environment is for the transformer to be completely replaced by one containing a harmless liquid.

A number of countries have banned the use of pcb in any form. Others continue with its use in transformers and capacitors. All recognise the potential danger that exists if a large local spillage does occur.

Within the last two or three years research has produced alternatives to pcb for transformers. It is to be hoped that the long-term effects of these new substances will be thoroughly and exhaustively investigated before they are adopted.

*Figure 11.3   Retrofilling of an askarel-filled unit in situ by
R F Winder Ltd.   The liquid is being replaced by
silicone under carefully controlled conditions.
Protective clothing is worn by the operators*

Other fire-resistant types

There are a number of liquids on the market for which suitability as a
transformer coolant and resistance to fire is claimed.   It is not
possible to examine these liquids in detail but one is described as a
synthesised ester and is marketed under the trade name of Midel 7131.

Another is described as a highly saturated paraffin oil and is
marketed under the name of Rtemp.

Probably the most well known, because of its long time use in

7

other industries is silicone fluid. This is marketed by a number of companies under their own trade names. Finally, a newcomer to the scene, is described as tetrachloro benzyl toluene and marketed under the trade name of Ugilec 141. It is the only true non-flammable liquid of the four mentioned. However, this contains 40% trichloro-benzene, a very toxic substance and the same solvent as used in pcb.

Of these four liquids silicone fluid is probably more highly favoured by engineers and consultants because it has been used for so many years and its characteristics are well known. Its viscosity is about twice that of ordinary transformer oil at 20°C; other character-istics make its overall performance not dissimilar to mineral oil, so that it can be accommodated within normal transformer design para-meters, fig. 11.4. One of the alternative high fire point liquids is quoted as having a very high viscosity value and would cause concern over the possibility of conductor insulation damage due to overheating. Special cooling would also have to be considered.

Figure 11.4   There is no difference in external appearance of a silicone-liquid-filled transformer and designs employing mineral oil or askarel. This transformer is rated at 500 kVA 3.3 kV/415 V and is installed in Southampton Docks (Parsons Peebles Distribution Transformers)

The cellulosic insulation materials commonly used in the manufacture of oil-immersed transformers are in general compatible with
silicone liquid. When impregnated with the silicone they can be
operated at higher temperatures than associated with mineral-oil-filled
transformers before thermal degradation takes place. Retrofilled units
may therefore be able to operate at a slightly greater rating, or
alternatively be assigned a greater overload capacity.

For this reason transformer manufacturers are looking at the future
designs of silicone-filled units to take advantage of the high temperature capabilities of the coolant. Such transformers might well result
in savings in weight and size.

Dry-type transformers

Dry-type transformers are defined by BS 171 as designs where the core
and windings are not immersed in an insulating liquid. Cooling is
usually by natural air circulation through the windings. Permissible
winding temperature rise depends on the type of insulation used on
the winding conductors and between the windings.

Transformer windings with Class A insulation are limited to a
temperature rise of 60°C. When Class C insulation is used 150°C is
the limit. All dry-type transformers with Class B insulation and
above are considered to be fire resistant to some degree because the
volume of combustible material is small and it does not maintain combustion. The modern Class C transformer, fig. 11.5, is almost
completely fire proof because the Nomex insulation used is self-
extinguishing. Temperature rise limits are discussed in detail later.

Two types of dry transformer are available. The conventional
arrangement was developed from the old Class B transformer. It uses
high temperature aromatic Polyaramid paper both for conductor covering
and solid insulation. Large air cooling ducts between the windings
and between the layers of the windings provide the cooling. This
arrangement has the advantage of low cost and many years of satisfactory service close to load centres in the normally dry environment of
an indoor installation.

It is not advisable, however, to leave this type of dry transformer
unexcited for long periods of time in a damp atmosphere without some
form of warm air circulation through the windings. Impulse voltage

9

levels of 60 and 75 kV are available for the modern Class C transformer.

*Figure 11.5 A 1000 kVA 11 kV/433 V Class C dry-type transformer
(Parsons Peebles Distribution Transformers)*

Because of the large cooling ducts between windings and the sub-
sequently high surge impedance the current chopping characteristics
of some vacuum circuit-breakers can produce very high transient voltages in dry-type transformers. It is advisable that transformer
manufacturers are made aware of the intention to use vacuum circuit-
breakers.

The newer development of dry-type transformer employs windings
that have been completely encapsulated in epoxy resin, fig. 11.6.
Designs are impervious to the ingress of moisture to the windings
and damp environments have very little effect. The thick covering of

mineral-filled epoxy resin gives more strength to the windings and this unit is more able to withstand the mechanical effects of a short-circuit. The epoxy resin encapsulated transformer, however, is very much more costly to produce than the Class C transformer with the open windings, and in many indoor installations this additional cost cannot be justified.

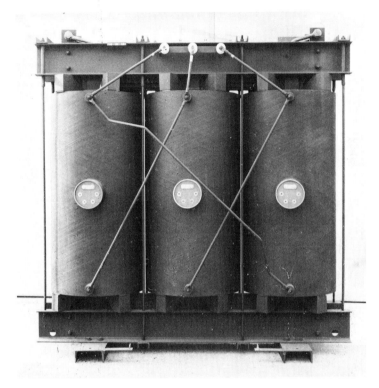

Figure 11.6 A typical cast-resin dry-type transformer rated at 2500 kVA 6.6 kV/433 V (GEC Distribution Transformers Ltd)

Both types of dry transformer need to be housed within a water-proof building and sited within an enclosure to prevent physical contact with any live parts in order to comply with the IEE Wiring Regulations for safety.

It has become practice in America and the UK to build dry-type transformers as self-contained units within a metal casing with h.v. and l.v. cable boxes mounted on to the sides as with the liquid-immersed type.

11

The development of the resin-encapsulated transformer in Europe led to these transformers being positioned inside wire mesh enclosures without any casing. When costs of these two units are considered the form of protection for the general public must be taken into account.

The windings of the Class C dry-type transformer are usually quite conventional, although with the introduction of newer and more sophisticated winding machinery, l.v. windings wound with wide strip aluminium or copper are becoming more popular with manufacturers.

The l.v. windings of resin-encapsulated transformers are almost always wound with wide strip conductor material, either aluminium or copper depending, to a large extent, on the method of resin encapsulation employed.

It is important in the design of the windings of resin-encapsulated transformers that the conductor material and the resin system have very similar rates of thermal expansion. This is achieved either by a mineral filler added to the resin mix before the encapsulation process or by adding glass rovings to the windings before impregnation.

PERFORMANCE

When a transformer is selected for a particular application prime cost should never be the only consideration. In many cases it plays a very small part in the overall cost. Factors which also govern choice of a particular transformer should include load factor, cost of losses and efficiency, maintenance costs, fire-resistant qualities and associated building costs, space limitations and ambient temperature as well as prime cost. These matters are discussed below but not necessarily in order of importance.

Prime cost is always a consideration. The amount of capital available for an electrical distribution network often governs the type of equipment that is purchased, irrespective of the many advantages and long-term financial benefits accruing from buying more expensive plant. The first cost of the various transformers discussed is shown by the nomogram, fig. 11.7, in which it will be seen that the mineral oil unit is the cheapest and the cast-resin design the most expensive at some 80% more. Locating the mineral-oil-filled unit close to load centres inevitably involves the installation of pits and drains and automatic fire protection. Special floor, roof and door construction are necessary. Even so, the cost of mineral-oil-filled transformers is so low relative to the fire-resistant alternatives that the decision to have the risk and limit the effect is taken over eradicating the risk. In any event there is some risk, even with fire-resistant transformers.

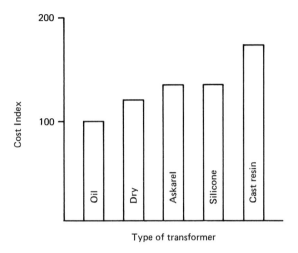

Figure 11.7 A nomogram showing comparative capital costs of various types of distribution transformers

Losses

No-load and load losses in a transformer result in loss of efficiency. They are the reason for the major running cost of a transformer. They have to be paid for, yet result in heat which is normally dissipated to the atmosphere.

The comparison between various manufacturers' liquid-immersed transformers can be made quite simply. It will be obvious that a transformer with a no-load loss of 700 W consumes 2628 units of electricity in a year less than a similar transformer with a no-load loss of 1000 W if they are both excited continuously.

The cost of load losses of course depends on the load factor (LF) and does not vary greatly between manufacturers for the same trans-former rating.

Quite large differences in losses do occur, however, between the various types of fire-resistant transformer and running costs could well be a deciding factor in the choice of a particular fire-resistant transformer.

Table 11.2 gives a comparison of losses between two types of fire-resistant transformer. The cast-resin values were taken from European manufacturers' published literature. The liquid-immersed losses are those which are available from a number of companies in the UK. It is quite evident that load factor and tariff structure play a most import-ant part in any economic comparisons.

Table 11.2 Comparison of losses of cast-resin and silicone-liquid-filled transformers

Rating (kVA)	Cast-resin				Silicone-filled			
	no load loss (W)	load loss (W)	total loss 80% LF (W)	total loss 50% LF (W)	no load loss (W)	load loss (W)	total loss 80% LF (W)	total loss 50% LF (W)
315	900	4000	3460	1900	470	4600	3414	1620
500	1250	6000	5090	2750	700	6800	5052	2400
800	1800	8700	7368	3975	1130	9700	7338	3555
1000	2200	10800	9012	4800	1380	11800	8932	4330

When examining this table the importance of the iron loss is more obvious at low load factors. For example at 50% load factor lower iron loss of the silicone-liquid-filled designs compared to the cast-resin makes them much more attractive than at higher load factors. At 80% there is not much to choose between either design while at 100% load factor the cast-resin transformers are more cost effective. In the UK the average industrial load factor on a transformer is prob-ably between 50 and 60% but where security of supply is of supreme importance the use of two transformers reduces this value to below 50%. Even lower load factors can apply where both load growth and supply security have to be taken into account.

The life of a transformer is an essential part of the overall cost equation. Mineral-oil-filled transformers have been in use on elec-trical supply networks for a great many years and the life expectancy of the average distribution transformer is known to exceed 30 years.

The silicone-liquid-filled transformer with normal temperature rise characteristics has an insulation system virtually identical to

14

mineral-oil-filled transformers and the viscosity of the fluid is not significantly different. The transformer life of the silicone-filled transformer can be assumed to be very similar.

The insulation system of the modern dry-type Class C transformer dates back to about 1960 in the UK. More than 20 years experience have shown this to be a very reliable unit.

The resin-encapsulated transformer was first introduced less than 10 years ago and its life has yet to be assessed. Values of 15 years quoted by manufacturers of these units may well prove to be pessimistic.

A Canadian manufacturer (Polygon Industries) has produced figures of electrical losses for all types of distribution transformers considered in this chapter and they are given as table 11.3. While it must be remembered that these values apply to the American 60 Hz system, it will be seen that no difference is made between the losses of any of the liquid-filled types and that these are considerably lower than the dry-types at all loads between 25% and 100%.

It is interesting to note the difference between the values given in tables 11.2 and 11.3 for the cast-resin and silicone-liquid-filled 1000 kVA transformer with regard to no-load and load losses. The 60 Hz system has a significant effect on the no-load loss.

The importance of assessing the value of the losses of the transformers for any contract cannot be over-emphasised. Most British manufacturers are in a position to offer low loss designs as standard because of their familiarity with those parts of the world where losses are highly capitalised.

These low loss units do have a higher prime cost but it may well be an economic proposition to pay a higher cost and take greater advantages in reduced running costs.

There are two sides to every story and although it may be proved that paying 20% more for low loss transformers can be justified by lower running costs, 20% fewer customers may be reached or the system may have a 20% lower capacity for revenue earning. In areas with a high rate of growth this second consideration may be of greater importance.

Table 11.3 *Electrical losses comparison of 15 kV 1000 kVA transformers with a BIL* of 95 kV*

	No load	1/4 Load			1/2 Load			3/4 Load			Full load		
		No load	Load	Total	No load	Load	Total	No load	Load	Total	No load	Load	Total
Oil ⎫ Askarel ⎬ Silicone ⎭	2.8	2.8	0.6	3.4	2.8	2.3	5.1	2.8	5.2	8.0	2.8	9.1	11.9
Dry-type, 150°C	3.2	3.2	0.8	4.0	3.2	3.3	6.5	3.2	7.4	10.6	3.2	13.2	16.4
Epoxy dry-type	3.2	3.2	0.7	3.9	3.2	3.0	6.2	3.2	6.7	9.9	3.2	11.8	15.0

*BIL = Basic insulation impulse level.

Temperature rise

In temperate climates the differences in allowable temperature rise of
liquid-filled and dry-type transformers are not important for most
installations. There are instances, however, where the high ambient
in which the transformer is sited may well limit the rating of a
standard transformer to something below the nameplate value. There
are also instances where the heat of the losses of a transformer could
affect the functioning of sensitive electronic equipment. An example
of both applications can be found in the first case where an oil-
immersed transformer is used to supply power to an induction furnace
or an annealing furnace. An arc furnace transformer must, because of
the very low voltage, be close to the furnace where ambient temperatures are very high.

An example of the heat of a transformer affecting the operation of
sensitive equipment can be found when power supplies to computers are
considered. A large dry-type transformer in an open installation
might well produce enough heat to create difficulties. Even power
diodes and thyristors have a very limited temperature range and care
is needed when transformers are sited for these applications.

Tables 11.4 and 11.5 are reproduced from BS 171 and indicate the
permissible limits of temperature rise for the two types of transformer. Where ambient temperatures are very high and transformers are
to be mounted indoors one might look favourably on the dry-type
Class C transformer with its capacity for operation at high temperatures. But in making such judgement other factors need to be taken
into account.

The susceptibility of the dry types to dust-laden atmospheres and
the exclusion of vermin therefore requiring frequent maintenance
checks might well exclude dry-types from overseas installations.

It should also be borne in mind that the temperature rise limitations specified in BS 171 assume the use of cellulosic materials with
a Class A limitation in mineral oil to BS 148. Tests on standard
solid insulating materials normally used with mineral-oil-immersed
transformers have shown that when these materials are impregnated with
silicone fluid they can operate for longer periods of time at elevated
temperatures without loss of transformer life and short time overloads
without thermal expansion problems.

17

Table 11.4 Temperature rise limits for dry-type transformers from BS 171: Part 2

1	2	3	4
Part	Cooling method	Temperature class of insulation*	Maximum temperature rise (°C)
Windings (temperature rise measured by the resistance method)	Air, natural or forced	A	60
		E	75
		B	80
		F	100
		H	125
			150[†]
Cores and other parts			
(a) Adjacent to windings	All		(a) Same values as for windings
(b) Not adjacent to windings			(b) The temperature shall, in no case, reach a value that will damage the core itself, other parts or adjacent materials

Note. Insulating materials may be used separately or in combination provided that in any application each material will not be subjected to a temperature in excess of that for which it is suitable, if operated under rated conditions.

*In accordance with IEC Publication 85, Recommendations for the Classification of Materials for the Insulation of Electrical Machinery and Apparatus in Relation to their Thermal Stability in Service.

†For certain insulating materials, temperature rises in excess of 150°C may be adopted by agreement between the manufacturer and the purchaser.

Table 11.5 Temperature rise limits for oil-immersed type transformers from BS 171: Part 2

1	2
Part	Maximum temperature rise (°C)
Windings: temperature class of insulation A (temperature rise measured by the resistance method)	65, when the oil circulation is natural or forced non-directed
	70, when the oil circulation is forced and directed
Top oil (temperature rise measured by thermometer)	60, when the transformer is equipped with a conservator or sealed
	55, when the transformer is neither equipped with a conservator nor sealed
Cores, metallic parts and adjacent materials	The temperature shall, in no case, reach a value that will damage the core itself, other parts or adjacent materials

Note The temperature rise limits of the windings (measured by the resistance method) are chosen to give the same hot-spot temperature rise with different types of oil circulation. The hot-spot temperature rise cannot normally be measured directly. Transformers with forced-directed oil flow have a difference between the hot-spot and the average temperature rise in the windings which is smaller than that in transformers with natural or forced but not directed oil flow. For this reason, the windings of transformers with forced-directed oil flow can have temperature rise limits (measured by the resistance method) which are 5°C higher than in other transformers.

19

It is also important to remember that where transformers are sited in areas of unusually high ambient temperatures or where very small transformers are essential that the transformer manufacturing industry is looking seriously into the advantages to be gained from designing high temperature transformers specifically for silicone fluid filling.

Using special high temperature insulation the overall prime cost of such a unit may well be higher than its low temperature counterpart. But it is reasonable to expect that a transformer of this nature would be physically smaller than any other transformer of the same rating.

Loading guide

The British Code of Practice CP 1010 'Loading guide for oil-immersed transformers' indicates how oil-immersed transformers may be operated in different conditions of ambient temperature and service, without exceeding the acceptable limit of deterioration of insulation through thermal effects. Although specifically related to oil-filled units similar reasoning can be applied to transformers cooled by other liquids.

The object of the guide is to give the permissible loadings, under certain defined conditions, in terms of the IEC Publication 76 rated power of the transformer, so that planners can choose the required rated power for new installations. Basically, the cooling-medium temperature is 20°C, but deviations from this are provided for, in such a way that the increased use of life when operating with a cooling-medium temperature above 20°C is balanced by the reduced use of life when it is below 20°C.

In practice, uninterrupted continuous operation at full rated power is unusual, and the guide gives recommendations for cyclic daily loads, taking into account seasonal variations of ambient temperature. The daily use of life due to thermal effects is indicated by comparison with the 'normal' use of life corresponding to operation at rated power in an ambient temperature of 20°C.

Two examples of the use of the curves are given in the Code and are reproduced here, see table 11.6. It is necessary to define the four symbols used in the tables in order to understand the examples. These symbols are:

K_1 = initial load power as a fraction of rated power

K_2 = permissible load power as a fraction of rated power (usually greater than unity)

t = duration of K_2 in hours

θ_a = temperature of cooling medium (air or water).

Note $K_1 = S_1/S_r$ and $K_2 = S_2/S_r$ where S_1 is the initial load power, S_2 is the permissible load power and S_r is the rated power.

Table 11.6 Loading guide for oil-immersed transformers (CP 1010)

	$K_1 = 0.25$	$K_1 = 0.50$	$K_1 = 0.70$	$K_1 = 0.80$	$K_1 = 0.90$	$K_1 = 1.00$
t = 0.5	+	+	1.93	1.83	1.69	1.00
t = 1	1.89	1.80	1.70	1.62	1.50	1.00
t = 2	1.59	1.53	1.46	1.41	1.32	1.00
t = 4	1.34	1.31	1.27	1.24	1.18	1.00
t = 6	1.23	1.21	1.18	1.16	1.12	1.00
t = 8	1.16	1.15	1.13	1.12	1.09	1.00
t = 12	1.10	1.09	1.08	1.07	1.05	1.00
t = 24	1.00	1.00	1.00	1.00	1.00	1.00

ONAN and ONAF transformers: θ_a = 20°C. Values of K_2 for given values of K_1 and t

Note   In normal cyclic duty the value of K_2 should not be greater than 1.5. The values of K_2 greater than 1.5, underlined, apply to emergency duties. (See Clause 3.)

The + sign indicates that K_2 is higher than 2.0.

Example 1.   A 1000 kVA ONAN transformer, initial load power 500 kVA. It is required to find permissible load power for 2 hours at an ambient temperature of 20°C.

Cooling: ONAN θ_a = 20°C K_1 = 0.5 t = 2 h

From table 11.6 K_2 = 1.53 but the guide limit is 1.5. Therefore permissible load power for 2 h is 1500 kVA (then returning to 500 kVA).

Example 2.   With θ_a = 20°C an ONAN transformer is required for 1400 kVA for 6 h and 800 kVA for the remaining 18 h each day.

1400/800 (S_2/S_1) = 1.75

From the curve drawn using the data of table 11.6, on the t = 6 line, the values of K_2 and K_1 giving K_2/K_1 = 1.75 are K_2 = 1.18 and K_1 = 0.68, see fig. 11.8. Therefore the rated power is:

$$S_r = 1400/1.18 = 800/0.68 = 1180 \text{ kVA.}$$

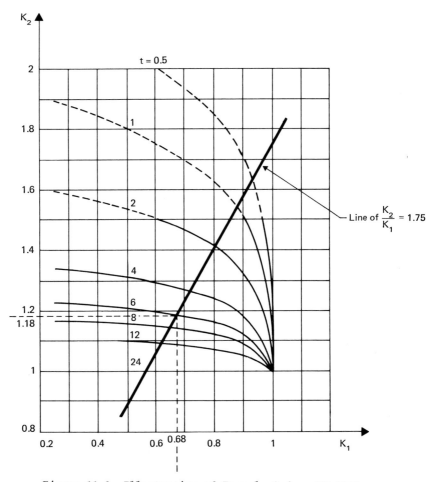

Figure 11.8 Illustration of Example 2 from CP 1010

It will be appreciated that the Code of Practice contains many more tables covering different thermal conditions and designs of transformers and the reader is advised to obtain a copy for use as required.

It must be pointed out that the preceding examples relate entirely to the transformer and the effect of cyclic loading on transformers.

If cyclic loading is anticipated, however, at the time of installation consideration must be given to the extra demand put on the switchgear. Mention must also be made that if settings of protective relays are to be adjusted to account for cyclic loading then the degree of protection against continuous overloads or faults is very much reduced.

Fire resistance

Dry-type and liquid-filled units already mentioned (except mineral oil), are designated fire-resistant designs but that does not mean that the materials used will not burn. Rather it refers to their high fire point (the temperature at which the material continues to burn when subject to a flame on the surface). This is the significant figure when considering fire resistance; it must be well above the maximum temperature reached by a transformer operating at its maximum overload condition in a high ambient. For reasons stated earlier askarel-filled units are not acceptable and so one is left with designs incorporating other fire-resistant liquids and the two dry-types.

Table 11.7 indicates the fire point temperature of some fire-resistant designs and shows that there is not much to choose between the different materials. But one must also consider the nature and toxicity of the smoke given off by materials when they are burning, together with other characteristics, to form a judgement as to the best to select.

The rate of heat release of a burning substance is also important for it governs the size and nature of the enclosure surrounding the transformer.

Table 11.7 Fire point temperature of some fire-resistant transformers

Material[*]	Fire point (°C)
Silicone liquid	360
Midel 7131	310
Cast resin	350
Class H	[†]

[*]For comparison purposes mineral oil is 170°C. Askarel is non-flammable.

[†]These designs are virtually fire proof.

Most fire officers agree that smoke is the most serious hazard to life in any fire for it blinds, confuses and suffocates and can cause deaths well away from the centre of the fire. Epoxy resins, like most solid polyesters, produce thick black smoke when burning, while silicone liquid generates a white vapour less dangerous in content and much easier to see through. Midel 7131 contains petroleum oils and certain synthetic oxyhydrocarbons but these are classed as of negligible toxicity when burning.

The rate of heat release of burning materials consists of two components, convective and radiative, the former being the higher value. The convective value provides a measure of the damage the burning material can do to a roof or any structure above the fire; the radiative indicates how much damage a fire could do to the walls and surrounding equipment. Table 11.8 shows these values for some fire-resistant materials.

Table 11.8 Values of rate of heat release (RHR) for some fire-resistant materials

Material	RHR	
	convective (kW/m)	radiative (kW/m)
Silicone 561	53	25
High fire point hydrocarbon	546	361
Epoxy resin	–	–

Also important is how a material reacts when burning. Silicone liquid forms a silica crust and this assists in extinguishing flames. Some tests on the burning characteristics of epoxy resin showed that when heated with a bunsen burner, the material continued to burn when the flame was removed but did not when a welding torch was the medium of the heat. Manufacturers of cast-resin transformers claim that their designs do not make any appreciable contribution to the fire hazard because of the very high non-flammable filler content. Many have been installed within the past few years and are giving satisfactory service.

TAPPINGS AND CONNECTIONS

Part 4 of BS 171 deals with tappings and connections of power transformers. This chapter, dealing as it does, entirely with distribution transformers will consider only tappings normally selected with the transformer disconnected from the supply.

A few years ago the standard distribution transformer had no tappings. It is argued, that with a fully regulated 10 or 11 kV supply system as exists in most western countries tappings on distribution transformers are entirely unnecessary. However, tappings on the h.v. windings have become part of the distribution scene and in areas where long feeders remain adjustment for h.v. variation can be useful.

The standard off-circuit tapping range is 10% with two taps of 2½% above normal and two taps of 2½% below normal. In specially difficult areas most transformer manufacturers would be quite happy to supply this range as all negative taps.

It is generally agreed that there should be some movement toward voltage standardisation within the European Community. Inevitably the recommendations for the standard voltage are almost as numerous as the countries involved and any rationalisation may well involve an extended tapping range.

Off-circuit taps on distribution transformers are normally selected by a switch on liquid-immersed transformers and links on dry-type transformers. Three- and five-position tapping switches are the most common in Europe. In certain difficult areas of the world it is not unusual to see off-circuit tapping ranges of 15% or even 20% specified. The costs of the special tapping switch and tapping arrangement make these non-standard arrangements very expensive and they should be avoided if at all possible.

Connections

Most 10, 11 or 13.8 kV distribution systems are supplied through system or network transformers where the l.v. winding is star connected. The system is therefore earthed via the neutral of the network or system transformer. For the satisfactory elimination of triple frequency harmonics it follows that the 10, 11 or 13.8 kV winding of distribution transformers should be delta connected. It is necessary on l.v. domestic distribution systems that phase-to-neutral voltages are available and that the neutral operates at or near to earth potential.

The most common winding connections are therefore either Dy 11,
Dy 1, Dy 5 or Dy 7 with Dy 11 or its equivalent being widely used
throughout the world. These connections are defined in BS 171 and
are shown in fig. 11.9. This diagram also includes other winding
connections including the delta zigzag which is discussed below. The
vector relating to the h.v. winding is taken as the vector of origin
and the secondary phase relationship is related to the clock face.
For example Dy 1 where the secondary star lags the primary by 30
degrees corresponds to one o'clock.

The choice of phase relationship between the primary and secondary
windings is unimportant if only one transformer is used for a given
site network. However, if more than one transformer is involved then
they must all have the same phase relationship or else it is impossible to parallel them or to switch over the supply to the network from
one transformer to another. More is said about parallel operation
under the appropriate heading.

Delta/zigzag connections. There are a number of special applications where other winding connections are important.

Local power supplies are often obtained from diesel engine or gas
turbine generating sets. Voltages generated are often too low for
economic power distribution and transformers are used to raise the
generated voltage to a satisfactory value for distribution then reduce
it back to domestic levels. Contractors often order two identical
delta-star transformers for this application which results in an unearthed and floating distribution system and a phase displacement
between generated voltage and user voltage of 60 degrees.

It is necessary in this case to arrange for the generator-
transformer to have a delta-connected winding connected to the
generator and a star connection for the transmission voltage. With
the connection Yd 1 there would be no phase displacement between the
generated voltage and the user voltage and the higher voltage distribution system would have a star point for earthing.

There are still many cases where unusual phase relationships exist
from old privately owned systems. Linking these into modern networks
can be made easier with the delta-interconnected star transformer or
the star/interconnected-star transformer. The interconnected star

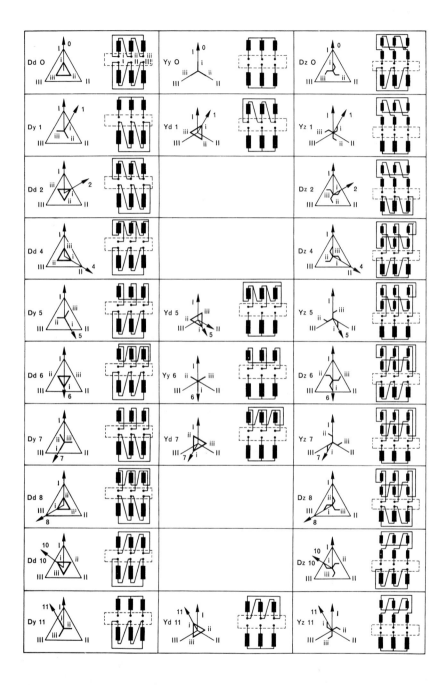

Figure 11.9   Designation of connections of some separate winding
three-phase transformers by connection symbols
(BS 171: Part 4)

winding, by varying the values of the winding sections, can be made to produce any phase relationship between primary and secondary windings.

Large supplies of d.c. are essential for certain industrial application. Furthermore 12- and 24-pulse systems of rectifier supply are necessary if harmonics in the supply are to be kept to a minimum. The interconnected star transformer winding provides the solution.

Terminations

Electrical connections to transformers are made with cable which is either carried overhead on poles or pylons or buried in trenches in the ground. The former uses fairly simple steel reinforced copper or aluminium conductors and relies on air spacing between conductors for insulation.

Electrical cable for underground power distribution has solid insulating material between conductors and overall and usually has a metal protection on the outer surface which is again protected against corrosion by an outer covering. At system voltage above 3300 V the underground cable becomes very much more complex and is beyond the scope of this chapter.

Generally speaking, distribution systems above 33 kV are by the overhead system and require bushing terminations on transformers. Distribution voltages of below 600 V in most of the cities and towns of Western Europe are by the underground method.

Underground cables have to be terminated by a method which does not expose the inner conductor insulation of the cable to the elements and this inevitably means some form of cable terminating box.

In the early days of power distribution the insulation most common to l.v. underground cables usually consisted of paper, cotton, jute, wax and hemp, etc. Although thoroughly impregnated with wax and oil these materials were quite prone to moisture absorption. Cable terminating boxes were compound filled. Cable jointing and cable box filling was a fairly complicated business which required considerable skill. In spite of every effort failures in cable boxes were fairly common.

The development of modern plastics such as polyvinylchloride and polyethylene, etc. and their use in the cable industry has done much

28

to simplify cable manufacture, cabling systems and termination. Almost all l.v. cable boxes are now air-filled with a simple compression gland securing the metal sheath of the cable. Low voltage transformer terminations are usually an 'all-in-one' epoxy resin bushing plate assembly with bolt-on connections.

The compound filling of 6.6, 10 and 11 kV cable boxes on distribution transformers has remained in many areas of the UK because the most common 6.6 and 11 kV cable is still paper insulated. Developments in the field of plastics have produced cross linked polyethylene cables where air-filled boxes with heat shrinkable sleevings eliminate the need for compound filling and greatly simplify the cable termination to transformers. Unfortunately costs for this type of cable are still high and in many areas considered to be prohibitive.

Dry-type transformers supplied in their own ventilated enclosures are generally treated as liquid-immersed transformers and have cable boxes mounted on the outside of the ventilated enclosure. Where the dry-type transformer forms part of a complete installation on h.v. and l.v. switchgear it is often required for the transformer to be supplied without an enclosure; h.v. winding connections are terminated in bolted connections just above the core and windings and l.v. connections are generally terminated on busbars.

Cable-end terminations for installations of this type can still follow the same form as the tankside cable box but with the three-phase bushings arranged and spaced for copper connections in air.

The resin-encapsulated transformer was developed originally in Germany where open installations are more commonplace. Special epoxy resin connectors have been developed by some companies and the incoming h.v. cable is simply laid into a moulded cable holder and the bared conductor bolted to metallic inserts.

COOLING

Transformers are identified according to the cooling method employed and the letter symbols used are indicated in table 11.9. The simplest form is where the windings are cooled by natural air flow over the heated surface of the windings and core. These are heated by the load and no-load losses respectively and the heat is transferred to the surrounding air by convection and radiation. This type of cooling is described as air natural or AN by reference to table 11.9.

Table 11.9 Letter symbols (BS 171: Part 2)

Kind of cooling medium	Symbol
Mineral oil or equivalent flammable synthetic insulating liquid	O
Non-flammable synthetic insulating liquid	L
Gas	G
Water	W
Air	A
Kind of circulation	
Natural	N
Forced (oil not directed)	F
Forced-directed oil	D

The natural movement of air over heated coil surfaces is not part-icularly efficient. Winding conductors, disc- and coil-separator winding shapes, and the roughness of conductor insulation all help to create eddies in the air flow over the windings and reduce the heat transfer from the winding to the air. Even a small amount of force-directed air flow over the windings improves the heat flow, and ratings are increased significantly.

A dry-type transformer cooled by direct forced air is designated as AF. A dry-type transformer which has natural cooling and the facility for automatic fan operation should the temperature of the windings increase beyond normal limits has two ratings specified followed by AN/AF. For example 1000/1250 kVA AN/AF dry-type Class C transformer.

The oil- or liquid-immersed transformer must by this definition have two sets of letters. One which describes the cooling of the winding and one which describes the cooling of the surface of the liquid. Hence the most common distribution transformer in which the windings and core are naturally cooled by oil and the oil is sub-sequently naturally cooled by air has the designation ONAN.

Forced-cooling equipment and its control are costly additions to any transformer and this cost can rarely be justified on distribution

transformers of the ratings covered in this chapter. However, the
same ruling that applies to forced cooling of dry-type transformers
also applies to the oil in an oil-filled transformer or the silicone
fluid in a fire-resistant transformer. Ratings can be increased significantly if air is forced over the cooling surface of the tank. An
oil-immersed transformer arranged to have fans automatically switched
on when the oil exceeds a certain temperature level would have the
dual designation of ONAN/ONAF. Yet a third condition of forced cooling is obtained when an oil pump is built into the oil flow system of
the transformer. The designation becomes ONAN/ONAF/OFAF.

The naturally cooled ONAN or LNAN distribution transformer above
the rating of approximately 50 kVA requires cooling surfaces in addition to the tank surface that would normally contain the core and
windings. At one time this additional cooling surface was provided by
tubes welded into the tank wall and, theoretically carried the hot oil
from the top to the bottom of the tank. In more recent years it has
become fashionable to manufacture plate radiators from pressings similar in pattern to the domestic hot water radiator and arrange these
in banks on the tank side. The plate radiator has the advantage of
reduced oil content and possibly results in lower manufacturing cost.

As early as 1925 manufacturers produced oil-immersed transformer
tanks with the tank walls made from deep corrugations of thin steel
plate. It was not until very many years later that machines (see p.4)
were developed to automatically form deep corrugations into a continuous strip of plate, automatically weld the edges of the corrugations,
insert and weld corrugation strengthening strips and shear to a predetermined length.

The transformer tank with all four sides formed from thin (1.2 mm)
corrugated steel plate with terminations and tapping switch all mounted
on the cover has become the most standard arrangement throughout Europe
and America, although standard supply industry terminations in the UK
make this cooling arrangement less advantageous over the tank with
radiators.

Ventilation of transformer enclosures

Transformers operating within an enclosed area inevitably reach a
higher temperature for the same loading conditions than they would when

operating in free air. It is important to the life of the transformer that this fact is appreciated and that substations or enclosures are designed so that this excess temperature is limited.

The problem of substation ventilation when fan extractors are used is very much more simplified than naturally ventilated enclosures. Natural ventilation does not rely on the functioning and maintenance (or lack of it) of fans and is therefore preferred.

The excess temperature of the substation or enclosure is a function of:

(a) The total losses of the transformer.
(b) The net area of the inlet and outlet ventilation areas.
(c) The effective vertical distance between the inlet and outlet ventilation areas.

The inlet ventilation area is positioned ideally low down, below the centre line of the transformer radiators with the transformer fairly close. The outlet ventilation area is required to be high, not immediately above the transformer, but on a wall remote from the inlet so that cooling air passes over the transformer.

The minimum height of the outlet above the inlet area should ideally be equal to 1.5 times the height of the transformer.

The net area of the inlet or outlet has been shown by empirical means to be approximately:

$$A = 0.06P$$

where P is the total loss dissipated from the transformer in kilowatts and A is in square metres.

With these conditions met the temperature of the substation air should not be more than 7-8°C above the outside ambient.

IMPULSE WITHSTAND

The main three-phase 11 kV distribution system in the UK is by underground cables and ground-mounted distribution transformers of 200 kVA and above connected to this system are not subjected to high level transient voltages of atmospheric origin because of the attenuating effect of the cable to steep-fronted waves. However, it is recognised that for a variety of reasons transient voltages do occur in cabled systems. Transformers can also be connected very close to an overhead

system and an agreed system of impulse voltage testing and impulse
voltage levels does give indication that a level of insulation strength
has been achieved in the basic design.

Table II of IEC 76, Part 3 gives the impulse voltage withstand
levels agreed by most countries of the world. Distribution voltages
of 3.6, 7.2 and 12 kV are covered by two values of impulse withstand
level. List I is for the transformer that is considered to be electrically not exposed to high voltage transients and list II with a
higher level for the electrically exposed. The 11 kV system of the UK
is considered by the supply authorities to require the 75 kV level,
while pole-mounted transformers connected to overhead lines are usually
tested to a higher level of 95 kV. Europe and Middle Eastern countries
standardise generally on the 75 kV level for distribution systems
between 10 and 11 kV.

At one time it was considered that dry-type Class C transformers
could be classified as electrically unexposed to transient voltages
because they could never be operated out of doors close to an overhead
distribution system.

The increasing use of vacuum circuit-breakers and their current-
chopping characteristics produce exceptionally high voltages in the
low capacitance, high surge impedance windings of the dry-type transformer. Impulse levels therefore became necessary for the dry-type
transformer and the list I level has been accepted as satisfactory for
the unexposed transformer.

OPERATION IN TROPICAL CLIMATES

A number of special problems exist when transformers are operated in
tropical climates. The effects of increased ambient temperature are
well documented and require little elaboration in this chapter. If
the average ambient temperature at site is 10°C higher than that
specified in normal operating conditions given in BS 171 then the
temperature rise of the transformer would either need to be designed
for 10°C lower or the transformer would need to be derated to a level
which produced a temperature rise 10°C lower. Other hazards exist
which are, perhaps, not so well documented. High isoceraunic levels
exist in some tropical countries and electrical storms can persist for
long periods of time. Standard impulse voltage levels may well be

insufficient for these areas and the added protection of surge arresters considered to be advisable. Standard bushings may again give insufficient creep and a higher voltage class considered necessary in these areas.

Temperature, intensity of solar radiation, rainfall, high wind, dust storms and humidity, all affect the life of paint applied as a protection against corrosion to the tank surface of liquid-immersed transformers. A standard paint finish generally consists of three coats. The first, the priming coat, is applied to the prepared metal. The second, the undercoat provides the key for the main protective top coat. This final coat is usually long lasting high gloss, the gloss providing the main protection. Generally this three-coat system provides adequate protection for a reasonable time, and is easy to maintain and replace when it has been damaged or worn. Thicker coatings can give extended life to any paint system. Special top coatings are available which again give extended life. It must be pointed out, however, that the more complicated the protective system, usually the more difficult it is to maintain and the integrity of any surface coating relies on adequate pre-treatment of the metal.

Dry-type transformers can be vulnerable to inadequate maintenance in tropical countries. Dust and sand are a natural hazard in many areas and in countries where the temperature drops to quite low values at night the warmth of a transformer installation probably seems to be quite a haven to a host of small creatures. Extra maintenance and vermin proofing of enclosures might, therefore, militate against their use.

PARALLEL OPERATION

Satisfactory operation of transformers in parallel means that each transformer will carry its share of the load according to its rating and for this condition to be met the voltage ratio, phase displacement and impedance must all be the same. Transformers in parallel must have the same secondary voltage for a common primary input.

The importance of phase displacement is obvious from fig. 11.9. A pair of three-phase transformers of similar characteristics and having the same connection symbols can be operated both physically and alphabetically. For example Dy 1 and Yd 1 can be safely connected together. The impedance (which governs the regulation) decides the proportion of the total load which is taken by each transformer. The resistances of each unit must be similar.

When connecting units in parallel or paralleling supplies from two separate transformers the phase rotation must be the same.

Other points to remember when parallel operation of transformers is being considered are:

(a) The tested impedance of transformers can vary by ± 10% of the guaranteed value. Two transformers to the same guaranteed value of impedance can have test values which vary by as much as 20%.

(b) The length and type of cable connections must be considered if additional transformer capacity is added to an existing system and sited away from the original unit(s).

(c) Transformers that have tapping ranges larger than 10% need to have the impedance variation throughout the tapping range considered. Very large variations between manufacturers can occur due to different winding arrangements.

PACKAGED SUBSTATIONS

A distribution substation consists essentially of h.v. switchgear (in many cases a ring main unit), a transformer and a fused l.v. distribution panel. Until recent years these were always supplied by different manufacturers as individual components. They were often sited in a small compound or building, and each component had its own termination system, usually cable boxes. The three equipments were electrically connected by short lengths of cable. Lack of available space, particularly in city areas, rationalisation in the electrical supply industry and manufacturing industries and growth in demand for electrical power all gave effect to the development of the British unit substation. The three equipments are still separate components, they can be purchased separately from different suppliers, each with its own particular characteristics and be brought together to form a substation because of the standardisation of terminal heights and flanges. Although a unit substation is often supplied with a ventil- ated steel or glass fibre housing each equipment is of weatherproof design and requires no more than a wire fence surround. Ventilated housings are preferred by many authorities at home and abroad and can be of very pleasing appearance. Lockable doors afford access to l.v. distribution panels and h.v. switchgear. As many as 12 three-phase fused outlets are available on the l.v. distribution panel. Housing doors can be interlocked with the h.v. switchgear.

The packaged substation is described in greater detail in chapter 2.

PROTECTION

Transformer protection is described more fully in chapter 19 but for completeness the various systems available are enumerated. Two systems of protection, peculiar to transformers, are described in more detail: they are gas and oil relays and winding temperature indication.

Differential protection

Differential protection is based on the principle of comparing the primary and secondary currents of the transformer and if these balance any fault is external to the unit. The winding connection of the transformer primary and secondary are usually different (delta-star for the most part in the power range we are considering) and have to be compensated for by connecting the appropriate CTs in star-delta. Both balanced current and balanced voltage systems are used.

Restricted earth fault

The three CT secondaries on each side of the transformer are parallel-ed together with a relay connected across them. A fourth CT is connected in the neutral of a star-connected winding. The relays only operate for an internal earth fault for it is only under these condit-ions that the CT outputs do not sum to zero, causing an unbalanced current to flow in the relay circuit.

Unrestricted earth fault

A single CT in the neutral of a star-connected transformer provides a measure of protection against earth fault but the relay also operates for earth faults outside the transformer.

Overcurrent

A standard idmtl relay can be used to provide overcurrent protection but it will of course cover the whole of the network beyond the transformer. Overload settings can be adjusted to discriminate with protection on the load side of the transformer. This type of relay is often installed to act as back-up protection.

Gas and oil relay

The double float gas and oil relay is fitted in the pipe between the main tank of the transformer and the conservator and is more commonly found on oil-immersed transformers above 2.0 MVA. The two pivotted floats carry switches which can be normally open or normally closed. One float is actuated when the oil level in the conservator and hence the relay falls to an unacceptably low level. The switch on the low level float is usually connected to an alarm circuit that gives warning of low oil level in the transformer. The other float operates when there is a sudden production of gas within the transformer. The float then operates on surge. Switch contacts on this float are usually connected to the trip circuit on the associated switchgear which then disconnects the transformer from the supply. A sudden production of gas is usually indicative of serious fault conditions hence the need for shutdown.

Flashover between connections, flashover to earth, breakdown between parts of the same windings, etc. produce different mixtures of gases. The most significant gases generated by the electrical breakdown of the oil are hydrogen, methane, ethylene and acetylene. Cellulose insulating materials, when broken down by an electric arc produce mainly carbon dioxide and carbon monoxide. An analysis of the gas collected from the gas and oil relay can give a very good indication of the materials involved in a gas-producing fault which initiated the operation of the relay.

It has been known for small quantities of gas to be released within a transformer immediately following installation and over a period of time the gas collects in the gas relay and eventually an alarm is given of low oil level. In this case an analysis of the gas will often show it to be no more than trapped air.

Pressure-relief device

One of the most useful developments in recent years is the

'snap-action' pressure-relief device. Manufactured by Qualitrol, this device, which is mounted on the tank, wall or cover, operates when a predetermined pressure is exceeded within the tank. The seal snaps open and the large orifice allows gas to be discharged at the rate of 283 m³/min. The Qualitrol pressure-relief device was developed for the oil-immersed sealed transformer but it has become widely accepted as a reliable explosion vent and has virtually replaced the old-fashioned diaphragm type. The Qualitrol device can be supplied with two single-pole double-throw switches. A brightly coloured plastics pin, located in the centre of the device, gives mechanical indication that the device has operated.

Winding temperature indicators

Unless the temperature of a winding can be measured by direct contact with the winding conductors, winding temperature indication can be no more than a close approximation and accurate over only a fairly narrow band of transformer loading.

The two main methods used by manufacturers in the UK to give indication of winding temperature are:

(a) A direct method whereby the temperature sensor of the instrument is held in close proximity to the l.v. winding.
(b) An indirect method whereby a 'thermal image' device simulates the winding-to-top-oil temperature differential.

Method (a) is used almost exclusively on dry-type transformers where large cooling ducts allow for the positioning of the instrument's temperature sensor and where the integrity of the winding insulation system is not impaired.

The indirect method of the thermal image device uses the standard mechanism of a dial-type temperature indicator. A current transformer mounted in the live connection to one winding supplies a proportion of the live current to a heater coil wound onto the operating bellows of the instrument. A calibrating resistor adjusts the current in the heater coil to a value that produces the correct winding-to-oil differential.

Rather more sophisticated methods are to be found fitted to larger transformers; one such method uses a standard 100 ohm platinum resistor as a sensing device. This is fitted in close proximity to

the winding. The instrument measures the resistance of the sensing
device which changes with winding temperature.

All winding temperature indicators can be fitted with contacts to
operate alarms and trip mechanisms. The instrument in common use can
be fitted with three or four switches to operate fans and pumps for
forced-air and forced-oil circulation.

SHIPMENT OF TRANSFORMERS
The preparation of a transformer for transportation depends on its
size, type, destination, the distance and method of transport and the
length of time the transformer is to remain in store before installation.

Liquid-filled transformers
Liquid-filled outdoor distribution transformers fitted with cable
boxes and for delivery within the UK are invariably dispatched by
road transport, securely anchored to open-backed vehicles with no more
packing than perhaps some protection for the cooling radiators or
corrugations. These, being of thin steel plate are easily damaged in
transit if vehicles are not carefully loaded. Smaller, pole-mounted
transformers, with exposed porcelain bushings require some protection
if damage to terminals is to be avoided during transport. A careful
arrangement of identical units with packing pieces spacing one unit
from another is normally sufficient for UK road conditions.

Larger units, even for delivery within the UK, require more consideration. The removal of conservators, bushings and radiators is
advised if the total load exceeds the width of a low loader. The
route to be taken by the vehicle, sharp bends (particularly at the
bottom of hills), road camber and low bridges are all hazards which
have to be considered when units larger than 5.0 MVA have to be transported. It is advisable to cover and protect dial-type instruments,
gas and oil relays, etc. from damage.

All transformers manufactured to BS 171 have lifting lugs as a
standard fitting. The weight of an 11 kV industrial ground-mounted
oil-filled transformer, with standard fittings is very approximately
22 $(kVA)^{0.75}$ tonnes and requires lifting capacity of 6 tonnes or less
for units of 1600 kVA or lower. Removal from the vehicle to site or

store in the UK or anywhere within the industrialised west should not present problems.

When oil-immersed transformers are shipped to overseas locations, particularly where handling arrangements are restricted and long distances have to be travelled overland on poor roads, then the type of packing employed and the method of transportation have to be given much more consideration.

The single isolated unit is the most vulnerable because most distribution transformers and unit substations, supplied in large numbers to the high growth areas of the world, are transported from manufacturers to users by containerised shipping. Many units are packed and sealed into 10 m long 40 m^3 volume containers by packing experts and the complete container is transported direct to site.

Larger transformers require the vulnerability of components, bushings, radiators, conservators, etc. all to be considered and it is often advisable to remove them and pack them separately in wooden crates.

Weight and freight restrictions often demand that oil-immersed transformers are dispatched dry with the oil packed in drums and shipped separately. No great problems exist here if the transformers are sealed with dry air or nitrogen and moisture is prevented from entering the tank and affecting the windings.

Sealed transformers are of course filled with oil and sealed at the manufacturer's works and are always dispatched filled with oil.

Dry-type transformers

Dry-type transformers must be very carefully crated and the core and windings protected against the ingress of moisture during shipment. It is usual for very robust close-boarded crates to be used and for these to be lined with polyethylene and made waterproof. Large quantities of silica-gel desiccators absorb any moisture that might manage to penetrate the polyethylene lining.

INSTALLATION

It is important to note that before installation transformers should be checked for any damage that may have been caused during transit. Liquid-filled units dispatched fully filled should be checked for

correct oil level and for any leaks that may have occurred. The
paint finish should be examined carefully for signs of damage. The
cores and windings of Class H and C transformers should be examined
for signs of mechanical damage to leads, connections and risers.
Coils should be examined for signs of insulation damage. The cast-
resin of encapsulated transformers can be easily chipped or cracked
by being knocked and thus needs to be examined very carefully.

Liquid-filled transformers

It is usual to have some form of containment and soakaway for all
liquid-filled transformers, be they mineral oil, silicone, askarel or
any other design, irrespective of whether they are installed indoors
or in the open. In some countries this is required by law. The soakaway is usually a pebble base contained within a low brick wall
enclosure. When installed in a building or substation without additional fire protection it may take the form of a catch pit, designed
as a pitched or lowered floor, pit or trench as shown in fig. 11.10.
It should be large enough to contain all the liquid to cater for the
possibility of a severe rupture of the tank. The American Factory
Mutual Research organisation has detailed this information in its
Factory Mutual Loss Prevention Data Sheet 5-4A/14-85.

The shape, size and materials used for the building should be
based on the rate of heat release of the transformer liquid when on
fire and discussion of these is outside the scope of this chapter.
The above mentioned Data Sheet also gives guidance on this aspect of
the subject.

Dry-type transformers

All dry-type transformers must be installed indoors with an earthed
metal enclosure around them. In the UK this usually takes the form
of a substantial metal framework, but there is no reason why the
lightweight mesh-screened panels, as used by the European continental
countries, should not be employed. This reduces the overall cost of
the installation.

Class C or H designs are generally not as tall as their cast-resin
counterparts, although other dimensions are similar. This slight
different in headroom might be important if the unit is to be

installed in an existing substation. The larger dry-type transformers, 500 kVA and above, are usually built on a framework of metal channels and are usually provided with wheels to allow movement of the unit for cleaning and maintenance.

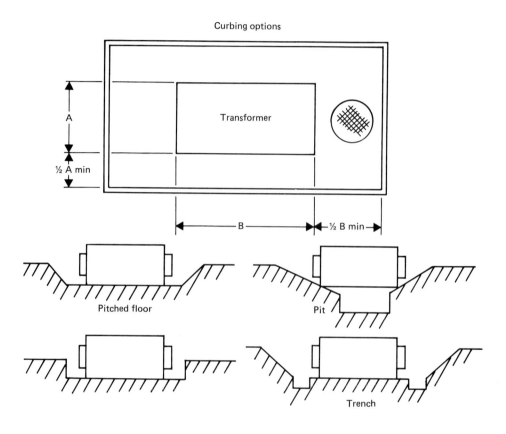

Figure 11.10 Some different arrangements of soakaways in a building or substation housing a liquid-filled transformer

CABLING

For the distribution transformers covered in this book cabling is usually PVC insulated and sheathed, although in special cases EPR or other forms of insulation may be employed. Copper or aluminium conductors are available. Armouring is usual for outdoor installations or where onerous soil conditions exist. A three-core design of h.v. cable is normal for both dry-type and liquid-filled designs. Termination is by compound-filled cable box for liquid-filled transformers and shrouded plug-in connections for dry-type designs.

Depending on the rating of the transformer, l.v. cables may be single-core or three-core. Termination methods are similar to those appertaining to the h.v. side possibly using heat shrink connections for dry-type units.

COMMISSIONING

Before proceeding with commissioning tests a careful examination of the transformer and its surrounds must be carried out, particularly if the unit has been installed for some time. It is not unusual to find tools and other extraneous matter lying on the unit in a position that could be highly dangerous if a high voltage was applied to the trans- former. For dry-type transformers, particularly those of Class C or H designs, the windings should be checked with an IR tester and then dried out as necessary. The drying out can be done electrically by passing a small current at l.v. through the windings or by the applic- ation of a 'gentle' external source of heat.

Where it is known that the dry-type Class C transformer is to remain in store for a long period of time or is to remain unexcited for long periods of time then it is advisable for the unit to be fitted with small heaters on the core and windings to circulate warm air during the time that the transformer remains inactive.

For liquid-filled units sent overseas it is important to ensure that the unit has in fact been filled with the correct fluid if the transformer was dispatched unfilled. Depending on the circumstances it may also be necessary to institute some form of winding drying-out procedure. In any case the fluid should be checked for electrical strength before commissioning.

Where relays are associated with transformers they should be examined to make sure there is no packing or safety lock incorporated as a protection against damage during transit. This should be removed. The position of the off-load tap change device must be set to corres- pond to the network conditions. If there is a conservator valve, ensure that it is open. If there are plastics caps covering breather pipes ensure that they are removed.

When all the connections and other matters have been checked the transformer can be energised and allowed to run on no-load for a

period long enough to ensure safe operation. Gradual loading can then
be introduced until full load is reached. During the commissioning
procedure instruments and protective relays should be observed for
correct functioning and it should be checked that readings are of the
expected order.

MAINTENANCE

It is not the intention to give full and detailed maintenance instructions here but to highlight the more important features related to the
various types of transformer included in the chapter.

Mineral-oil-filled units

Maintenance of the insulating oil is necessary, as laid down in British
Standard Code of Practice CP 1009 which, although published in 1959 is
still suitable for present day use. Oil is subject to deterioration
or contamination in storage, in the course of handling or in service.
Accordingly it requires periodic examination and possibly treatment to
maintain it in a good condition. After many years in service it may
even require replacement.

Provision is usually made on all mineral-oil-filled transformers
for samples of the oil to be drawn off, and this operation should be
done while the oil is warm. A limited but useful amount of information
can be obtained from the colour and odour of the oil. Cloudiness may
be due to suspended moisture or suspended solid matter such as iron
oxide or sludge. Moisture can be detected by the crackle test.

If the oil is dark brown it may contain dissolved asphaltenes;
if green the presence of copper salts is indicated, and it may be
expected that further deterioration will be rapid.

An acrid smell is often indicative of volatile acids which can
cause corrosion and which may render the oil unsuitable for treatment
on site. A petrol-like or acetylene odour may indicate a low flashpoint due to a fault or some other cause.

Tests are laid down in CP 1009 to determine free water, acidity,
electric strength, sludge, flashpoint and resistivity and suggested
minimum safe limits are indicated. Frequency of testing is also indicated which varies from 6 months up to 2 years depending on the test
concerned and the environmental conditions. It is important that the
oil level is maintained.

At regular intervals it is strongly recommended that breathers
and breather pipes are checked. If a silica-gel dehydrator is fitted
then the condition of the oil bath and crystals should be checked.
An oil-immersed transformer should never be allowed to breathe through
silica-gel crystals supersaturated in moisture. They should be
changed as soon as the colour changes from blue to pink.

The Code also recommends that the protective paint finish of the
tank is checked for damage and that there are no leaks.

If oil temperature and winding temperature indicators are fitted
operation of the switches should be checked. Gas and oil relays and
pressure-relief devices fitted with switches should also be checked
occasionally for ease of movement.

Fire-resistant liquid-filled transformers

For reasons stated earlier askarels are being replaced in transformers
and so the maintenance of these units will not be discussed.

Of the other fire-resistant liquids only silicone fluid is covered
here. At the time of going to press insufficient was known of the
long-term reliability or stability of the many other fire-resistant
fluids available. Manufacturers of other fluids should be approached
for details of the maintenance requirements for their liquids.

The thermal stability and non-polarity of silicone liquid
indicates that the need for maintenance is much less than for mineral
oil, because it will not degrade in the useful service lifetime of a
65°C rise transformer. Maintenance of the fluid itself is thus
reduced to restoring its original dielectric quality in the event of
contamination.

The same type of equipment that is used for cleaning mineral oil
can be used with silicone. The best method of removing contaminants
is usually a combination of a cartridge filter to extract particulates
and a conventional vacuum degasifier to remove dissolved water. A
standard filter press can also be used. Table 11.10 details
recommended maintenance tests for silicone liquid. Interfacial
tension and acid number are included in the table but due to the
stability of the fluid the significance of these values is not documented. However, because of the unique gas-absorbing properties of
silicone fluid and its affinity to water, transformers filled with

Table 11.10 Recommended maintenance tests for silicone transformer liquid

Test	Acceptance values	Unacceptable values indicate
Minimum		
Visual	Crystal clear, free of particles	Particulates, free water colour change
Odour	Odourless	Arced or burned paper, volatile contamination (solvent, pcb)
Dielectric breakdown (ASTM D877)	35 kV new 25 kV in transformer	Particulates, water
Additional		
Water content (Modified Karl Fisher photovolt aquatest)	100 ppm	Water
Interfacial tension ASTM D971	————	Contamination
Power factor ASTM D924	< 0.1%	Polar/ionic contamination
Viscosity ASTM D445	50 cs	Fluid degradation, contamination
Fire point ASTM D92	> 340°C	Contamination by volatile material
Acid number BCP ASTM D974 & D664	————	Degradation of cellulose insulation, contamination

this liquid are sealed. There is no contact with the atmosphere, neither can the fluid be contaminated by air-borne pollutants. Silicone-filled transformers need only be checked for leaks and paint finish.

Dry-type transformers

The most important aspect of maintenance is that of ensuring that all cooling air ducts are kept free of foreign objects. A vacuum cleaner can be used for this purpose. Any blockage can cause the winding temperature to rise to levels that could affect the performance and life characteristics of the insulation. If a transformer is taken out of service for any length of time, and heaters have not been fitted, it is a wise precaution to dry out the unit by the means suggested earlier under commissioning. This is particularly true of the Class C or H designs. Before connecting any supply to the transformer for this purpose the terminations at both ends of the h.v. windings, the pressure rings and the insulators should be dried with a cloth. The l.v. winding can then be short-circuited and a low current passed through the h.v. winding. The whole drying-out operation should not take more than about 5 hours. Alternatively, fan heaters can be employed to circulate warm air through the windings.

Should a winding repair become necessary it is difficult, if not impossible, to effect this on a cast-resin unit, and so the encapsulated winding has to be completely replaced. It is relatively easy to repair the conventional Class C dry-type, although it is best carried out by the manufacturer or a reputable repair organisation, preferably a member of the Association of Electrical and Machinery Trades (AEMT).

Chapter 12

Switchgear

R. W. Blower, BSc(Eng), CEng, FIEE

P. Stott, CEng, MIEE

YS Consultants Ltd and
GEC Distribution Equipment Ltd

SPECIFICATION AND TESTING

The general characteristics of all forms of switchgear are guided by
the existence of a considerable number of international and national
standards. These are under continuous review and changes are always
being considered in the light of changes to the technology of switching devices and to the techniques of control and protection.

British Standards nowadays tend to be closely related to the corresponding IEC recommendations, but there are some differences, often
arising because of differences in the dates of issue and the continuously changing pattern of use referred to above. This aspect is
particularly relevant to l.v. switchgear and is enlarged on later.
These standards lay down a number of criteria for the rating of switchgear and the conditions of use for which it is intended. Also, a
considerable amount of space is given to the subject of testing.

It is obviously impractical to subject every switching device produced to a series of tests which will simulate all the likely switching
conditions which it might meet in service, in order to prove to the
purchaser that it meets its specification. Therefore the quality control policy is followed of subjecting a sample piece of equipment
(very often a prototype) to a comprehensive series of major type tests,
and then to carry out routine tests on each production equipment of
that type to ensure that it matches the type tested article in all
essential characteristics.

The major type tests are: short-circuit proving up to full rated
breaking current at rated voltage; high voltage (h.v.) tests; temperature-rise tests at rated normal current; and mechanical endurance
tests.

The routine tests are: operational tests to ensure opening and closing operation is as the prototype; voltage tests on insulation; and resistance measurement to compare with the temperature rise on the tested prototype.

All circuit-breakers (cbs) have to be able to close and open satisfactorily under all conditions of service. In particular they must interrupt all currents from zero to full rated breaking current with all possible combinations of power factor, current asymmetry and recovery voltage that occur. Figure 12.1 illustrates the typical form of the current and recovery voltage which occurs when a fault current is interrupted. The asymmetry which is illustrated in this single-phase example arises as a function of the instantaneous value of the system voltage when the fault occurs, and the power factor of the system voltage under fault conditions. This reduces from the usual operating figure in excess of 0.8 to a much lower figure such as 0.1 to 0.3. This creates much more severe conditions for arc interruption as the current zero now occurs at a time when the supply voltage is closer to its peak. The high frequency transient recovery voltage is a function of the system inductance and capacity.

In addition to the fault condition, cbs (and switches) often have to be able to switch light currents of a highly inductive nature (low lagging power factor) or of a capacitive nature (low leading power factor). Special conditions attend these operations.

Light inductive currents

As illustrated in fig. 12.2, the available arc extinguishing effort may tend to force the current to zero prematurely. When this happens energy is trapped in the inductance of the load and subsequently transferred into capacitive energy stored in the leakage capacitance of the system. This process continues in an oscillatory manner as part of an augmented transient recovery voltage and eventually dies away as the energy is dissipated as heat in the resistive circuit elements. Some of the energy is also lost (maybe as much as 30%) by iron losses if the load has an iron core as is usually the case, since these conditions normally arise when switching transformers and motors on no-load. It is a necessary part of the cb designer's job to ensure that the degree of 'current-chopping' (as this phenomenon is often called), is not allowed to reach a level capable of generating dangerous overvoltages.

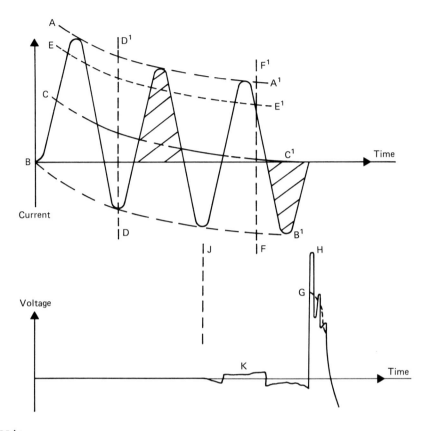

AA' } BB' }	Envelope of current wave
CC'	Displacement of current wave zero line
DD'	Typical contact separation point for asymmetrical breaking duty
EE'	RMS value of symmetrical current wave measured from CC'
FF'	Typical contact separation point for symmetrical breaking duty
G	Peak value of 50 Hz recovery voltage
H	Peak value of high frequency transient recovery voltage
J	Assumed contact separation point to illustrate typical voltage across circuit-breaker contact gap
K	Arcing voltage

Figure 12.1 Typical fault current and recovery voltage diagram

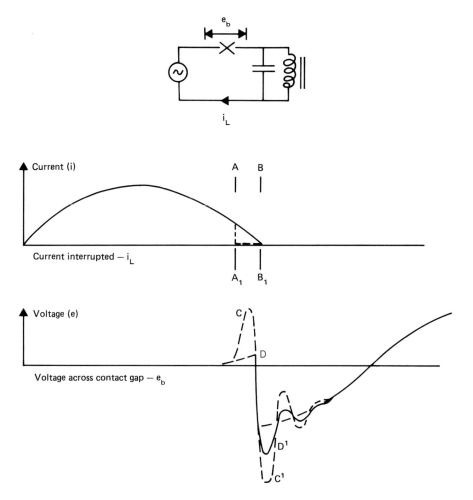

AA$_1$ Current interruption point with 'current-chopping'
BB$_1$ Current interruption at natural current zero
CC' Recovery voltage with 'current-chopping'
DD' Recovery voltage with interruption at natural zero

*Figure 12.2 Conditions occurring when interrupting small inductive
currents (cos θ ≃ 0 lagging)*

Light capacitive currents

Conditions here are again special, since a d.c. charge is trapped in
the capacitance once the current flow ceases and the contact gap is
quickly stressed to a value of double the peak phase voltage as the
polarity of the a.c. recovery voltage changes. This is illustrated

in fig. 12.3 and again the cb or switch designer has to ensure that the contact gap does not break down under these conditions, however early the initial clearance occurs, as this could lead to the build-up of even higher voltage stresses.

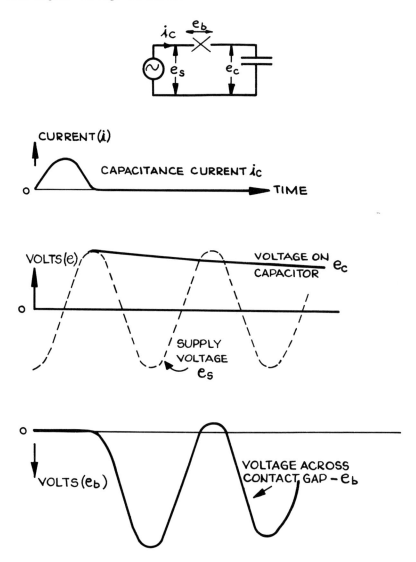

Figure 12.3 Conditions occurring when interrupting capacitance currents (cos θ ≈ 0 leading)

DEFINITIONS

Switchgear

A general term covering switching devices and their combination with associated control, measuring, protective and regulating equipment, and also assemblies of such devices and equipment with associated interconnections, accessories, enclosures and supporting structures, intended in principle for use in connection with generation, transmission, distribution and conversion of electric power.

Metal enclosed switchgear.   Switchgear assemblies with an external metal enclosure intended to be earthed, and complete except for external connections.

Metalclad switchgear.   Metal enclosed switchgear in which components are arranged in separate compartments with metal enclosures intended to be earthed.   There will be separate compartments at least for the following components: each main switching device; components connected to one side of a main switching device, e.g. feeder circuit; and components connected to the other side of the main switching device, e.g. busbars.

Circuit-breaker

A mechanical switching device, capable of making, carrying and breaking currents under normal circuit conditions and also making, carrying for a specified time and breaking currents under specified abnormal circuit conditions such as those of short-circuit.

Indoor circuit-breaker.   A cb designed solely for installation within a building or other housing, where the cb is protected against wind, rain, snow, abnormal dirt deposits, abnormal condensation, ice and hoar frost.

Outdoor circuit-breaker.   A cb suitable for installation in the open air, i.e. capable of withstanding rain, snow, dirt deposits, condensation, ice and hoar frost.

Switch

A mechanical switching device capable of making, carrying and breaking currents under normal circuit conditions, which may include specified operating overload conditions, and also carrying for a specified time currents under specified abnormal circuit conditions such as those of short-circuit. It may also be capable of making, but not breaking, short-circuit currents.

Disconnector (isolator)

A mechanical switching device which provides in the open position an isolating distance in accordance with specified requirements.

A disconnector is capable of opening and closing a circuit when negligible current is broken or made, or when no significant change in voltage across the terminals of each of the poles of the disconnector occurs. It is also capable of carrying currents under normal circuit conditions and carrying for a specified time currents under abnormal conditions such as those of short-circuit.

Note - Negligible currents imply currents such as the charging current of busbars, bushings, etc. and a current not exceeding 0.5 A is deemed to be a negligible current for the purpose of this definition.

Summary

As will be seen from the foregoing definitions, the most versatile switching device is the cb, as this is the only equipment capable of interrupting short-circuit currents and then restoring supply a number of times without requiring maintenance or the replacement of any parts. The least versatile device is the disconnector which is only capable of carrying short-circuit currents and has to be operated off-load.

Because of the need to interrupt short-circuit currents, the design and mode of operation of a cb tends to be dominated by this requirement and it is usually categorised by the arc extinguishing medium used for this purpose. In this chapter we consider only a.c. cbs, as the interruption of d.c. is a very limited specialist requirement.

CIRCUIT-BREAKING

An essential element in the operation of any a.c. cb is the electric
arc, which permits the current in the circuit to continue flowing
after the contacts have parted, until a suitable current zero occurs.
As has already been mentioned, the sudden cessation of current flow
at any time, other than very close to a natural current zero, has
undesirable consequences in all normal distribution systems, so the
existence of the arc as a natural commutating device is a very
important factor in the operation of a.c. cbs.

An ideal cb is one which acts as a perfect conductor until current
zero is reached, at which point it becomes a perfect insulator. As
no practical cb meets this condition, the result is modified to a
greater or lesser degree by the cb characteristics. The objective of
the cb designer is to create the necessary conditions to sweep away
the ionisation products in the contact gap at current zero and replace
them by a medium which will withstand the application of a very
rapidly rising voltage of considerable amplitude, the transient
recovery voltage.

HIGH VOLTAGE SWITCHGEAR

In the United Kingdom it is general practice for switchgear manufacturers to supply completely factory assembled switchgear (FBA). This
means complete cubicles containing busbars and all circuit components
up to the cable terminations including the cb and its isolating means.
It is, therefore, almost equally general for the switchgear to be
type tested in its completely assembled form. This is not always the
case for l.v. switchgear. Also h.v. switchgear is designed principally
for use with separate protective relays and therefore has a short time
rating, usually equal to the breaking current for a period of three
seconds, or in some cases of very heavy fault levels, a one second
rating may be assigned. It also has to be able to close fully against
a short-circuit making peak equal to 2.5 times the rated breaking
current. It also has to be able to interrupt under conditions of
rated breaking current with a degree of asymmetry which will depend
upon the opening time of the cb being considered. With some of the
modern types such as vacuum or sulphur hexafluoride (SF_6) this time
can be quite short and the d.c. component correspondingly large.

A figure of 50% d.c. component is not uncommon under these circumstances.

TYPES OF SWITCHING DEVICE

Circuit-breakers

An important feature in considering the application of any form of cb is the behaviour of its operating mechanism. Because of its protective duty, it is essential that a cb always be in a condition to open even if the power supply to the mechanism closing device has been interrupted. This is achieved by biasing the cb towards the open position by springs in various ways. The cb is then held in the closed position by some form of catch which can either be released manually or, more usually, by an electrical solenoid or trip coil.

Because cbs could at any time find themselves being closed onto a faulty network, it is now usually forbidden for them to be closed by direct manual means. Therefore all cb closing mechanisms require some form of stored energy to operate them. The two most common devices in use have either a solenoid and armature providing the necessary closing force, or springs which may be either hand charged or charged by an electric motor. The spring close mechanism has the advantage that it can always be operated even if the source of supply has been disconnected. The solenoid requires a heavy duty d.c. source, usually a secondary battery. Where such a source exists for other purposes, such as emergency lighting, then the solenoid operating mechanism has certain advantages.

At the distribution voltages considered here, up to 11 kV, by far the most common arc extinguishing media used until recently were oil, and air at atmospheric pressure. For particular heavy duty there have been a limited number of cbs made using compressed air as the interrupting medium, but this is more usually confined to designs of cb for use at transmission voltages. Today, increasing use is being made of cb using either vacuum, or SF_6 as the interrupting medium.

Oil circuit-breakers.   The oil used in oil circuit-breakers (ocbs) complies with BS 148 and is a hydrocarbon oil of fairly low viscosity and good insulating properties. When the contacts part considerable

heat is generated and this not only vaporises the oil but disassoc-
iates it into its hydrogen and carbon constituents. The hydrogen is
then thermally ionised which generates the electrons and positive ions
which carry the current across the space between the contacts in the
form of an electric arc. To control the flow of gases in the arc
region the contacts are normally enclosed by an arc control device,
fig. 12.4. The intense heating of the hydrogen gas and the dissociation of the oil generates pressure which is utilised within the arc
control device to improve the efficiency of operation.

Figure 12.4 Contacts and arc control device of an oil circuit-breaker

During the arcing period the presence of the arc tends to prevent the exhaust of gases from the arc control device through its side vents, but as the current reaches current zero these gases are released and sideways displacement of the ionisation products occurs due to the high pressure gas which surrounds the arcing zone. As the recovery voltage is impressed upon the arc gap which contains clean gas that should easily withstand the rapidly rising restriking transient. In an ocb of this type the effort required to extinguish the arc increases as the current rises, but so does the energy injected into the electric arc. Consequently, the extinguishing effort rises to match the increasing fault current.

The arc voltage, see fig. 12.1, is important for two basic reasons. Firstly, the arc voltage controls the amount of energy being generated in the arc and this has an important effect on the mechanical design of the enclosure. Secondly, the arc voltage plays a part in modifying some of the electrical parameters concerned with the circuit-breaking operation such as the power factor and the high frequency transient recovery voltage.

The ocb exists in two main forms:

Bulk oil circuit-breaker. This is the type most usually met in the British Isles and very large numbers are now in service in all kinds of distribution systems. In addition to interrupting the arc, the oil also serves as the main insulating medium, the cb operating parts being contained within an earthed metal enclosure. The most important aspect of this enclosure is the joint where the oil tank meets the top plate, which carries the six bushings between the cb itself and the system to which it has to be connected. The metal enclosure is fitted with some form of exhaust system which is baffled to prevent the oil leaving the tank with the exhaust gases created by arcing.

In addition to the arcing contacts contained within the arc control device, cbs with heavy current ratings, e.g. in excess of 1250 A, often have main contacts which are in parallel with the arcing contacts and usually connected outside the arc control device. It is then important to ensure that when the cb opens, the main contacts break circuit well before the arcing contacts start to open.

Small oil volume circuit-breaker.   This is largely a continental development in which the use of insulating materials for the tank of the cb allows for a considerable reduction in the amount of oil. This presupposes the availability of materials of sufficient strength to withstand the internal pressures. Many continental manufacturers offer such equipment and its connection to the fixed part of the switchgear is usually by horizontal withdrawal. In operating principle it is exactly the same as the bulk ocb but the contact structure is always of the single-break type.

Magnetic air circuit-breaker.   The basic principle of an acb con- sists in creating an arc voltage which is too high to be maintained by the system voltage. Under these circumstances the arc cannot persist.

   This is usually achieved either by forcing the arc to extend itself close to solid materials which extract heat from the arc, or by breaking the arc up into a series of arcs in which case the anode and cathode voltage drops are added to the total arc voltage to assist in achieving the objective. Designs exist where both methods are used in combination. A typical acb is shown diagrammatically in fig. 12.5 and it will be seen that the arc extension means is contained in the arc chute. The arc is encouraged to enter this device by the arc runners to which the arc roots transfer when the contacts open. Magnetic circuits are provided to generate a field within the arc chute which will cause the arc to move into the plates of that chute. A typical arrangement has moulded plates with ribs which are arranged so that the ribs on one of the parallel plates interlock with the ribs on the other plate gradually causing the arc to take a more and more serpen- tine path as it is driven deeper into the arc chute.

   Figure 12.6 illustrates the arcing and extinction process and shows how the arc voltage rises to quite high values during this process. It should be compared with fig. 12.1 which shows the same condition for the ocb.

   At very low currents of the order of 100 A the magnetic field may be inadequate to cause the necessary arc entry into the chute. To assist this operation at such low currents it is usual to fit an air 'puffer' comprising a piston operating within a cylinder connected to a nozzle under the contacts. This gives the necessary impetus to the low current arc to ensure its early extinction.

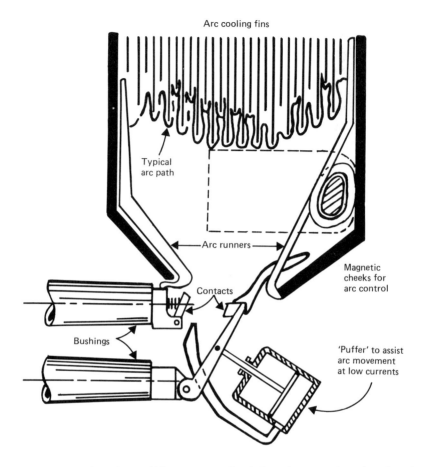

Figure 12.5 Sketch to illustrate principle of magnetic air circuit-breaker

Vacuum circuit-breaker. In the vacuum circuit-breaker (vcb) the contacts and arc control devices of the traditional cb are replaced by a vacuum interrupter. The vacuum interrupter is a sealed vessel with insulating walls which contains two contacts. One of the contacts is fixed to one of the end shields and the other contact is free to travel in an axial direction and the vacuum is maintained by metallic bellows connected between the moving contact and the other end shield. Inside the vacuum interrupter are metallic screens between the contacts and the inside walls of the insulating tube. The performance of the vacuum interrupter is dependent upon three factors: the existence of a sufficiently hard vacuum within the device; the selection of a

60

suitable contact material for the contacts; and the provision of some
form of magnetic control for the arc.

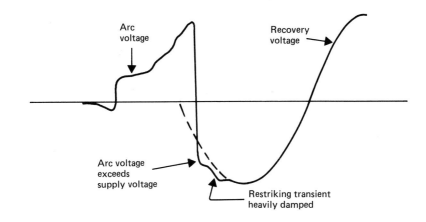

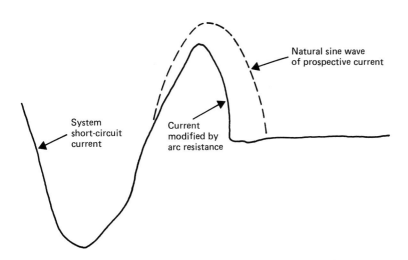

Figure 12.6 Arc extinction process in a magnetic air circuit-breaker

The vcb has contact gaps of the order of 10 mm up to 11 kV.
Therefore the necessary operating power is much reduced from that
needed in the traditional designs considered earlier. When operating
within its designed breaking current limit the contact gap in the
vacuum interrupter restores its full dielectric strength within one
microsecond of current zero. This makes for an extremely efficient

interrupting device. With the very short travels required the contacts parting, the maximum arc duration usually experienced is of the order of 13 milliseconds in a three-phase switching operation. The arc voltage is also normally very low because of the short gap and the type of arc which exists and thus the total arc energy per interruption is very much less than in a traditional cb.

These factors lead to two particular advantages which the vcb has over other types. The first is the exceptionally long contact endurance which the vacuum interrupter possesses, typical devices being quite capable of interrupting fifty or more full short-circuits at maximum rating and still being capable of further interruptions. This means that in many applications the vacuum interrupter would never need to be replaced during the economic life of the switchgear. So long as the operating mechanisms are also designed specifically with the object in view of guaranteeing very long operating lives without maintenance then the total switchgear becomes almost maintenance free.

The second advantage, more specifically in comparison with the ocb, lies with the elimination of flammable materials within the cb itself.

These two specific advantages give the designer of the cb considerable freedom in the way in which he can incorporate the various cb elements and give the user the ability to plan his system operation to take advantage of the contact endurance. In industrial applications particularly, the negligible fire risk, elimination of exhaust gases and negligible dynamic foundation loads give the user much greater flexibility in the siting of the substation.

In the UK particularly, all manufacturers of vacuum switchgear have introduced designs in which the cb is not isolated from the system by withdrawal from the switchgear unit, taking advantage of the much reduced need for maintenance. Typical equipment is shown in fig. 12.7.

Sulphur hexafluoride circuit-breakers. SF_6 is a heavy, chemically inert, non-toxic and non-flammable gas, which is odourless and colourless. It is only within the last 20 or 30 years that it has been found to have considerable possibilities for use as an insulating and arc extinguishing medium. At atmospheric pressure its dielectric strength is between two and three times that of air, while at an

62

*Figure 12.7   Typical vacuum switchgear unit with fixed circuit-
            breaker*

absolute pressure of about three bars it equals the dielectric
strength of insulating oil. The superior arc quenching ability of
this gas is partly attributable to the fact that it is electronegative,
which means that its molecules rapidly absorb the free electrons in

the arc path between the cb contacts to form negatively charged ions, which are ineffective as current carriers compared with the existence of the free electrons. This electron gathering action results in a rapid build up of dielectric strength at current zero.

In order to interrupt fault currents of the magnitudes found in today's distribution systems it is necessary to cause significant relative movement between the arc and the gas. In typical distribution cbs of the ratings being considered here this can be achieved in two or three ways. Until comparatively recently the most used technique was to have a piston connected to the moving contact which generated a blast of gas through a nozzle surrounding the contact gap. Today designs have appeared on the market which use magnetic fields to rotate the arc within the gas either using this relative motion alone to develop the necessary extinction power or using a secondary arc which generates thermal energy thus expanding the gas and driving a flow across the primary arc.

The gas is used mainly as the arc extinguishing medium but can also act as the insulating medium. In the latter case the cb can be contained within an earthed metal enclosure while in the former case the cb is normally housed in an insulating enclosure. For effective use in arc interruption the nozzle dimensions are usually chosen such that the arc blocks the gas flow during the main current period and then releases the gas as current zero is approached. This considerably reduces the necessary energy requirements in the cb. In those cbs, usually of the highest ratings, which utilise the puffer type of operation, the operating energies are of the same order of magnitude as those required for oil or magnetic acbs. SF_6 cbs using magnetic arc extinction have a somewhat smaller operating energy. The arc voltage generated during arcing in SF_6 lies between that of the vcb and the ocb. While SF_6 gas is very stable some decomposition occurs on exposure to an electric arc, the dissociation products being the lower order fluoride gases, SF_2 and SF_4, plus some metallic fluoride in the form of an insulating powder. These gases may be readily absorbed by filters of activated alumina. By this technique of absorbing the breakdown products the SF_6 cb is capable of a considerable number of short-circuit interruptions without requiring replacement of any active parts.

64

Oil switches

An oil switch has to fulfil all the duties performed by the cb except the interruption of currents much in excess of normal load. The parting of contacts in an oil bath normally suffices to interrupt low currents at voltages up to about 15 kV and the addition of some simple form of arc control device permits the switch to interrupt load currents satisfactorily at voltages up to around 36 kV. The addition of some relatively simple spring-operated mechanism to open the con-tacts in a controlled manner can lead to the development of a switching device capable of interrupting normal load currents at reasonable power factors, say in excess of 0.7, and to have some limited capability of interrupting inductive currents and capacitive currents of a few amperes. The same spring-operated mechanism can also be designed to close the contacts fully home satisfactorily in the event of closing on to a full short-circuit.

Such switches can be combined with fuses which can then clear short-circuit currents. These combinations are much used in the UK for secondary distribution systems where distribution transformers are connected to primary substations in the form of rings connected by cables. The fuse switch protects the transformer, while a switch is used to connect each of the ring cables. The three switches together with the fuses and the necessary cable termination arrangements can all be included in a single non-extensible device normally referred to as a ring main unit. Rings are operated with a normally open point, so that the use of load-breaking switches makes it possible to change the open point without disconnecting any of the load.

Other switches

For many years continental manufacturers have marketed air-break switches, usually using some form of gas-generating plastics to form an arc control device surrounding the contacts. The gases produced assist in the extinction of the arc in air and enable them to have a load-breaking rating. Given a suitable spring-operated mechanism such switches may also have a making capacity thus enabling them to be rated in the same way as the oil switch. They can also be combined with fuses to form ring main equipments. The use of modern plastics insulating materials can enable such air switches to be manufactured in a very compact form although this adds considerably to the cost.

With the introduction of the new technologies referred to earlier using the properties of vacuum and SF_6 gas, new designs of switches are also being placed upon the market using these materials. Where these are used they confer upon the switch device the same advantages that they currently confer upon the cb. However these are not currently in use in very large numbers and only time will tell whether an effective and economic substitution can be made.

COMPARISON OF CIRCUIT-BREAKER TYPES

Table 12.1 compares some of the main characteristics of the four different types of h.v. cb discussed. The rate at which the market is turning towards the newer technologies is evidence that the advantages which they offer mainly in terms of reduced fire risk and hence improved safety to operating personnel, and the reduced maintenance requirement which offers financial inducements to the user of such designs, are proving attractive to users.

HIGH VOLTAGE SWITCHBOARDS

It is essential to mount the cbs in either metal enclosed or metalclad housings. In practice the usual difference is that the current transformers (CTs) and cable terminations are accommodated in one compartment in a metalclad equipment. Whatever form of cb is housed in the cubicle some means of isolating the cb, at least from the busbars, has to be provided. This takes one of three forms: vertical withdrawal; horizontal withdrawal; the use of disconnectors or switch between a fixed cb and the busbars.

The last arrangement has only been used in recent years with vcbs, to take advantage of their very low maintenance requirements. Otherwise the bulk ocb, and some forms of vcb use the vertical isolation technique, while the magnetic acbs and the continental small oil volume cbs generally use horizontal withdrawal. The SF_6 cb is available in both forms, usually matching the national design of oil-filled switchgear.

The switchgear cubicle needs to be able to accommodate CTs and voltage transformers (VTs) usually connected in the circuit side of the system. In addition some mounting facilities for instruments and relays are usually provided, and it is necessary to make provision for the termination of cables. Typical metal enclosed switchgear units incorporating vacuum and SF_6 cbs are shown in figs. 12.7 to 12.10.

Cable termination is increasingly making use of modern air insulated techniques. The introduction of heat shrinkable plastics sleevings, some of which can be semiconducting which facilitates the grading of the electrical stress along insulation between the cable core and the sheath at the termination, have facilitated the adoption of this technique. These techniques can be used with paper insulated cables although originally introduced for the termination of polymeric insulated cables.

As the switchgear usually forms the most convenient point at which access can be gained to the main conductors of a distribution network it is usual to provide safe facilities for making connections to those main conductors. When the cb is withdrawable, then access to either the busbars or circuit side conductors can be obtained through the orifices into which the cb is normally plugged. When the cb is of the fixed type then separate orifices for testing and access to circuit conductors are provided.

Interlocking and padlocking. In order to ensure safe operation of switchgear, particularly when obtaining access to conductors for such operations as cable fault detection, phasing out, testing of cables, etc., it is usual to provide mechanical interlocks or padlocks to control access. The first interlocking requirement on all forms of withdrawal switchgear is to ensure that the cb cannot be withdrawn or plugged in while it is closed. Generally, metallic shutters are provided which automatically cover the plugging orifices when withdrawable cbs are removed from the switch cubicle. Similarly, facilities are made available so that these shutters can be padlocked in the closed position to maintain the full safety of the metal enclosed equipment.

Operation and maintenance. The most common position of the cb is in the normal service location so that when it is closed it connects the circuit to the switchboard busbars. It is usual for metal enclosed switchgear to incorporate secondary connections between the cubicle and the cb which are automatically made when the cb is racked into the service location. To ensure correct operation in service the interlock used to prevent the withdrawal of a closed cb must be in the correct position for cb operation.

67

Table 12.1 Comparison of h.v. switchgear characteristics with various interrupting media

Characteristic	I Air-break	II Bulk oil	III Vacuum	IV Sulphur hexafluoride
(1) Switching small inductive currents	At low currents the acb has a gentle extinguishing action and arcs for several half-cycles. This results in negligible 'current-chopping' and therefore negligible voltage surges.	Oil is a good insulator and arc extinction is more efficient than in acbs giving short arc duration and a greater degree of 'current-chopping'. The current chopped is less than 10 A and gives rise to measurable overvoltages in highly inductive circuits. The value of these overvoltages is not sufficient to cause damage to system insulation.	The vcb practically always interrupts at the first current zero, irrespective of current value. As the arc plasma is formed from metallic vapour derived from the contact surfaces, the stability of the arc at low values of current is a function of the contact material. The contact material in the interrupters made in the UK restricts current-chopping to values below 7 A, which is no worse than in ocbs.	The current-chopping behaviour depends somewhat on the means of arc extinction employed but is generally of the same order of magnitude as the oil and vcbs.
(2) Switching capacitance currents	For the same reason that acbs are gentle at extinguishing currents in inductive circuits they are prone to restrike when interrupting capacitance currents and have a very limited capacity for such duty.	Bulk ocbs employing two breaks per phase at 12 kV have a build-up of dielectric strength across each pole sufficient to ensure restrike-free capacitance current interruption.	The dielectric recovery of the vacuum gap is extremely fast, giving restrike-free interruption of capacitive currents up to the full load current rating.	With the electronegative characteristic the contact gap de-ionises quickly and restrike-free capacitance switching is assured.

(3) Mechanical behaviour

The international standards require 1000 no-load operations to be performed without attention and with negligible wear. Regular lubrication at this sort of operational interval is envisaged in the design.

The short travel and low energy require-ments assist the designer to construct a robust mechanism capable of matching the maintenance-free life of the vacuum interrupter. At least 10000 maintenance-free operations are usual.

The energy requirements usually fall between those of ocbs and vcbs, those with 'puffer'-type arc extinction needing the most energy which will obviously increase with rating. These cbs are also intended for long inter-vals between servicing - intervals of 10000 operations being normal.

(4) Disturbance during fault operation

(a) Pressure development

The rapid establish-ment of a heavy current arc in the arc chute generates high pressure and shock waves which have to be withstood by the mechanical construction. This leads to large and heavy arc chutes which are accordingly expensive.

The dissociation of oil into hydrogen and hydrocarbons by the arc current generates very high pressure within the arc control device, and this con-tributes to arc extinction. In the bulk ocb a proportion of this pressure is transmitted to the metal tank but the existence of an adequate air cushion in the top plate of the breaker helps to keep the tank pressure to modest proportions and the cylindrical design makes it a simple matter to con-tain this residual pressure rise.

The metallic vapour produced during arcing increases the vapour density in the contact region synchronously with the current. There is no general pressure rise within the interrupter, the envelope of which only has to withstand external atmospheric pressure.

Internal pressure is developed during fault interruption maybe two to three times the normal static pressure, but the insulating chamber is designed to allow for this.

Table 12.1 (contd)

Characteristic	I Air-break	II Bulk oil	III Vacuum	IV Sulphur hexafluoride
(b) Exhaust gas emission	Large quantities of hot ionised air are discharged from the arc chutes, creating a need for insulating cooling and ducting arrangements for safe discharge.	Modest quantities of exhaust gases are discharged from the ocb after passing through a baffle compartment within the top-plate which both cools the gases and separates the gas from the oil.	The vacuum interrupter is permanently sealed and all metal vapour produced during arcing condenses immediately. There is no emission of any sort.	The breaker is totally sealed so there is no gas emission. Some of the gas is dissociated into other SF compounds plus free sulphur. These other gaseous products are absorbed by special filters inside the cb.
(c) Mechanical reaction on foundations	Very heavy	Heavy	Negligible	Slight
(d) Noise generation	Heavy	Moderate	Negligible	Slight

(5) Fire risk

While no oil is used and no flammable gases are emitted, the hot exhaust gases produced during fault interruption con-stitute a minor fire risk.

The use of oil as the interrupting medium and the emission of flammable gases (hydrogen, acetylene, methane, etc.) during operation must con-stitute a fire risk. In practice, reputable designs rarely give rise to any fire unless some serious malfunct-ion occurs. The quant-ity of oil is not a factor either in the liability to fire or in the amount of damage created in the event of fire. In environments where fire could have serious consequences enclosed substations with fire precautions may be necessary.

Fire risk is neglig-ible as no flammable materials are used and no gases of any sort are emitted.

As for vacuum switch-gear.

Table 12.1 (contd)

Characteristic	I Air-break	II Bulk oil	III Vacuum	IV Sulphur hexafluoride
(6) Maintenance requirements				
(a) Routine	With conventional cbs routine maintenance involves the cleaning and lubrication of mechanisms, together with an examination of the contacts, arc control devices and insulating media with cleaning and replacement as found necessary. The frequency of this attention is dependent upon the duty required. It can vary from monthly servicing in a heavy duty industrial situation with several load switching operations every day to intervals of 3 to 5 years in many public supply installations. Oil cbs in frequent use need oil changes more often than any other attention, those with restricted quantities of oil requiring significantly more frequent attention than a bulk ocb.		Vacuum switchgear routine 'maintenance' consists of an inspection of the unit at infrequent intervals. This enables the condition of insulation and isolator to be examined and maybe the interrupter contact wear to be noted from the indicators provided. A record of the total number of operations can be kept from the counter which is connected to the mechanism. Experience soon indicates the desired interval between such inspections. In public supply installation it is unlikely that any replacement of parts will be necessary during the economic life of the gear, while for heavy duty industrial situations such replacement might be necessary after an interval of a few years.	SF$_6$ switchgear is designed for long life and infrequent maintenance. The rapid transfer of the arc from the contacts to the arcing nozzles assists this longevity. Ten year maintenance cycles are frequently the minimum requirement although regular visual inspection is always desirable. If access is required some simple safety precautions have to be observed and refilling with gas requires specialised equipment.

(b) Post-fault	It is normally recommended that maintenance after operation on fault is undertaken at the earliest opportunity so that the condition can be restored to the usual standard of security.		Post-fault maintenance is not necessary. It is suggested that units which have operated on fault should have an extra inspection when a suitable opportunity occurs in the normal course of operation.	As for vacuum switchgear
(7) Suitability for industrial systems	Industrial systems often result in onerous environments for the switchgear installation and add frequent operating duty as well. The comments above together with the operating duty require frequent maintenance attention, particularly in respect of insulation surfaces.	Very suitable for industrial applications, the only drawback being the need for oil and contact changes when the operating duty is severe. Oil maintenance is more frequent for small oil volume units.	Industrial situations with frequent operation provide the application where the advantages of vacuum switching are more apparent. The annual costs of vacuum switchgear in this environment are markedly less than the traditional types.	It is usually in the industrial environment that the infrequent maintenance is of greatest advantage. The mechanical requirements should be studied if frequent operating is required particularly if closing energy is high.
(8) Operational facilities				
(a) Integral fault-making earthing facilities	Except on heavy and expensive UK equipment designed mainly for power-station auxiliaries, air-break switchgear rarely has this feature. When required separate earthing trucks are used.	The vertical withdrawal with bulk ocbs used with bulk ocbs makes it simple to provide safe, integral, fault-making earthing by cb transfer.	Fixed cb vacuum switchgear has a system using the selectors for integral, fault-making earthing under padlock control. Otherwise operated as columns I or II depending on manner of isolation.	As for columns I or II depending on whether vertical or horizontal isolation is employed.

Table 12.1 (contd)

Characteristic	I Air-break	II Bulk oil	III Vacuum	IV Sulphur hexafluoride
(b) Injection test facilities		Require the removal of the cb and then test sticks can be inserted into the isolating sockets.	On fixed cb versions, separate test orifices are provided enabling test sticks to be inserted while the circuit is earthed as above. Other types as for columns I and II.	As for columns I or II.
(9) Factors in substation design	Substation width is dictated by the depth of the switchgear unit augmented by an access passage for cable termination at the rear of the units and a wide aisle in front of the switchboard to provide space for cb withdrawal and maintenance. The cost of the roof structure increases more than linearly with the span so this dimension plays a large part in determining costs. Switchgear types imposing dynamic loads on the floor during operation require expensive, rigid foundation arrangements. With switchgear having a fire risk, if there is a serious possibility of extensive consequential damage it may be decided to install fire-fighting equipment, e.g. CO_2 or other inert gas or sprinklers. Even if the risk is not considered great enough to warrant fire-fighting equipment, the larger switchboards are often sub-divided by fire walls, built across the substation, to reduce the likely damage in the event of fire.		With the fixed cb designs no maintenance or withdrawal space is needed so the substation depth can be minimised. No fire walls or fire-fighting equipment are required, floor loadings are light and the unit width is small so that substations can be smaller and lighter in construction than for traditional switchgear types, significantly reducing building costs. When withdrawable cbs are employed a deeper substation will be needed but savings in fire walls and fire-fighting equipment will still be made, thus contributing to more economical substation design.	SF_6 switchgear always has withdrawable cbs and the substation needs to leave space for this purpose, but as fire risk is negligible, fire walls and fire-fighting measures are unnecessary, leading to simple and compact substations.

74

Factors in sub-
station design
(contd)

The substation length is a function of the width of each switchgear unit plus the space taken up by any fire walls and associated busbar trunking. Because of the use of oil as the main insulation medium in the bulk ocbs this type would normally be narrower than either air-break or small oil volume for comparable ratings (see (2) above).

(10) Special factors

Air-break switchgear can be made with very heavy fault ratings and normal current ratings. As it is generally considered to have less fire risk than any ocb it is frequently chosen for installations where these factors outweigh a higher first cost. The frequency of maintenance is likely to be less than that for ocbs of comparable rating, but the high first cost and high sub-station costs together with the high cost of spare parts detract from this advantage.

Bulk oil switchgear has a long history of satisfactory performance under arduous conditions. Maintenance is frequent when service conditions call for a large number of operations per month but this is easy to do and costs of spares are reasonable. It is compact, which makes for smaller and hence cheaper, substations than air-break or small oil volume.

In many cases the vacuum switchgear sub-station can be sited where other types of switchgear would be unwelcome and this can usually lead to other economies, e.g. in cable costs. Running costs of vacuum switchgear show substantial savings over other types so the 'life-cycle' cost of a vacuum switchgear installation is usually significantly less than other types even when the effects of economic inflation are ignored.

Gas leakage is usually guaranteed at less than 1% a year and a gauge is often provided for monitoring purposes. Overhaul is likely to be rare, but when required needs more care and special equipment than the other types of cb reviewed here.

Figure 12.8   Typical vacuum switchgear unit with withdrawable circuit-breaker

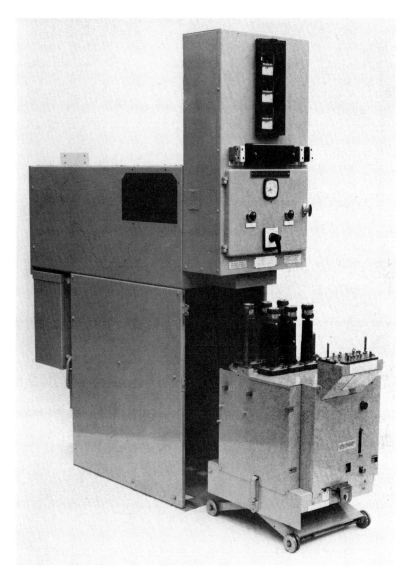

Figure 12.9 Typical SF$_6$ switchgear unit

Figure 12.10 SF$_6$ switchgear unit with horizontal withdrawal

Earthing.   It is standard British practice for earths to be applied
to distribution systems by using a proven fault-making device such as
the cb itself. The application of an earth to any system is normally
controlled through a permit-to-work system. This ensures that all
the necessary switching operations to make the relevant circuit dead
have been carried out before the system is earthed.

78

With vertically isolated switchgear it is convenient to use the facility of moving the cb into and out of the unit to provide earthing locations. These are illustrated in the case of a typical bulk oil switchgear unit in fig. 12.11. This shows typically the disposition of the VTs, CTs, instrument panel, etc.

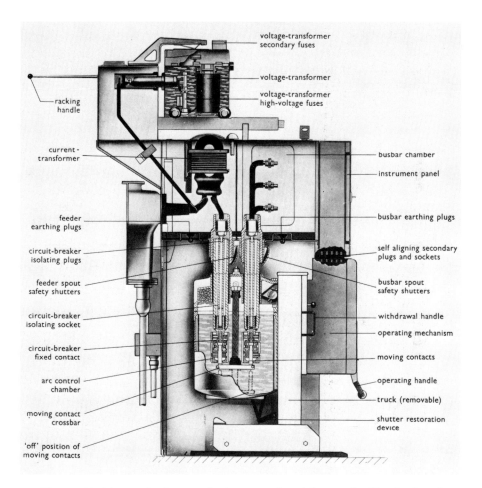

Figure 12.11 Typical UK switchgear unit with vertically isolated withdrawable bulk oil circuit-breaker

The selection of the correct location in which to raise the cb into either the service, circuit earth or busbar earth position is under padlock control.

Other methods in use for providing earthing facilities with proven fault-making capability are the provision of extension plugs for the cb itself so that it can be used in the service location with an earth connection to the other side of the cb. A further way is the provision of a special fault-making earthing switch which is interlocked with the cb so that the cb must be removed from service before the switch is used. Finally, the most expensive way of achieving fault-making earthing is by the provision of an alternative device which replaces the cb and its carriage and is so designed as to contain a fault-making earth switch, usually with facilities for carrying out tests as well.

Maintenance.   The maintenance of electrical switchgear is covered in some detail by BS 5405. This divides maintenance into three sub-headings of inspection, examination and overhaul.

Inspection, as its name implies, means a visual study of the switchgear and could include an operational check to ensure that all is in working order. It is normally necessary to take the cb out of service so that it can be inspected.

Examination means the dismantling of certain parts of the equipment so that hidden parts can be inspected in more detail. This generally means taking the unit out of service so that covers can be removed for testing of insulation or cleaning of busbars or other similar operations.

Finally, overhaul is the operation of refurbishing or replacing certain parts of the equipment to restore it to its original condition.

It is impossible to give detailed information on the various aspects of cb maintenance in a handbook such as this. Each manufacturer provides detailed instructions as to what operations to carry out and assistance and guidance as to the frequency of inspection, examination and overhaul.

LOW VOLTAGE SWITCHGEAR

Over the last few years there have been fundamental changes to the specifications for l.v. switchgear. These have been brought about chiefly by the introduction of IEC requirements. A typical single panel l.v. switchboard is shown in fig. 12.12.

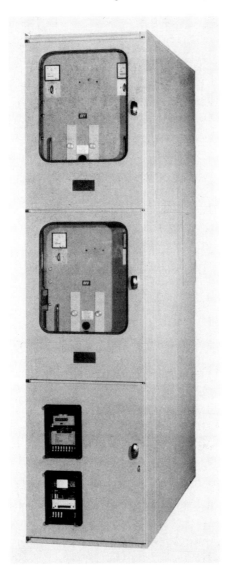

Figure 12.12 General arrangement of a typical l.v. switchgear panel mounting two air circuit-breakers

Today all l.v. circuit-breakers should be designed, manufactured and tested to IEC 157-1: 1973. BS 4752: 1977 is identical to IEC 157-1: 1973.

However, there are certain aspects of the current specification with which the user needs to be familiar:

(a) short-circuit categories

(b) method of short-circuit tests

(c) temperature-rise limitations/thermal ratings.

Short-circuit categories

IEC 157-1 has two categories of short-circuit performance outlined in table 12.2.

Table 12.2 Short-circuit performance categories

Short-circuit performance category	Rated operating sequence for short-circuit making and breaking capacity tests	Condition after short-circuit tests
P1	O - t- CO	Required to be capable of performing reduced service
P2	O - t - CO - t - CO	Required to be capable of performing normal service

O   represents a breaking operation.

CO represents a making operation followed, after the appropriate opening time (or immediately, that is without any intentional time delay, in the case of a circuit-breaker not fitted with integral overcurrent releases) by a breaking operation.

t   represents a specified time interval.

It can be seen that the P1 cb has to be capable of a type test duty O - CO at its ultimate short-circuit rating, while the P2 cb has to be capable of a type test duty O - CO - CO.

However, the most significant difference between categories P1 and P2 is that a P1 cb need only be capable of reduced service condition after the test, whereas the P2 cb has to be capable of continued normal service.

The reduced service condition of the P1 circuit-breaker means:

(a) It may not be capable of carrying its rated current without significant overheating, thus causing possible insulation degradation. Indeed, many P1 cbs will not carry more than 25% of their rated current satisfactorily after the O - CO duty.

(b) It may not operate automatically on overload in accordance with its tripping characteristic, thus endangering future discriminat- ion demand, but more importantly, failing to protect the circuit since it is unlikely to operate within the 1.45 × circuit rating limit as required by the 15th Edition of the IEE Installation Regulations.

It is clear, therefore, that the user would have little alternat- ive but to replace a P1 cb under these circumstances. The P2 cb can be reclosed for satisfactory continued service after completion of the short-circuit type test sequence.

It is therefore necessary that the user fully understands the differing aspects of the short-circuit categories and indeed should stipulate clearly in any specification for plant equipment whether a P1 or P2 category of performance is required.

Method of short-circuit tests

IEC 157-1 does not stipulate that a cb should be tested in an enclos- ure. However, what it does stipulate is that screens should be placed around the cb during short-circuit tests to simulate the proximity of the earth metal of an enclosure.

Unfortunately, this is too loosely interpreted by certain manu- facturers and testing authorities, since what is carried out is the placing of a wire mesh a certain distance above the cb arc chute vent. Assuming this test is satisfactory, this dimension is that usually quoted by the cb manufacturer in his literature as information con- cerning the mounting of the cb in an enclosure.

Unfortunately, the majority of switchboards are not constructed with mesh immediately above the arc chutes and if they were, there could still be restrictions above the mesh preventing exhaust of the arc products in the same manner as when the cb was short-circuit tested.

If the switchboard is constructed using a solid sheet a distance above the arc chutes, then when the cb operates under short-circuit conditions the arc products will reflect from this solid sheet and will be vented in a manner quite different to when the cb was origin- ally short-circuit tested.

The arc products consist of ionised gas which until adequately cooled and expanded readily conduct and permit an electrical discharge to either earth metal or live phase conductors, thus causing a secondary fault actually within the cb enclosure, while the cb is attempting to interrupt. The cb then fails to interrupt satisfactorily and this would probably result in an explosion in the switchboard.

Hence it is essential that the cb be short-circuit tested in an enclosure substantially the same as the enclosure in which it would be mounted in service, see fig. 12.13, and the short-circuit test certification the manufacturer produces for his equipment must be in this form.

IEC 157-1 does not clearly stipulate that a cb should be tested with the live connections to either terminal of the cb. The short-circuit performance of a cb can be considerably reduced when the live connections are connected to the lower terminals, unless the cb has been specifically designed for the same short-circuit performance irrespective of whether the live connections are connected at the top or bottom. (This reduction could be to only 25% of the short-circuit rating obtained with the live connections to the top contacts.)

Many cbs are not marked to state they should only have live terminals connected to the top contact, nor is the fact outlined in many manufacturers' catalogues.

If a cb is used as a bus-section or interconnector, then the live side could change dependent upon the method of connection of the distribution system. Hence the cb could be connected within the system in a manner which would result in it not being able to interrupt a short-circuit satisfactorily in the event of one occurring.

It is essential therefore that for this type of application the user must satisfy himself that the cb has been tested with the live connections to both the top and bottom contacts.

Temperature-rise limitations

Table 12.3 shows the temperature-rise limits specified in IEC 157-1. It can be seen, for example, that the temperature rise of a silver-faced contact in air is only limited by the necessity of not causing damage to the insulation, or adjacent parts. Hence the only limitations for acbs could be regarded as the temperature of the terminals at 70°C and the temperature of the manual operating means, i.e. 15°C (metal) 25°C (insulation).

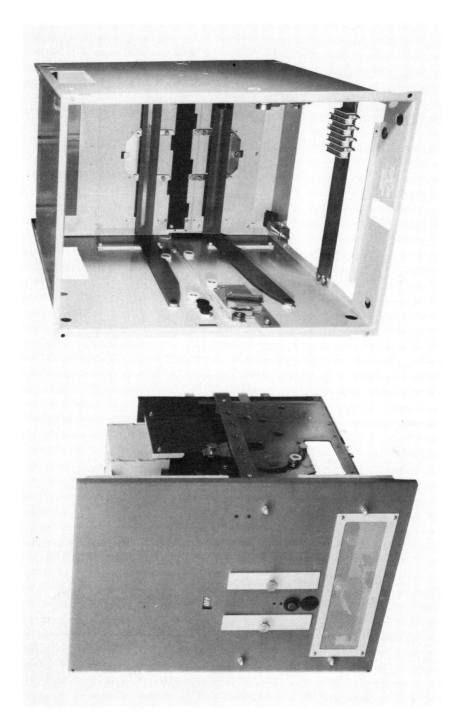

Figure 12.13 Low voltage air circuit-breaker with its housing for controlling the operating environment

*Table 12.3   Temperature-rise limits for the various materials and
parts*

Type of material, description of part	Temperature-rise limit (measured by thermocouple)
Contact parts in air (main, control and auxiliary contacts):	
copper	45 °C
silver or silver-faced*	(1)
all other metals or sintered metals	(2)
Contact parts in oil	65 °C
Bare conductors including non-insulated coils	(1)
Metallic parts acting as springs	(3)
Metallic parts in contacts with insulating materials	(4)
Parts of metal or of insulating material in contact with oil	65 °C
Terminals for external insulated connections	70 °C (5)
Manual operating means:	
parts of metal	15 °C
parts of insulating material	25 °C
Oil in oil-immersed apparatus (measured at the upper part of the oil)	60 °C (6)

*
The expression 'silver-faced' includes solid silver inserts as well
as electrolytically deposited silver, provided that a continuous
layer of silver remains on the contacts after the endurance tests and
the short-circuit tests. Contacts faced with other materials, the
contact resistance of which is not significantly altered by oxidat-
ion, are treated as silver-faced contacts.

(1) Limited solely by the necessity of not causing any damage to
    adjacent parts.
(2) To be specified according to the properties of the metals used and
    limited by the necessity of not causing any damage to adjacent
    parts.
(3) The resulting temperature shall not reach a value such that the
    elasticity of the material is impaired.
(4) Limited solely by the necessity of not causing any damage to
    insulating materials.
(5) The temperature-rise limit of 70 °C is a value based on the con-
    ventional test of Clause 8.2.2.2. A cb used or tested under
    installation conditions may have connections the type, nature and
    disposition of which will not be the same as those adopted for the
    test; a different temperature rise of terminals may result and
    this will have to be agreed.
(6) May be measured by thermometer.

Thermal ratings.   The ampere rating a manufacturer quotes for his cb is a 'Thermal current rating'. This rated thermal current is defined as the rated thermal current of unenclosed equipment, equipped with suitable overcurrent releases, if applicable. It is the maximum current stated by the manufacturer that the equipment can carry in an 8 hour duty when tested in free air, without the temperature-rise of its several parts exceeding the limits specified in table 12.3. Free air is defined as that obtained under normal indoor conditions reasonably free from draughts and external radiation. Unenclosed equipment is equipment without an enclosure of equipment supplied by the manufacturers when an enclosure forms an integral part of this equipment.

The definition above of rated thermal current is more comprehensive than the definition at present in IEC 157-1, but this is the interpretation of the clause used by cb manufacturers. Hence, ampere ratings quoted in manufacturers' catalogues are 'free-air ratings' and users must understand this rating is not necessarily the rating of a cb when mounted in a switchboard.

Enclosed ratings.   The enclosed rating of a cb is defined as the rated thermal current of enclosed equipment. It is the maximum current stated by a manufacturer that the equipment can carry in an 8 hour duty when mounted in a specified enclosure without the temperature-rise of its several parts exceeding the limit specified in IEC 157-1.

This rating is not defined in IEC 157-1, but it is the one the user should consider. The normal full load current of a cb must not exceed its enclosed rating. Many basic cb units are incorporated in what is generally known as a withdrawable cradle. This is a simple housing without a top and hence does not control the environment of the cb when it is installed in a switchboard. Therefore, dependent upon the switchboard environment, the enclosed rating of a cb can be considerably less than the rated thermal current, since the rated thermal current of the cb will have been established when the unit has been tested in free air.

Hence for totally satisfactory operation of the equipment in service, the ampere rating of the cb must be established in the switchboard, since the enclosed rating can be affected by the degree of ventilation afforded in the switchboard, the size of connections to the cb and the size of cables installed by the user. It is also dependent upon the number of cbs installed in a pillar.

It has now been recognised that considerable confusion has been caused by categories P1 and P2 primarily because the specification does not clarify adequately the fundamental differences between a cb designed to meet a P1 performance only and one designed to meet a P2 performance. Basically, a P1 cb requires to be inspected and possibly replaced after a short-circuit operation, as outlined earlier.

For total reliable and satisfactory performance of the switchgear when installed in service, the cb must have been certified in its full operating service environment. It is essential that the cb and switchboard construction be short-circuit tested to verify satisfactorily the performance of the cb when mounted in the switchboard, and the suitability of the connections from the cb in the switchboard, under fault conditions. The revision of IEC 157-1 which is now being prepared will stipulate these requirements, and also clarify their interpretation.

Responsibility

In consequence of the arguments outlined, it is clear that the manufacturer of a switchboard, whether he be the original manufacturer of the cb supplying a product of integrated design or a switchboard builder who incorporates a cb in his own cubicle design, is responsible for verifying that the total switchboard unit performs satisfactorily in service. This necessitates producing test certification which directly relates to the parameters of the environment in which the cb is to operate in service.

Switchboard assembly

Segregation.   To restrict a fault in one section from spreading to another, simplicity is often the key to reliability. Tools, etc., left in the switchgear after a maintenance period are known to be the most common cause of internal faults, hence the simpler the construction of the equipment the less likelihood of a mislaid tool being overlooked. A fault on one circuit must not be permitted to develop

88

into a fault on another. If a tool is left inside a switchboard and a fault develops, the fault will move away from the power source along the power connections until a restriction is reached. If this is a busbar fault then the fault can run from one unit to the next if inter-unit segregation in the form of barriers is not installed.

If segregation is fitted, then the fault is restrained at the barrier and will not spread into the adjoining section while the cb clearing the fault operates.

Any fault produces a high degree of ionised gas and the ultra-violet light during arcing encourages the striking of arcs in other regions. Hence segregation between one circuit and the next is essential if the fault on one circuit is to be restrained from developing on other healthy circuits.

Busbar and cable accommodation. In general, busbars consist of a three-phase, four-wire arrangement, i.e. three phases plus neutral, and run throughout the length of the switchboard. They should be certified to confirm the design will withstand the system fault level, including the neutral busbar, which under certain circumstances can be subjected to a full short-circuit current, for at least the period of time the protective device requires to clear the fault condition. The busbars themselves should be physically disposed with respect to each other such that the short-circuit forces which exist during fault conditions are minimised.

The main circuit supplies to and from the switchboard in the majority of installations are through copper or aluminium cables and particular consideration to the physical arrangement of cable accommodation should be made. In particular the space allocated for the glanding and trifurcating of three- and four-core cables should be in accordance with BS 5372, see fig. 12.14.

The design of the cable glanding arrangements should be such that it is possible to bond it to the system earth, to maintain earth continuity and minimise the earth loop impedance of the protective earth sheath of the cable. A typical arrangement of busbars and cable terminating facilities is shown in fig. 12.15.

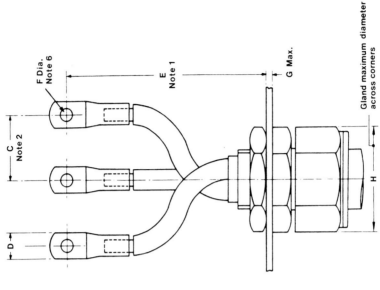

CABLE SIZE mm²	CONDUCTOR MATERIAL	E mm	D PALM WIDTH mm	F FASTENER mm	G GLAND PLATE mm MAX.	H GLAND A C mm MAX	SEE NOTE
2·5	STRANDED COPPER	70	16	M6	5	35	5
4		80	20	M8	5	41	5
6		85	20	M8	5	54	
16		125	22	M8	5	54	5
25		140	22	M8	5	54	
35		155	22	M8	5	58	5
50	SOLID ALUMINIUM	180	25	M8	5	58	5
70		205	27	M8	5	73	
95		225	30	M10	6·5	73	5
120		235	32	M10	6·5	100	5
150		255	35	M12	6·5	100	
185		280	40	M12	6·5	100	5
240		315	45	M16	10	110	
300		355	50	M16	10	110	5
400	STRANDED ALUMINIUM	180	65	M20	10	100 SINGLE CORE ONLY	5, 7

NOTES:

1. Drawing based on BS5372:1976 (Cable terminations for electrical equipment) with allowance for cable gland nose projection.
2. Dimension 'C' shall permit a minimum clearance of 19mm between:
   (a) Live parts of differing phase (AC)/polarity (DC) ⎱ When associated cables
   (b) Live parts to earth—   ⎰ are fitted.
3. This drawing is applicable to 1, 2 & 4 core cables as well as the 3 core illustrated as typical.
4. This drawing is applicable to the use of glands to CEGB standard 120502 (draft) BS6121 or BS4121.
5. Generation division rationalised cable size.
6. Gland & terminal centres must be in nominal alignment (single core cables only).
7. Clamping washer to BS4320, Table 2, Form C, large diameter, normal thickness, steel cadmium plated.
8. Fasteners of M10 and below shall be of brass to BS2874 Class C2114 (hard) or Class C2116, or steel, or equivalent.

Figure 12.14 Cabling details for l.v. switchboards

90

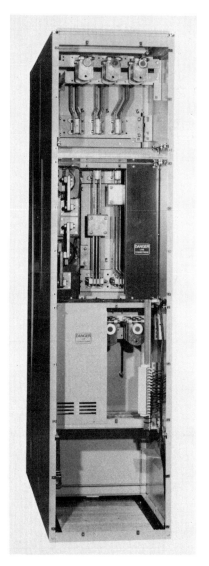

Figure 12.15 Low voltage switchgear unit showing metal segregation
of busbar and cable side connections

Circuit-breaker

<u>Mechanical and electrical interlocking</u>.   Interlocking prevents the
failure of the plant due to maloperation of the equipment by the
operator. For example, interlocks are required on withdrawable cbs to
ensure that a closed cb cannot be removed from the busbar or put onto
the busbars.

Table 12.4 Earth loop and protective conductor impedance[*]

Z_s (1)	$I_{\Delta H}$ (2)	Z_B (3)	$I_{\Delta H} \cdot Z_B$ (4)	t (5)	Max. fuse ratings GEC 'T' Type	Max. mccb rating without E/F relay	
						Max. thermal setting	Max. magnetic setting
(ohms)	(A)	(ohms)	(V)	(s)	(A)	(A)	(A)
4	60	0.85	51	4.6	20		
3	80	0.65	52	4.1	25		
2	120	0.45	54	3.4	32		
1	240	0.2	48	5.0	63		
0.9	266.6	0.19	50.6	4.7	63		
0.8	300	0.17	51	4.6	63		
0.7	342.86	0.15	51	4.6	80		
0.6	400	0.125	50	5.0	80		
0.5	480	0.1	48	5.0	100		
0.4	600	0.085	51	4.6	125		
0.3	800	0.065	52	4.1	160	160	700
0.2	1200	0.04	48	5.0	200	250	1100
0.1	2400	0.021	50.4	4.8	355	400	2100
0.09	2666	0.019	50.66	4.7	400	630	2400
0.08	3000	0.017	51	4.6	400	630	2400
0.07	3428	0.015	51.4	4.4	450	800	3000
0.06	4000	0.013	52	4.1	500	800	3000
0.05	4800	0.01	48	5.0	630	800	4000
0.04	6000	0.0085	51	4.6	710	800	5000
0.03	8000	0.007	56	3.0	800	800	7000

[*] Typical earth loop and protective conductor impedances relating to GEC acbs, fuses and mccbs, which will ensure automatic disconnection in case of an earth fault on a 240 V phase-to-earth system in less than 5 seconds, complying with the protection against electric shock requirements of the 15th Edition of the IEE Wiring Regulations.

[†] Maximum full load current.

[‡] Time multiplier setting.

(1) Earth loop impedance.
(2) Maximum possible earth fault current at 240 V phase-to-neutral.
(3) Maximum impedance of protective conductor.
(4) Touch voltage on earthed metal of equipment.
(5) Permissible duration time of touch voltage.

Max. acb rating with CT 271 relay		Max. acb rating with CDG 11 relay		Max. acb/mccb rating
Relay set at 60% MFLC[†] (A)	Relay set at 10% MFLC (A)	Relay set at 40% MFLC TMS at 1.0 (A)	Relay set at 10% TMS[‡] at 0.1 (A)	With EFD relay operated from core balance CT
80	500	30	400	Any ratings of
100	600	35	500	acb or mccb can
150	1000	40	800	be tripped
350	2000	150	1600	within 60 ms by
370	2200	166	1600	an earth fault
400	2500	166	2000	detector relay
476	2800	190	2280	operated from a
550	3000	250	2500	core balance CT.
666	3500	300	3000	The relay is
833	3500	330	3500	preset at any
1100	3500	363	3500	earth fault
1600	3500	750	3500	setting from
3300	3500	1400	3500	10 A to 100 A.
3500	3500	1550	3500	
3500	3500	1666	3500	
3500	3500	1710	3500	
3500	3500	1818	3500	
3500	3500	3000	3500	
3500	3500	3333	3500	
3500	3500	2000	3500	

<u>Operation during earth fault and overcurrent conditions</u>. The whole
aspect of the cb function is to interrupt and isolate the circuit
safely in the event of fault conditions. Apart from its operation
during short-circuit conditions, which has been referred to under
'Specification and testing', the operation during earth fault and
overload conditions must be carefully understood.

An earth fault can develop on a system but may only result in a
relatively low fault current flowing, which could be substantially
less than the normal full load current of the cb, and hence not sensed
by the cbs integral protective device as being a fault condition. It
is essential, however, that this type of fault be detected and isolated
as soon as possible in order to avoid injury to personnel and the
possibility of a serious fire risk.

It is usual for earth fault protection to be incorporated within
the switchboard which trips the cb via a shunt trip mounted within its
mechanism. It is important, however, that the installer of the switchboard recognises that the earth loop impedance of the system needs to
be matched to the type of protective device fitted, and typical
examples are given in table 12.4.

A circuit cannot withstand an overload indefinitely and therefore
for adequate protection the cb overload device should be set to interrupt the circuit in less than 2 hours at an overload no greater than
1.45 times the circuit rating. One important aspect that should be
recognised referring back to the section on short-circuit categories,
is that a P1 cb after interrupting a short-circuit may not operate in
accordance with this criterion since its overload device may have
suffered damage due to the short-circuit. Hence if the cb were to be
closed after the fault had been rectified, it might not operate automatically in less than 2 hours if an overload of 1.45 times the
circuit rating occurred, resulting in possible overheating and permanent damage to the circuit.

<u>Disconnection</u>.   Positive disconnection of the circuit is essential,
particularly during maintenance. Circuit-breakers which incorporate
the ON/OFF indication as part of their operating handle will generally
only achieve full disconnection of the circuit when the handle is in
the OFF position, i.e. disconnection of the circuit may not be achieved

in any other position. Circuit-breakers which incorporate a separate
indicator to the operating handle, generally give positive contact
position, irrespective of the handle position, since the indicator is
usually driven directly from the contact system. However, it is
essential that the safety procedure of ensuring the circuit is dead
should be adhered to before work on any circuit commences.

Discrimination

The requirement that a fault on one circuit should not spread or
affect another circuit has been discussed with respect to the mechanical configuration of the switchgear, i.e. segregation. However, it
is also important to consider discrimination since a lack of full
discrimination results in a fault on one circuit affecting another
circuit, equipment of which is mechanically separate from that of the
faulty circuit.

In the event of a fault on the system the cb nearest the fault
should be the only one that operates even though other cbs could be
seeing some aspect of fault contribution. If full discrimination is
not obtained during short-circuit or overload conditions, then the
supply to healthy circuits is affected and this is totally unacceptable
where high reliability and the need for essential supplies is required.

Short-time rated cbs.   If fault discrimination is required, cbs with
only an instantaneous rating cannot be considered since during short-
circuit conditions their tripping times will be similar. This will
result in the unit close to the fault and cbs nearer the supply tripping. If the user requires full discrimination during both overload
and short-circuit conditions, it is essential he uses cbs with a
short-time rating. This means that unless the cb is close to the
fault, it should be capable of withstanding the fault without tripping,
while the cb close to the fault clears.

Typical ratings of short-time cbs are 50 kA for one second, which
indicates that the cb is capable of carrying that fault current for
one second without tripping or damage that will affect performance.

Instantaneous circuit-breakers.   Feeder circuits furthest away from
the power source can be simple instantaneous devices, i.e. they do

not need to discriminate. Typical ratings of instantaneous devices
are 50 kA with a fault clearance time of 0.025 second.

Current-limiting circuit-breakers.   These cbs are also instantaneous
units, but operate in considerably less than 0.025 second. The unit
operating in 0.025 second will let through the full peak value of the
short-circuit. Hence, the risk of serious damage and fire cannot be
ignored. The current-limiting cb, see fig. 12.16, restricts the fault
energy let through, thereby reducing the serious risk of fire.
Typical operating times for current-limiting cbs are for clearance of
the full short-circuit in less than 0.01 second. Figure 12.17 shows
clearly that for a prospective peak short-circuit value of over
100 kA, the cb 'cuts off' the fault, such that the maximum peak that
is attained is less than 50 kA.

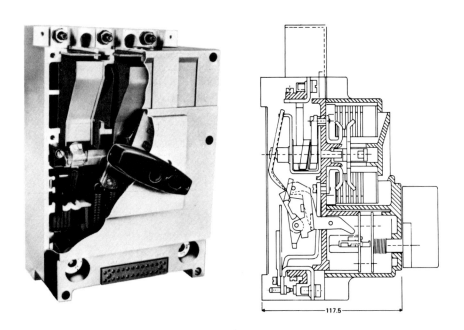

Figure 12.16   Typical current-limiting circuit-breaker

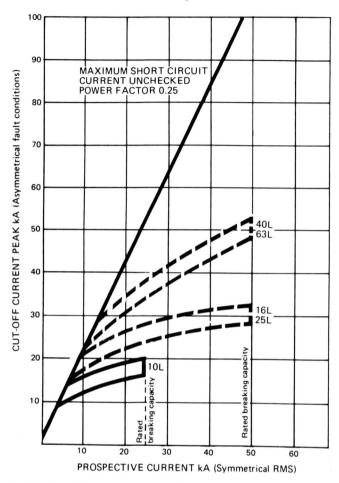

Figure 12.17 To illustrate the effect of a current-limiting circuit-breaker on the prospective fault current

Low voltage switchgear protection

Low voltage cbs are either fitted with electromagnetic protection devices or thermal/magnetic protection devices, but it is not uncommon for units to be supplied also with their protection fed from auxiliary relays. Auxiliary relays are generally used since their greater flexibility over both the electromagnetic and thermal/magnetic units can enable full discrimination to be obtained on an extensive and complex distribution system. However, auxiliary relays need auxiliary supplies and require space on the switchboard assembly and these can be expensive.

Static overcurrent protection devices.   The advent of new semiconductor techniques over the past few years has led to the development
of static overcurrent protection units.   These units are self-contained
and are generally mounted on the cb, since they require no auxiliary
supplies.   They provide a highly reliable and accurate means of protection, in addition to offering the same degree of flexibility as the
conventional type of auxiliary relay referred to earlier.

Low voltage distribution systems are often controlled and protected
by combinations of the following: acbs, mccbs and fuse switches.

Difficulties in achieving full discrimination between these three
types of switchgear are sometimes encountered due to the differences
in their operating characteristics.   Air circuit-breakers are usually
controlled by relays or direct-acting series overload devices, both
having an inverse time overcurrent characteristic combined with an
instantaneous characteristic which usually produces a high knee-point
on the overall time current curve.   Fuses have an extremely inverse
time characteristic which is almost a straight line.

The solution is to replace the inverse time overcurrent protection
on the acb with a solid state relay having the combined facilities of
both very inverse time overcurrent and independent time overcurrent
characteristics both of which can be selected to suit the system.
Hence, instead of having the limitation of conventional protection, an
acb fitted with solid state units can be adjusted to any one of a
number of curves as illustrated typically in fig. 12.18.

The advantages of solid state units over conventional relays can
be summarised as follows:

Solid state device has no moving parts.

Characteristic unaffected by differences in temperature.

Flexibility of time/current characteristic.

High degree of accuracy.

High reliability.

Ease of testing (plug-in facility).

Maintenance free.

Close overload protection assured due to the ease of selection of
control settings.

Earth fault protection available.

98

No external auxiliary supplies necessary.

Close pick-up/drop-off ratio.

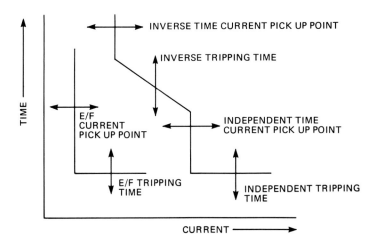

Figure 12.18   *Illustrating the wide range of adjustable operating*
curves provided by solid state protection devices

The solid state unit operates from CTs generally fitted within the cb module and these provide adequate power to operate the electronic circuitry and also to trip the cb, i.e. no external supplies are required with this method of protection, fig. 12.19.

Figure 12.19   *Type CTZ solid state protective relay*

99

ERECTION OF SWITCHGEAR

The switchgear cannot be assembled in the factory and shipped to site as a complete plant, so it is necessary to pack the equipment in its individual cubicles, ship to site and eventually erect it. Erection includes the setting in place of these cubicles, their interconnection both mechanically and electrically, the fitting of any extra relays together with the power and control cables. The chambers may have to be filled with insulating media of different types.

Once the equipment has been erected it needs to be commissioned, which is defined as the work of testing and finally placing in service of the installed apparatus. Before being put into service tests must be carried out on the complete equipment to prove that it meets the required specification.

Storage

It is best to deliver the switchgear cubicles at a time convenient for their immediate erection. However, it sometimes happens that the site works are delayed in which case the switchgear must be stored carefully until it is needed.

On delivery it is important to check that all items are present and correct in accordance with the delivery note and then to store these components carefully to ensure that no parts go astray. At all times, care must be taken to maintain the condition of the stored items, precautions must be taken to ensure that the equipment is properly stacked, for example, and that it is kept clean and dry. If possible, arrangements should be made to keep the building temperature in excess of the dew point so that condensation on the equipment is prevented and thereby the plant is protected from corrosion.

Erection

Before commencing erection it must be ensured that the workforce is in possession of all the required drawings and instructions required to erect the equipment, which are normally provided by the manufacturer. The substation in which the switchgear is to be erected should be as clean and dry as possible and all debris should have been cleared away. During erection particular attention should be paid to a number of points.

Exclude dirt and debris from partially erected cubicles. All openings that are not in immediate use should be blanked off or covered by clean sheets. All electrical insulation should be kept clean and dry by being kept covered and if necessary, heated. Materials which have been issued from the stores and not yet used on erection should be stored safely and tidily. When handling the cubicles and major components care should be taken to observe the correct lifting arrangements and to make certain that slings are attached to the manufacturer's designated lifting points. This ensures that no parts are subjected to undue strains or sudden stresses which could result in disturbed settings or other damage.

Foundations. The successful erection and operation of the switchboard depends very largely on the accuracy of the foundations. The most useful form of fixing medium for the type of switchboard considered here is some form of proprietary channel embedded in the floor, containing captive adjustable nuts. These channels should be assembled truly parallel and level and should project slightly above the surrounding floor. This is so that the switchgear can be clamped to the channels themselves which are then known to be at the correct level. Less commonly nowadays holes may be cast in the floor in which suitable foundation bolts can be grouted after the switchgear has been erected carefully.

General assembly. It is normal to commence the assembly of a distribution switchboard from the centre unit. This minimises any effect of a build-up of errors as the equipment is erected. Any inter-unit tie-bolts are loosely positioned as erection proceeds, and all units lined up onto the centre unit. Plumb lines should be used on each unit to ensure good alignment. When all units have been placed in position and checked for alignment the inter-unit bolts may be tightened and checks made that any withdrawable portions may be entered or withdrawn smoothly. Instrument panels and any other component details should then be added to the switchboard.

Busbar and circuit chamber assembly. The actual section of the busbars to be used should be quoted on the manufacturer's drawings and care must be taken to ensure that the appropriate section is used for a particular unit.

Contact surfaces must be cleaned carefully before assembly using fine emery cloth where the surface of the contact is of natural finish and using a proprietary silver polish if the surfaces are plated. Where the connections have threads these should be cleaned with a fine scratch brush. After cleaning, the joint faces must be wiped with a clean lint-free cloth to remove any dust, and the joints assembled as soon as possible.

Normally, the lower busbar is connected up first, with the joints insulated as required, ensuring that a good electrical connection is made between all copper faces and that all securing nuts are tight. The next bar to be assembled will be the centre one and finally, the top one.

The same treatment of joint faces must be carried out on all other connection joints within the circuit chamber, such as connections for VTs.

The manufacturer's instructions should be checked carefully to see whether any or all of the joints which have been made on site require to be insulated. If this is required then the components needed should have been supplied with the equipment and the instructions given by the manufacturer should be followed carefully, particularly in respect of any recommended safety precautions.

Cabling. The preparation of the cables for connection to the switchgear is a specialist occupation and an experienced jointer should be employed for this purpose. The cable has to be laid carefully to avoid tight bends and the length to the cable lug measured very carefully to avoid any stress on the cable once the joint has finally been made. Minimum bending radii for cables are specified in BS 6480: 1969.

Insulation of the exposed cable insulation and of the joint is frequently provided by means of heat shrinkable plastics sleeves. These should be applied and terminated in accordance with the manufacturer's specific instructions.

Occasionally, paper cables are still terminated in compound-filled boxes and where this is the case care should be taken to ensure that the compound used is continually stirred during the melting period to avoid excessive heating and possible burning of the compound at the bottom of the boiler. Care must be taken to ensure cleanliness of the cable box and all utensils associated with this operation. The cable box itself, and any buckets or ladles which are used in the operation, must be pre-heated before use and the compound at the appropriate temperature should be poured slowly to avoid splashing and the inclusion of air bubbles. When the cable box is filled to its indicated level, the compound should be allowed to cool slowly, avoiding draughts. If the compound falls below the indicated level on cooling, it should be topped up while still warm to ensure a good bond between the main mass and the topping layer.

Earthing. Each unit forming part of any installation must be earthed by means of a copper strip fastened by a bolt or stud connection. This earth strip must be continuous and connected to all units and fastened to the main earth. All joints must be cleaned and treated as busbar joints. Special attention should be paid to the earthing of cable sheaths at cable glands.

Oil filling. Where chambers have to be filled with insulating oil on site it should first be checked that the oil supplied is in accordance with the manufacturer's recommended grade. All electrical oils must conform with BS 148 and the oils must be tested for electrical breakdown before filling, as described in BS 148 and BS 5730. The equipment must be filled to the indicated level, and it is advisable to fill VTs after they have been positioned on the switchgear. The indicated level is usually based on an ambient temperature of 15°C, and if the actual site temperature differs considerably from this then due allowance should be made.

Small wiring. It is usually necessary to complete small wiring connections between the instrument panels on adjacent cubicles and to connect external multicore cables to the control cable terminating boxes which are usually mounted at the rear of the switchgear units. If it is not already contained on the wiring diagram, a useful aid to ensure correct connection for multicore cables is to list the cores

103

in order and record the appropriate connection to be made to each
core at each end of the cable.

Final inspection

After the switchboard has been finally erected, all securing bolts
tightened, all busbars and other connections completed, all insulation
finished, cables connected and small wiring completed a final inspection should be made. The following is a typical, but by no means
exhaustive, check list.

(a) Before fitting covers, all chambers should be checked for complete
     cleanliness and the absence of all foreign matter.
(b) Once the covers have been fitted, it should be checked that all
     fixing screws are in place, and secure.
(c) All labels, where required, should be fitted and visible.
(d) Any mechanical interlocks should be checked; safety shutters,
     where fitted, must be checked to be operative.
(e) All withdrawable items should be proved to be capable of extract-
     ion and isolation as required.
(f) All fuses and links should be inserted in the appropriate holders.
(g) All exposed insulation surfaces must be clean and dry.
(h) A final check should be made for continuity of earthing.
(i) All tools used in the erection of the switchboard should be care-
     fully accounted for.

ELECTRICAL TESTING AND COMMISSIONING

Routine factory tests will have been carried out during manufacture in
order to check design criteria and the maintenance of the supplier's
standards. These tests provide a valuable reference when any query is
made concerning the apparatus during its commissioning tests and operational life. Commissioning tests are conducted on site after
installation of the equipment. These are to ensure that the apparatus
will perform its duties in service, that interconnection with other
equipment is correct and to provide data for future maintenance and
service work. The conducting of these tests also provides valuable
training for the purchaser's operating staff. Normally, such tests
are carried out once only, after installation, prior to putting the
apparatus into service. The most common form of commissioning test is

to simulate operating conditions using portable voltage and current sources. A test log should be maintained listing all tests carried out, the results and objectives.

Typical commissioning tests include: visual checks, earth impedance measurements, insulation resistance checks, current and voltage transformer checks, portable primary current injection testing, cb operation checks, control and scheme tests, secondary current injection testing and load testing.

Visual checks. The object of such a check is firstly, to ensure the mechanical integrity of the equipment. Then all electrical connections made on site should be checked to the appropriate diagram to ensure their correctness. Check that all fuses and links are in place and have been fitted with the appropriate fuse wire or cartridge.

Insulation resistance checks. Insulation resistance measurements on all small wiring should be carried out at 500 V d.c. This test is to ensure that such wiring is in good condition. Any apparatus which may be damaged by application of such a voltage, e.g. static protective devices for instance, should have the appropriate terminals short-circuited for the duration of this test. When measuring the insulation resistance to earth of the individual circuit, all other circuits should be normal, i.e. earth links closed and d.c. circuits normal. This ensures that the insulation of the particular circuit is satisfactory both to earth and to all other circuits.

It is impractical to give a definitive lower limit for the resistance measurement from this test. Such readings are dependent on the cable length, the size of cores and the number of parallel paths. As a guide, any reading of less than 1 megohm at 500 V d.c. should be investigated.

Current and voltage transformer checks. Normally the VT and CT wiring will have been completed at the manufacturer's works and only if this wiring has been disturbed is it necessary to carry out any tests on site. Should this be the case then one essential test to be carried out is to ensure that the CT secondary winding has been connected correctly in relation to the primary winding. Should this have been reversed in any phase then the operation of the protection will have been seriously affected.

All CTs have some means of identifying the primary and secondary terminals, common practice is to identify as P1 - P2 (primary 1 and 2) and S1 - S2 (secondary 1 and 2) as recommended by BS 3938, with test windings identified as T1 - T2.

The following test is recommended to prove these relative polarities: fig. 12.20. A low reading d.c. voltmeter is connected across the CT secondary winding terminals and a battery across the primary. If relative polarities are correct, on closing the circuit a positive 'flick' is observed on the voltmeter, and on opening the circuit a negative 'flick' is seen. Where CTs are mounted in transformer bushings it is necessary to short-circuit the main transformer l.v. winding, thus reducing the equivalent impedance of the transformer to give a good deflection of the instrument needle. Voltage transformers may be checked in similar fashion.

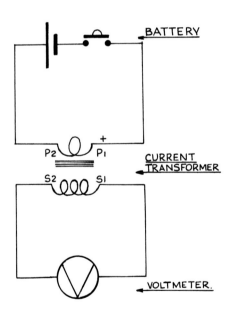

Figure 12.20 Circuit required to test for CT terminal polarity

Proving of protection.   The operation of the various forms of protection which can be fitted to distribution switchgear is covered in chapter 19. Suffice it to say here that the operation can be

simulated either by injecting heavy currents through the CT primaries
or by the injection of suitably chosen currents into the CT secondary
circuits. In some instances the CTs may be fitted with a special
tertiary winding intended for test purposes in this way. Whichever
method is adopted, the intent is to inject currents which represent
fault conditions of various types and to check that the relevant
relays operate correctly, and that any auxiliary relays which are
called upon to perform, do so also in a correct manner.

To adjust the current settings it is normal to use a variable
auto-transformer to provide the supply. As the waveshape of the test
current can have an influence on the behaviour of the relay it is
recommended that as much series resistance as possible should be
included in the injection circuit.

High voltage tests.   If called for in the contract documents h.v.
tests can now be applied to the insulation. The test values should be
those laid down in the appropriate standard for site testing and
should be applied by an a.c. h.v. test set or, particularly if the
cables have been connected, an equivalent d.c. test set. Where vcbs
are in use it is usually recommended that a commissioning voltage test
be applied across the open interrupter as a check that the vacuum is
still in perfect condition.

Circuit-breaker operation tests.   Following the completion of insulation testing the cbs should be checked for operation. These checks
should cover tripping and closing operations from both local and
remote positions. These tests should preferably be carried out at
minimum and maximum supply voltages. It should be checked that
correct indication of the closed and open position is given both by
the mechanical and any electrical indicators which are fitted. The
correct operation of the interlocks should be checked. Not only
should one ensure that the permitted operations can be undertaken but
that the interlocks prevent the carrying out of prohibited operations
as intended.

Before carrying out these tests care must be taken to ensure that
the circuit is isolated from any source of power supply.

Load testing.   Once all the checks on the equipment have been carried out, the operational tests are satisfactory, the voltage tests passed, and all the functional tests on relays, etc. completed to the customer's satisfaction, the equipment can be energised. Once the circuit is on-load it can be checked that all the instruments and indicators are reading correctly.

If test blocks are available or the relays have test plug connections it may be worthwhile doing a final check to see that the CT polarity is correct and the instrumentation is giving correct readings.

Chapter 13

Rotating Machines

D. B. Manning, CEng, MIEE
Mawdsley's Ltd

Electricity is a particularly attractive form of energy in that it
can easily be produced, transmitted and converted into some other
form. The commonest form of energy into which electricity is
converted is mechanical driving energy and more than 60% of electrical
energy produced is utilised in this way. Conversion of energy from
its electrical to mechanical form is achieved using electric motors.
The vast bulk of industrial electric motors is used to drive pumps,
fans and compressors. All industrial installations, whether manufacturing units or complex process plants, include electric motors often
of many types, sizes and voltages to suit a wide variety of applications.

Often much abused, electric motors are expected to perform
efficiently and reliably for many years with the minimum of maintenance. In relation to the cost of the energy they convert they are
extremely inexpensive. Typically, the electrical energy costs of
supplying a motor can equal the prime cost of the motor in only two
months of operation. Installation, cabling and control gear costs
will perhaps double or even treble this period but this is still a
small cost in the normal expected machine life. Many motors supplied
over 50 years ago are still performing well in plants around the
world.

Therefore, selection of the right type of machine for the application and duty and correct installation and maintenance of the
machine is as important as the machine design itself.

This chapter concentrates on motors but does make reference where
appropriate to alternators. Similarly, reference is limited to machines up to 11 kV.

MOTOR TYPES

All motors fall into one of two classes, those suitable for use on
a.c. supply and those suitable for d.c. systems.

Alternating current motors

There is a large range of a.c. motors available, the most widely used
being the cage design.

Cage motors.   Three-phase cage rotor induction motors are available
in ratings up to 10 MW. Essentially simple and robust in construction
they have a distributed stator winding which establishes a rotating
field and a rotor comprising copper or aluminium bars welded or brazed
at each end to a short-circuiting ring. It is the 'cage' appearance
of the rotor which gives rise to the name by which the machines are
known. In smaller motors the cage must be cast in aluminium alloy
such as LM6.

The rate at which the field rotates is determined by the number of
poles on the distributed stator winding and on the supply frequency.
The more common rates or synchronous speeds are given in table 13.1.
The synchronous speed, Ns is given by

$$Ns = \frac{f}{p} \times 60 \text{ rev/min}$$

where f is the supply frequency (Hz) and p, the number of pole pairs.

Table 13.1 Synchronous speeds

No. of poles	Synchronous speed (rev/min)	
	50 Hz	60 Hz
2	3000	3600
4	1500	1800
6	1000	1200
8	750	900
10	600	720
12	500	600
14	428	514
16	375	450
18	333	400
20	300	360

Cage induction motors do not run at a synchronous speed because
the torque they produce depends upon the speed difference or slip

between the speed of the rotating field (synchronous speed) and the lower speed of the rotor. The slip however is quite small, can be predetermined within limits by motor design, and will be about 5% on a small 10 kW motor reducing to less than 1% on motors above 100 kW.

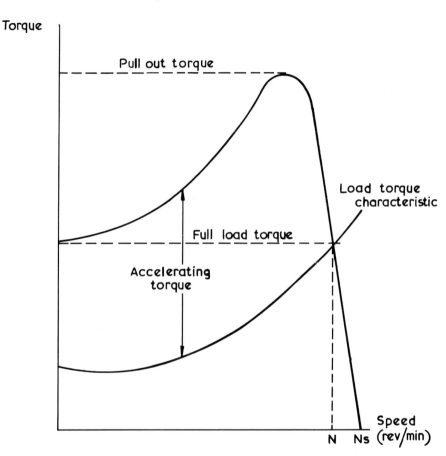

Figure 13.1 Cage motor speed/torque curve

The speed/torque relationship of fig. 13.1 is typical in shape for a cage motor started direct-on-line. The motor operates at the point where its speed/torque curve intercepts the load characteristic at speed N. Slip rev/min = Ns - N. The vertical difference between motor and load speed/torque characteristics is the accelerating torque. Clearly therefore the motor torque available must always exceed the load requirement up to the operating speed if the load is ever to reach full speed.

111

Starting currents. These are quite high and are up to eight times full load current for machines up to 30 kW and up to six times for larger motors. Except at the extremities of supply lines the system capacity is normally adequate to supply these currents without too much voltage drop. Where the starting currents are likely to be an embarrassment special high resistance or deep slot rotor bars can be used which reduce the starting current to below five times full load current. These are by definition special machines and more costly so that reduced voltage starting is a more usual method of restricting the starting current (chapter 15).

Whether star-delta or auto-transformer reduced voltage starting is employed it is important to remember that while the starting current will be proportional to the applied voltage, the starting torque will theoretically be proportional to the square of the applied voltage, see table 13.2. In practice, the effect of stray losses reduces further the available starting torque at reduced voltage.

If reduced voltage starting is used then a careful check must be made to ensure that accelerating torque is available.

Table 13.2 Nominal starting currents and torques

Starter type	% applied voltage at start	% full load current at start	% full load torque at start
Direct-on-line	100	700	120
Star-delta	58	400	40
Auto-transformer	80	560	77
Auto-transformer	70	490	59
Auto-transformer	50	350	30

Slip ring induction motors. Much less widely used are slip ring induction motors where the cage rotor is replaced by a distributed wound rotor, the three-phase rotor winding being connected to slip rings mounted on the shaft. Under normal operation the slip rings are short-circuited and the rotor behaves exactly as a cage rotor. The advantage of the wound rotor slip ring machine lies in the possibility of inserting external rotor circuit resistances during the starting period.

The rotor control gear can be arranged to be switched sequentially, automatically reducing the values of resistance in the rotor circuit as the motor runs up to speed. A family of speed/torque characteristics, one for each resistance value, is generated as shown in fig. 13.2.

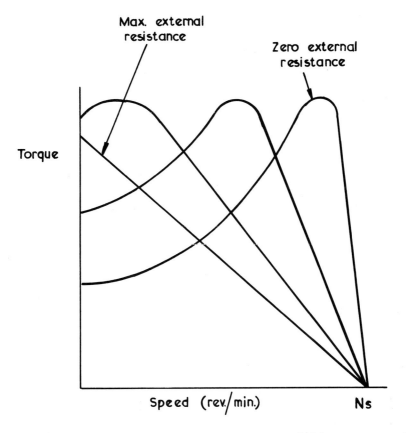

Figure 13.2 Family of speed/torque curves for different external rotor resistances on a slip ring induction motor

The number of resistance steps can be chosen appropriate to the starting torque requirements and starting current limitations. The external resistors usually take the form of metallic grids and if appropriately rated, allow the motor to run for long periods at reduced speeds. Very large slip ring motors may still from time to time employ liquid rotor resistors for starting. These are better able to dissipate the heat generated and the speed variation during start up is stepless. The high losses appearing as heat in the rotor circuit resistances prevent this system being more widely used for economic continuous reduced speed running.

The principal disadvantages of the wound rotor motor compared with the cage machine are higher prime cost of motor and starting equipment and increased maintenance due to the slip rings and brushes.

Synchronous machines.   Synchronous machines are most commonly encountered as alternators in the range up to 5 MVA as standby power generators or even as main base load generators in remote areas. As motors, synchronous machines above 5 MVA are used mostly where their ability to generate reactive power and so improve the power factor of the installation, coupled with their slightly higher efficiency offset their higher cost when compared with the cage motor.

Synchronous machines are almost always brushless. The increased availability in recent years of thyristors and diodes has enabled design engineers to dispense with slip rings and to opt for static excitation and brushless systems.

The construction of the majority of brushless synchronous machines comprises a stator with a distributed winding and a rotor with salient pole field windings. These are supplied through a rotating diode rectifier assembly fed by a shaft mounted exciter as shown in fig. 13.3. For economic reasons the exciter for larger power ratings is itself controlled using a pilot exciter or static excitation regulator. Although the machine runs at synchronous speed without any slip the rotor lags behind the rotating field by a variable angle, known as the load angle. This is approximately proportional to the load imposed upon the motor. Starting of synchronous motors depends upon the size and rating. Smaller machines, say up to 10 MW, are usually started as cage motors utilising pole face damping windings or linked solid pole faces as the cage. Above that rating they may employ pony motors or even variable frequency power sources to accelerate from rest to almost synchronous speed.

High speed (two-pole) synchronous machines almost certainly have cylindrical rotors due to the problems of centrifugal forces on salient poles although in general turbo-type machines are available only at powers in excess of 10 MW.

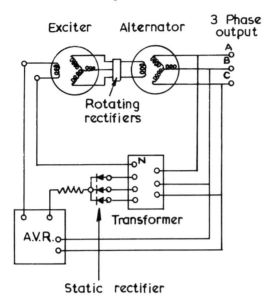

Figure 13.3   Three-phase brushless alternator with automatic voltage regulator

Synchronous reluctance motors.   The majority of fixed speed drive applications tolerate the slip rev/min associated with induction motors.   Nevertheless some applications do require a precise known drive speed.   Synchronous reluctance motors, available up to about 250 kW, fulfil this need.   An example of their application is as a drive machine on a buffer or uninterruptible power supply where the output frequency of the alternator must remain the same as the input frequency to the motor alternator set.

Essentially the synchronous reluctance motor has a stator with a distributed winding for the appropriate number of poles or speed.   A shaped laminated rotor with a cage winding follows the rotating field at exactly the same speed but with a variable load angle.   A typical machine is shown in fig. 13.4.

Started as cage induction motors they draw large starting currents and run at relatively low power factor.   On the other hand, they are extremely robust and inexpensive.

115

*Figure 13.4 A typical Mawdsley synchronous reluctance motor rated at
15 kW and 1500 rev/min*

Direct current motors

Far from being old fashioned, d.c. motors continue to be widely used
even though few factories have a d.c. power distribution system. Once
again it is the thyristor regulator which, in conjunction with one or
more d.c. motors, provides a very formidable and flexible variable
speed drive system. Direct current motors have apparently changed
little over the years and still retain a salient pole stator to
accommodate the field or excitation windings and interpoles. The
rotor is a distributed winding in slots soldered, brazed or welded to
the segments of a commutator.

In fact the construction has changed to recognise the particular
characteristics of thyristor regulators. Modern d.c. motors have
laminated poles and the smaller machines even laminated yokes. The
laminated construction helps to improve commutation by allowing the
magnetic circuit to respond more quickly to flux changes occasioned
by thyristor regulators. Square frame designs recently appearing on
the market have much improved power/weight ratios together with other
advantages, fig. 13.5.

One outstanding advantage of d.c. motors is the accessibility of
the field winding and the possibility therefore to influence the

excitation by field forcing to achieve very fast response drives.

Figure 13.5   A Mawdsley's square frame industrial d.c. motor rated at 250 kW with forced ventilation

VARIABLE SPEED DRIVES

Increasing energy costs are resulting in a widening acceptance of variable speed drives. Particularly on pump and fan drive applications, large energy cost savings are possible by adopting variable speed drives in preference to throttling by valves or dampers, fig. 13.6. The energy cost savings can quickly repay the capital cost of the speed control equipment.

In the example given in fig. 13.6 a pump running at 100% speed is delivering 40 m³/min and operates at point A where its head/volume characteristic, 1, intercepts the system characteristic, 3. The pump flow is to be reduced to 30 m³/min. Two possibilities exist:

(a) The pump flow may be restricted or throttled which produces a new system characteristic, 4 and the pump then runs at intercept B.

(b) The pump speed may be reduced by 16% which gives a new pump head/volume characteristic, 2 and the pump then operates at intercept C.

117

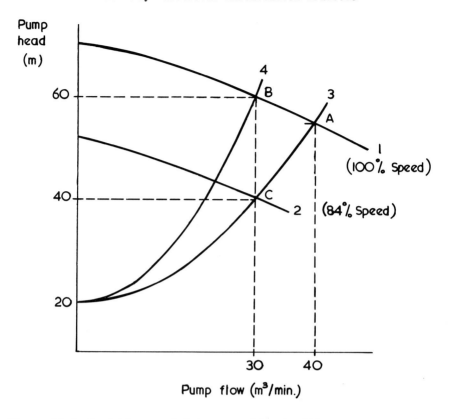

Figure 13.6 Variable speed drives provide significant energy savings

The power absorbed by the pump at B is approximately 330 kW and at point C, 220 kW. Thus in this example the power saving possible by pump speed adjustment rather than by throttling is 110 kW.

For process and process line control, for example in continuous production processes such as rubber, plastics, paper and metals, variable speed drives are essential. The ability to control motor speeds means that other process variables can be accommodated and that product quality and production rates can be optimised.

Alternating current variable speed drives

There are a number of a.c. variable speed drives available, the choice often being dictated by the requirements of the application. Gaining in popularity are variable speed inverter controlled cage motors, especially for single motor pump and fan drives.

Variable frequency inverters.   Apart from single motor drives,
variable frequency inverters have for some time been employed on
multiple motor drives such as steel mill run out table applications.
The advantage here is that several usually identical motors can be
supplied in parallel from a single inverter in order that they all run
at the same speed at any time and the speed of the group can be controlled as a whole.

Thyristor regulators are presently in use which provide controlled
adjustable frequency outputs up to 15 MW. Depending on rating, the
regulators may comprise one of two predominant systems.

Fixed voltage d.c. link.   The link is supplied from a free running
diode bridge which in turn feeds a thyristor or transistor chopper
unit. The chopper output is a series of pulses which build up an
alternating current, fig. 13.7. This is known as a pulse width modulated (pwm) system in which the voltage output is controlled normally
in proportion to frequency output so that the motors they supply
receive constant flux conditions.

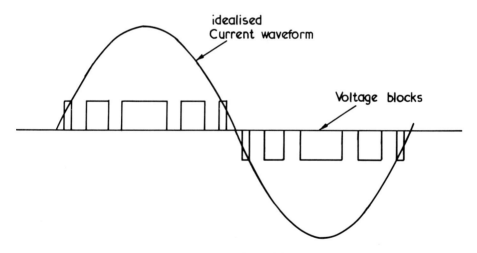

Figure 13.7 Output waveforms of pulse width modulated (pwm) inverter

Variable voltage d.c. link.   These are current or voltage fed
inverters which have a conventional thyristor regulator as the input.
The chopper unit is more simple, its output frequency being determined
by the d.c. link voltage. Known as quasi square-wave inverters they

119

also maintain constant output voltage to frequency ratio and commutate or switch only at output frequency rate, see fig. 13.8.

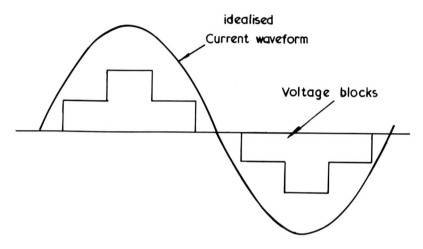

Figure 13.8   Output waveforms of quasi square-wave inverter

Variable frequency inverters are used to control the speed of cage motors up to 800 kW. Above 800 kW the machines used are synchronous motors because they are able to provide the reactive kVA necessary for commutation. The inductance of the cage motor distributed stator windings has a profound smoothing effect upon the current in the stator. The current thus approximates closely to a sine wave. Obviously any harmonic currents present produce heat without contributing to the output torque of the motor. In general, the harmonic currents present require derating of both cage and synchronous motors by between 10 and 15%.

Additional motor derating is probably necessary if they are to run below normal full speed for extended periods unless the cooling system is independent of speed.

Static Kramer drives. Based upon the slip ring induction motor the static Kramer drive relies on extracting energy from the rotor and recovering it either electrically or mechanically. The rotor energy at slip frequency is rectified and fed via a line commutated inverter back into the a.c. supply, fig. 13.9a. A transformer is usually necessary to match the recovered and supply voltages. Alternatively, the rectified rotor energy may supply a d.c. motor mounted on the a.c. motor shaft, fig. 13.9b.

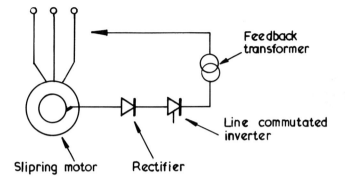

Figure 13.9a Electrical slip energy recovery of static Kramer drive

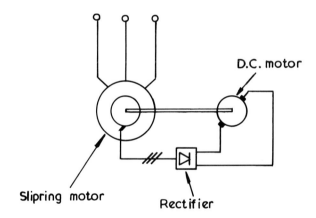

Figure 13.9b Mechanical slip energy recovery

The speed control is stepless and is from sub-synchronous speeds down to zero. However, the rating of the energy recovery equipment is proportional to the speed range and the system is therefore economical only for short speed range applications such as pump drives. The ratings of static Kramer drives can be anything between 50 and 5000 kW.

Static Scherbuis drives.   When the energy recovery equipment assoc-iated with static Kramer drives is arranged to inject power into the slip ring induction motor rotor, as well as to extract it, then the drive is known as a static Scherbuis system and although more complex than the Kramer, it is capable of speeds above synchronous.

Alternating current commutator motors.   The rotating brush arm Schrage and regulated NS motors are Scherbuis drives from which the static Scherbuis has been developed.

All the drives described except the inverter fed cage motors are not now so common due largely to their higher costs and maintenance requirements.

Eddy current couplings.   The attraction of eddy current couplings is their ability, in conjunction with conventional cage motors, to provide a variable speed output by control of the coupling excitation. Sub-synchronous speeds only are possible since they operate effectively as slipping clutches. They also at reduced speeds dissipate energy in the form of heat and are usually limited to ratings below 15 kW. Much larger couplings are available up to several hundred kW but these require water cooling to dissipate the heat generated and are therefore not popular or economical.

Direct current variable speed drives

Variable speed d.c. drives have been widely used for many years in particular for process line speed control. They have always proved to be very reliable in service and planned maintenance techniques have successfully increased mean times between failure due to the funda-mentally simple commutator and brush assembly, to periods much longer than associated control equipment.

The original Ward Leonard systems were superseded by magnetic amplifiers and mercury arc rectifiers and then, in the early sixties, by thyristor regulators for the speed control of d.c. motors.

A more recent development has been that of the switched reluctance motor.

Switched reluctance drives.   This type of drive uses a reluctance motor which has salient poles on both rotor and stator. The distrib-uted three-phase winding on the stator is replaced by a number of salient pole d.c. field windings. The number of poles, as in the case of d.c. motors, does not determine motor speed. The rotor is built up of shaped laminations and carries no winding at all.

Unidirectional current pulses are applied sequentially to the field poles at a rate determined by the required speed and rotor position. Control of the pulse timing is derived from a position transducer mounted on the motor shaft. By appropriate pulse timing either positive or negative torques can be achieved and full four quadrant control is available over a wide speed range and both constant torque or constant power characteristics can be provided.

<u>Thyristor controlled d.c. drives.</u>   The development of thyristors having increasing current carrying capacity and reliability permits d.c. motors to retain predominance as the most popular form of variable speed drive. Almost all present designs are for fully controlled thyristor regulators.

Anti-parallel connected suppressed half or circulating current regulators in conjunction with d.c. motors allow full four quadrant control. Armature control provides a d.c. motor with constant torque characteristics and field control provides constant power characteristics. Combined armature and field control is common on winder and coiler drives.

The thyristor controlled d.c. motor is usually fitted with a tachogenerator which provides a speed related signal for comparison with the reference signal. It is the error or difference between these signals which advances or retards the firing angle of the thyristors in the regulator to correct the d.c. voltage and hence speed of the motor, figs 13.10a and 13.10b. In addition to, or instead of using the motor speed, other parameters such as current, load sharing, web or strip tension and level may be employed.

MOTOR APPLICATION
For reliable performance, the correct motor must be selected for the application. Torque and starting requirements can easily be identified. The choice of motor type is largely determined by rating and whether fixed or variable speed is necessary.

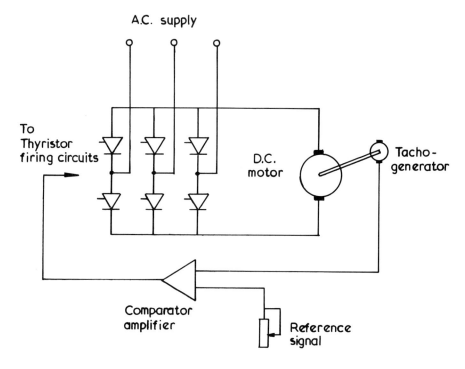

Figure 13.10a   A three-phase six-pulse thyristor bridge and d.c. motor

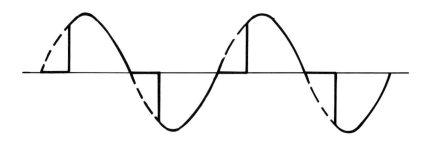

Figure 13.10b   Delayed firing of thyristor reduces mean d.c. voltage

Voltages

On a.c. motors, the supply voltage is determined by motor rating. It is difficult to lay down hard and fast rules when relating voltages to motor outputs. Up to 150 kW it is usually l.v. There is a grey area between 150 and 750 kW when the supply voltage can be from 380 V to 6.6. kV. Higher voltages of around 11 kV would be expected on ratings above 750 kW.

Mounting

Mechanically, the type of load determines whether the motor shaft is to be horizontal or vertical and the particular mounting necessary.

Bearings

The types of bearing incorporated depend on rotational speeds and radial or axial shaft loadings. Designers pay particular attention to bearings to maintain the highest level of operational reliability. Modern anti-friction bearings, of the ball and roller type, are selected to give an L10 life of 100000 hours. This means that, given lubrication in accordance with manufacturer's recommendations, fewer than 10% of the bearings will fail within the 100000 hour life.

The larger and high speed motors incorporate oil lubricated sleeve bearings. Typical threshold ratings for sleeve bearings are for two-pole machines, 2000 kW and for lower speed machines, 5000 kW. Oil lubrication may be of the oil bath type or, for higher bearing loadings, forced oil circulation.

Enclosure

A motor installed outside in a coastal situation must have a different form of enclosure from that of a motor installed down a coal mine or in a computer room.

The degrees of protection to which motors are constructed are specified in National and European standards such as BS 4999, Part 20 and IEC 34-5. For a clean environment an 'open' machine may be perfectly acceptable. Screen protected, drip proof, splashproof and totally enclosed machines are commonplace.

The degrees of protection, or IP numbers most commonly met are:

IP 21 Screen protected against solids greater than 15 mm and against vertically falling dripping water.

IP 22 Protected against solids greater than 15 mm and against dripping water falling at any angle up to 15 degrees from the vertical.

IP 23   Protected against solids greater than 15 mm and against water
         falling as a spray at any angle up to 60 degrees from the
         vertical.

IP 44   Protected against solids greater than 1 mm and against water
         splashing from any direction.

IP 54   Protected against dust and against water splashing from any
         direction.

IP 55   Protected against dust and against water jets from any
         direction.

The letter 'W' inserted between IP and the designation numbers
indicates that the machine is also weather protected to limit the
ingress of rain, snow and airborne particles.

Ventilation and cooling

Some heat is produced in all electrical machines as a result of
copper, iron, friction and windage losses. The main loss and therefore greatest heat produced is in the windings as a consequence of
copper losses. These equate to the I^2R in the windings. Improved
winding and slot insulation allow motors to run hotter without necessarily shortening the machine life. A hotter machine provides greater
kW/unit volume, i.e. smaller machine for a given output. Smaller
motors are less able in general to dissipate the heat produced and
often incorporate some external method of heat removal. The accepted
forms of cooling are specified in BS 4999, Part 21 and IEC 34-6. Some
of the methods most often encountered are indicated below.

Self-ventilating (IC 01).   A fan is mounted on the rotor shaft which
draws surrounding air through the motor from one end to the other and
discharges it to the atmosphere. This method cannot be used in a
dirty or moist environment without adversely affecting machine life.

Force ventilated (IC 06).   An independent separately driven fan is
mounted on the machine which forces air through the machine. The
separately driven fan can be fitted with filters to remove dirt in the
air, although if the environment is dirty the filters would quickly
become choked and the motor overheat. Where filters are fitted it is
usual to provide protection in the form of a differential pressure

switch to measure the pressure drop across the filters and to shut
down the plant, or at least raise an alarm when the pressure drop
becomes excessive.

Force ventilation is used in particular for variable speed drives
where a shaft driven fan becomes ineffective at reduced speeds.

Totally enclosed fan cooled (IC 0141).   Here the motor is totally
enclosed and the fan mounted on a shaft extension external to the
machine. It draws air from the surrounding atmosphere and a simple
cowl directs the air over the surface of the motor along its length.
The body of the motor normally incorporates cooling fins to increase
the surface area exposed to the cooling air. An internal shaft driven
fan is fitted to move the air inside the motor to minimise hot spots
in the windings.

This method of cooling is particularly common on cage induction
motors up to about 500 kW which are produced in vast quantities.

Closed air circuit, air cooled (IC 0161).   Usually encountered on
machines above 500 kW which are required to operate in dirty or difficult environments, the motor has a shaft driven fan which circulates
cooling air through the machine and around a closed circuit. An air-
to-air heat exchanger, itself cooled by a separate fan, shaft or more
usually separately driven, extracts the heat from the closed air
circuit. This cooling system is usually referred to as CACA.

Closed air circuit, water cooled (ICW 37A81).   In this case the heat
exchanger of the CACA machine is replaced by an air-to-water heat
exchanger. The material from which the water tubes are made depends
upon water quality. This method of cooling is more efficient than the
air-to-air exchanger so that, for the same output, a closed air
circuit water cooled (CACW) motor tends to be smaller than one which
is CACA. However, water is not always available and when it is the
attendant pipework, valves, pumps and installation costs do not always
favour CACW.

In order to extract the heat within the motor, air is forced
through axial holes in the rotor core and often also through radial
slots in the rotor. Design of the machine cooling is exacting,

requiring that temperatures within the machine are kept as even as possible from one part to another so avoiding hot spots. Keeping the temperatures even increases the utilisation of material and minimises size and cost. Typically the temperature variation from one part of the winding to another is about 15°C. It is of course the highest temperature which determines the motor rating.

Noise

The ventilation system is a major contributor to the noise generated by a motor. For effective cooling the air has to be turbulent within the motor and heat exchanger with a good scrubbing action. This applies also to totally enclosed fan cooled machines which generate additional noise due to the air being directed by a cowl and rudimentary fan.

Larger and more modern motors often incorporate sound absorbing material into their construction.

A two-pole cage motor with CACA ventilation may produce a noise level of 95 dBA if not acoustically treated while a lower speed CACW motor with acoustic treatment may produce only 75 dBA. Because the dB scale is logarithmic a noise level of 95 dBA is ten times greater than one of 75 dBA.

Noise levels in industry are becoming important considerations and the subject of various codes and standards. This is due to the permanent damage to hearing resulting from excessive exposure to high noise levels.

Insulation

Improvements in insulation materials and techniques permit higher temperatures. Insulation materials do not suddenly break down at some threshold temperature, they gradually age and deteriorate. The temperatures permitted by British and European standards for each class of insulation are such as to give an insulation life of 15 years. Exceeding the allowed temperature reduces the insulation life by about half for each additional 10°C. Conversely, the insulation life is doubled for each 10°C working temperature below the stated limit. The absolute temperature of the windings and insulation is the criterion but these are always expressed in terms of a temperature rise above an

ambient temperature, normally of 40°C. It is rare in the UK and many
other countries to find an ambient temperature of 40°C even though the
ambient is the air immediately surrounding the motor rather than the
outside temperature. For water cooled machines the accepted datum for
water temperature is 30°C.

Clearly the temperature rating of a motor is more of an art than a
precise science and it may be perfectly acceptable to exceed allowable
temperatures for short periods, such as during starting, providing
that subsequent running is at a lower temperature level. The insulation life can then be estimated and providing it is not less than 15
years there may be no need to use a larger and more expensive motor.

However, it is obviously essential to determine the frequency of
starting, starting currents and other duty cycle data in order to
size a machine correctly.

Winding temperature protection can be provided by motor makers in
the form of thermostats or thermistors embedded in the stator windings. Unfortunately it is not possible to fit them in the rotor
windings but the motor designer is aware of the temperature gradients
in the machine and is able to select a protection operating temperature
which is appropriate. On d.c. machines the temperature detectors can
be fitted in the interpole windings. While not in the armature windings, they are at least in the armature circuit and do more accurately
monitor the armature temperature. The protection is usually arranged
to shut down the plant although on some essential duties additional
protection may be fitted which operates at a lower temperature in
order to give an advanced warning of an impending shut down. At least
the warning will give the operator an opportunity of initiating a controlled plant shutdown.

STORAGE

Efforts should be made to minimise the deterioration of the machine
during storage on site or in a warehouse. Dry conditions, protected
from damp and condensation and from extremes of temperature, are
obviously desirable. Ingress of dust to a machine on site should be
avoided, especially of concrete dust which may be present if building
and civil work are still going on. Machines should not be stored in
an area which is subject to vibration since this could cause damage to

the bearings. If some degree of vibration cannot be avoided then the shaft should be turned by hand every few weeks to load different parts of the bearings.

Where doubt exists about the dryness of the storage area and the machine is fitted with anti-condensation heaters it may well be worth considering using the heaters during storage. If the heaters are used for this purpose the safety aspects should be borne in mind and terminal box covers be replaced and warning notices attached. It is important to inspect the machine in storage every six months or so and to maintain protective coatings on bright parts which may be liable to rust.

INSTALLATION

Careless installation can affect the life and operation of a machine. Contractors and users are urged to follow the machine manufacturer's instructions. General considerations are indicated below.

Checking

Machine manufacturers are not always made aware of any need to pack machines specially for prolonged storage. Storage, for however long, may have been under unsuitable conditions and it is essential to check before installation that the motors have not deteriorated. While signs of rusting are obvious, the insulation resistance may have been affected by moisture. If, on checking, the insulation is found to be less than 1 megohm the machine must be thoroughly dried out.

However careful the manufacturer may have been to pack the machine for difficult storage conditions, damage can occur in transit. The storage period may be considerably longer than was envisaged at the time the machine was despatched. Close inspection of the machine prior to installation is therefore essential. Included in the check should be the nameplate data to ensure that it is appropriate for the actual site supply and other operating conditions. Machines should certainly not operate in flammable, dangerous or corrosive conditions unless they have been specifically designed and supplied for the purpose.

Any dust should be blown out of the machine and a detailed inspection, particularly of any machines fitted with commutator or slip rings, should be undertaken to ensure that no damage has resulted from exposure due to chemical and corrosive fumes.

Bearing grease, except in the case of sealed for life bearings, must be checked and if necessary replaced if it has deteriorated during storage. Shaft clamps which may have been fitted to minimise the risk of brinelling during storage should also be removed.

Erection

The machine must be mounted on a solid and level foundation in order to avoid vibration. For a foot mounted machine design the foundation is often a bedplate of fabricated steel upon a reinforced concrete plinth. Where this is the case the bedplate foundation bolts must be adequately proportioned and the bedplate packed so that when it is finally pulled down onto the plinth it is flat and correctly aligned. Only when flatness and alignment are established should the bedplate be grouted down to provide a solid homogeneous base for the machine.

The cost of manufacture and installation of bedplates is high and machines are now often bolted down directly onto a concrete foundation using foundation pads set into the concrete, fig. 13.11.

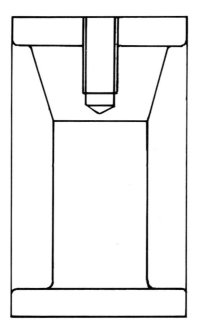

Figure 13.11 Cast iron foundation pad

Foundation pads are usually cast iron with a top machined face and longitudinal tapped hole. The body is normally fluted for the best possible bond in the concrete. The pads are bolted onto the machine feet and the machine itself packed up on the concrete foundation for correct alignment. When the machine has been aligned the foundation pads are permanently grouted into pockets in the concrete. After final alignment and level have been satisfactorily established, dowel holes are drilled through diagonally opposite motor feet and into the foundation pads and dowel pins inserted, fig. 13.12. The use of dowel pins greatly facilitates any subsequent reinstallation of the machine on its foundation. Once the foundation pads have been permanently grouted in they behave and function in exactly the same way as a conventional fabricated or cast bedplate.

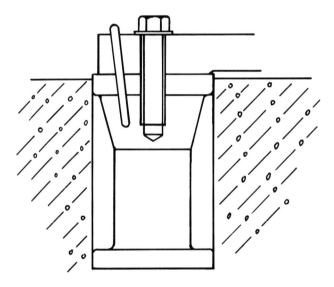

Figure 13.12 Dowel pin in place

Minor alignment or height adjustments or a change of machine are accommodated by the use of shims under the machine feet. On metric machines, the height of the shaft centre line above the underside of the feet has been standardised and that dimension in millimetres incorporated into the frame size nomenclature. Thus a 400 frame size machine has a shaft centre line height of 400 mm. The only tolerance on this dimension is negative to allow one machine to be replaced by

132

another of the same shaft height dimension with only feet shim changes. Bedplate mounted machines are also dowelled after grouting and final machine alignment adjustments.

Large machines with pedestal mounted bearings are usually built upon and supplied with a cast iron subframe or bedplate for mounting directly onto prepared reinforced concrete foundations.

Flange mounted or vertical machines are usually erected on a specially designed subframe or machined facing which itself forms the baseplate or foundation. Vertical motors are often mounted on fabricated skirts, especially for pump drives, and the skirts are treated as bedplates described above.

Alignment
Accurate alignment is an essential requirement if damage to bearings and flexible couplings is to be avoided. Alignment between an electrical machine and its prime mover or driven machine has to be established before the coupling may be connected.

The faces of the coupling must be parallel and any separation dimension between the faces established in accordance with the coupling manufacturer's recommendation. The final coupling alignment would normally be established and checked using a dial gauge, fig. 13.13. If the machine is to be coupled to an internal combustion engine it is necessary to remove engine spark plugs or injectors to facilitate alignment so that the set may be turned easily by hand.

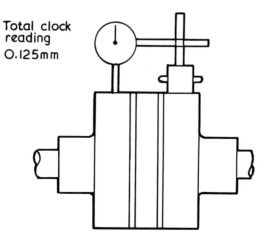

Total clock reading 0.125mm

Figure 13.13 Using a dial gauge to check alignment of a flexible coupling

Two-bearing electrical machines are usually coupled to their prime mover or driven machine by means of a flexible coupling. The purpose of a flexible coupling is not to permit any misalignment but to minimise transmission of bearing shock loadings.

Single-bearing electrical machines are coupled to their prime mover or driven machine using a solidly bolted coupling. They cannot be connected by flexible couplings since these are not designed for, or capable of, supporting the downward thrust due to the weight of the machine rotor.

Mechanical erection is completed when the coupling halves are connected but some further checks are necessary before power can be applied. These should include ensuring that cooling air flows are not restricted by obstructions to air intakes or exhausts. Insufficient space between air intakes and adjacent walls can cause overheating. Ensure that covers have been replaced and that any doors which have to remain open while the machine is running are clearly marked. Check that auxiliary equipment such as blowers, tachogenerators, external coolers, filters, bearing vibration or temperature sensors and bearing oil circulation equipment has been satisfactorily fitted.

On machines fitted with air/water heat exchangers the water flow rate must be measured by means of a separate flow meter to ensure that it is in accordance with the flow rate specified on the rating plate of the machine. If a separate flow meter is not available the flow rate can be calculated by measuring the volume of water leaving the outlet over a set period of time.

Cabling and protection

Power and control cables to any machine should be of adequate current carrying capacity and voltage grade. Effective and positive termination of cables onto machine terminals is necessary for good and lasting electrical contact. The machine is provided with earthing studs and it is essential that a proper earth is made in accordance with local regulations prevailing on site. Special regulations apply to increased safety Ex(e) and flameproof or explosion proof Ex(d) machines. These require special attention to earthing and to the use only of copper cables.

The power supply to which the machine is connected must have an

appropriate fault clearance level in relation to the fuses and other
protection devices being used in the system. Thermal protection
relays are necessary to protect the machine against over temperature
resulting from overcurrent. However, excessive temperature may also
result from obstruction of the cooling medium or operation at an
excessively high ambient temperature. An overcurrent protection
device will not of course recognise this. A protection device which
directly monitors winding temperature, such as thermistors or thermostats if fitted, detects high temperatures whatever the cause.
Current-dependent thermal protection relays must be provided in
addition to any winding temperature detectors.

Current relays should be selected to provide thermal protection
under short-circuit, single-phasing, locked rotor or other fault conditions. The protection device should isolate the machine from the
supply and, for an Ex(e) machine, within the t_e temperature-rise time
of the appropriate ignition group.

The t_e time is the time in seconds taken for the hottest surface
of the machine and its windings to reach the ignition group temperature under stall conditions after it has reached its steady state full
load temperature in an ambient temperature of 40°C.

COMMISSIONING

Having installed and cabled up the machine correctly, a further
inspection should be made to ensure that bearings are appropriately
lubricated, cooling systems functioning properly and that cooling air
inlets or exhausts are not obstructed in any way. Power may be
applied to any separately driven ventilating fan in order to confirm
that it is rotating in the correct direction. This is normally indicated by an arrow on the fan casing. Providing that the fan motor has
been connected with the correct phase rotation as specified in the
connection diagrams this test should be just a formality but nevertheless an important formality since wrong fan rotation will almost
certainly significantly reduce its effectiveness with consequent
overheating of the main machine. This overheating would not be
detected by any overcurrent relay as already stated and damage to the
main machine windings could result.

Direction of rotation should similarly be checked on the main machine itself. Again the correct direction is indicated or specified on the nameplate or elsewhere. Often machines, particularly the larger ones, are designed for rotation in only one direction. Reversing the direction of rotation therefore may require some mechanical alteration, albeit only a change to the shaft driven fan. Unidirectional fans are more common on larger motors since they are both more efficient and less noisy.

Alternators which have been in storage for some time may have insufficient residual magnetism to allow proper excitation to build up. Larger alternators having a permanent magnet pilot exciter should not suffer this problem. Some manufacturers provide the normal exciter with pole face permanent magnets embedded to eliminate the possibility of failure to excite.

When failure to excite is experienced and a maximum voltage regulator setting is not successful and any rotating diodes have been examined for correct functioning, flashing of the exciter field winding is necessary. This can be achieved by running the alternator up to speed and by touching the leads from a 6 or 12 V battery across the exciter field terminals in the correct polarity.

Checking of a rotating rectifier system requires each diode in turn being removed from its mounting plate and its forward and reverse resistances being measured. The forward resistance should be low and its reverse resistance high. If both resistances are approximately equal a failed diode is indicated and this should be replaced by an identical unit.

When refitting a diode a silicon heat sink compound should be lightly smeared on the diode seating to improve heat transfer and inhibit corrosion. A torque spanner to the correct setting must always be used when tightening semiconductors to their mounting plates or heat sinks.

Insulation resistance tests can be made on a brushless alternator using a 500 V or 1000 V instrument but not on the rectifiers themselves. Similarly, high voltage flash tests should not be attempted unless the rectifiers have first been short-circuited and any auxiliary equipment such as the voltage regulator disconnected.

Once the preliminary tests have been completed and the machine is running and loaded it is desirable to check for vibration and to monitor and log all meter readings and speed.

MAINTENANCE

Rotating electrical machines are inherently robust and reliable and require little maintenance. Generally, maintenance involves maintaining standards of cleanliness and regular inspection. A machine which is running within its design parameters is likely to need very little attention. The areas to be given most attention are, obviously enough, the bearings and, if fitted, the brushgear and associated slip rings or commutator.

Bearings

Large machines which are fitted with anti-friction ball and roller bearings normally have bearings which require re-lubrication. Grease is forced into the bearing through grease nipples while the machine is running. A grease gun may be used or sometimes bearings are fitted with Stauffer greasing facilities. In either case, air bubbles in the grease should be avoided if lubrication is to be effective and the grease must be of the recommended type. Cleanliness is essential to avoid dirt and grit being forced into the bearings. Some bearings have grease escape valves to prevent overfilling the bearing and consequent overheating. The excess grease can be cleaned away periodically without adverse effect on horizontal shaft machines. On vertical shaft machines this excess grease is sometimes led to a container located below the bearing and this must be emptied at the recommended intervals to prevent grease entering the windings. The interval between re-lubrication depends upon rotational speed, bearing size and loading and whether the machine is horizontal or vertical. Typically, the period is 4000 running hours for a ball bearing and approximately half that period for a roller bearing of similar size. Specific recommendations will be given for each machine by the manufacturer but the period between re-lubrication should not exceed one year.

At longer intervals of about 8000 - 12000 running hours the bearings should be inspected by removing the outboard bearing cap and noting any serious discolouration of the grease. If serious discolouration is evident the bearing should be removed from the shaft, cleaned and examined more closely. Replacement of the bearing is indicated if it shows signs of blueing, cracking, brinelling or excessive wear.

Small machines are often fitted with sealed-for-life anti-friction
bearings which do not require re-lubrication. Inspection of a sealed-
for-life bearing is not possible so that where malfunction is suspected
it should be replaced. Listening to a bearing through a sounding rod
or stethoscope can give a useful indication of its condition but some
experience is necessary before drawing too many conclusions. A high-
pitched whistling sound may indicate defective lubrication while a
low-pitched rumbling probably results from dirt or damage.

Removal of anti-friction bearings from a shaft involves some dismantling of the machine although it may not be necessary to remove the
rotor from the stator. Bearings are an interference fit onto the
shaft so that correct withdrawing tackle, which can apply even pressure
round the bearing, should be used. Tapping or hammering of the outer
race will almost certainly damage the track. Pre-heating of the new
bearing to about 95°C in an oven assists in pressing it onto the shaft
and a lightly tapped drift assists in pressing the bearing home
squarely onto its seating. The drift should be applied to the inner
race if the bearing is being fitted onto a shaft and to the outer race
if into a housing.

Oil lubricated sleeve bearings require an oil viscosity appropriate
to the ambient temperature. The oil level in the bearings must be
maintained and the oil replaced completely at regular intervals or at
any sign of overheating.

Brushgear

Machines fitted with slip rings or a commutator have brushgear. To be
effective the slip rings or commutator must be in good condition and
free from surface defects. Slip rings which are badly scored need to
be skimmed in a lathe. For removal of minor grooves a commutator
stone can be used, rested on a brush arm as the rotor is slowly driven
round. Finally, the surface can be polished using a piece of 00 grade
glasspaper wrapped around the square end of a piece of wood as the
rotor is turned by hand.

A similar technique can be applied to commutators but 'stoning' is
a dangerous operation which should be carried out only by someone
experienced in this work. A commutator which is in good condition
should have developed a smooth brown surface patina. When this low

friction patina is present the commutator surface should not be stoned
or polished. Raised commutator bars or mica are indicated by heavy
and uneven blackening and then skimming and undercutting are required.
When the commutator is uniformly black, cleaning and polishing should
be considered.

Longitudinal undercutting of the mica insulation between commutator
segments is always necessary after skimming in a lathe, fig. 13.14.
Although the bars of the commutator should be chamfered lightly, the
bar width must not be reduced.

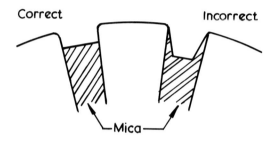

Figure 13.14 Correct and incorrect undercutting of the mica

It is sometimes impossible to achieve the brown surface patina
which provides long brush life. The cause is usually light load
running and insufficient brush current density. So often margins are
built into the specified machine rating that light loadings are inev-
itable. However, where this is the case, it is worth considering the
removal of some of the brushes. An equal number of brushes may be
removed from the same track on each brush arm so increasing the current
density of the remaining brushes. The machine manufacturer is always
willing to give advice as to the number of brushes required per arm
for the actual loadings on site.

Inspection of the brushgear will show up excessive or uneven brush
wear and the presence of carbon dust. All carbon dust should be
vacuumed or blown out of the machine at each inspection. The brushes
should be checked for wear and for freedom of movement in the brush
holder. Although brushes may be allowed to wear down almost to the
metal of the pigtail, it is worthwhile replacing them much earlier.
If replaced when they are only reduced 50% in length the brushes are
most unlikely to require attention, or cause an unscheduled plant

stoppage, before the next routine inspection. Many d.c. motor manufacturers now offer brush wear detection facilities which provide
early warning of advanced brush wear and reduce the possibility of an
unscheduled stoppage for maintenance.

Coolers

After a period of time any heat exchanger whether air/air or air/water
will have developed some dirt build-up which reduces the cooling
effectiveness. Cleaning of the air passages, tubes and water tubes is
therefore necessary from time to time. Filters fitted to force ventilating blowers need to be inspected and, if necessary cleaned or
replaced depending upon the type.

If the machine is to be shut down in freezing conditions any water
circuits should be drained. Condensation forms and accumulates in the
air/water heat exchanger and could be drawn into the machine through
the air passages and enter the windings. When a machine is to be shut
down for any time the cooling water flow should also be stopped to
limit the build-up of condensation. Even under normal operation this
condensation can be significant and justify raising the water temperature in the cooler and reducing the ambient humidity to reduce the
quantity of condensation formed.

Windings and insulation

A machine which has been out of service for a long period could have
too low an insulation resistance to allow it to return to operation.
If the resistance is less than 1 megohm on an l.v. machine, or equivalent value on h.v. machines, the windings need to be dried out. The
machine can be placed in an oven or dried using a hot air blower. In
either case the temperature should not exceed 90°C or damage could
result to rotating diodes for example. Initially, the insulation
resistance will fall and then slowly increase to a maximum level. The
resistance readings should be monitored as the drying out process
proceeds and, to avoid misleading readings, the temperature should be
kept as constant as possible.

Before taking any insulation resistance measurements, any diodes
or capacitors should be disconnected or short-circuited. High voltage
insulation breakdown tests should be avoided since they have a progressive effect in causing deterioration of the winding insulation.

Chapter 14

HBC Fuses and Fusegear in Low Voltage Systems

J. Feenan, CEng, FIEE, FIMechE
Technical Director
GEC Fusegear Ltd

When the 15th Edition of the IEE Wiring Regulations was launched in early 1981, there were references made to the first set of Regulations which were introduced in 1882 and attention was drawn to extracts from this first Edition regarding 'Protection of the wires', in which the fuse is mentioned as the protective device. The 15th Edition of the Regulations naturally contains far more specific Regulations but two important points still remain. First, the 15th Edition is largely about the protection of 'the wires'; secondly, the fuse, in the form of the hbc fuse, is still a major protective device after nearly a century; its action under fault conditions ensures required disconnecting times. In fact, the 15th Edition, more than any previous Edition, gives precise Rules regarding overcurrent protection in which the l.v. hbc fuse emerges as a unique short-circuit protective device as well as giving the necessary overload protection to PVC-insulated cables which are acknowledged to be the most difficult to protect under overload condition.

Design of the hbc fuse has progressed during the last 60 years until it has become a highly sophisticated protective device with very precise characteristics. The British and International Standards covering l.v. fuses have also progressed during these years and in June 1981 agreement was finally reached in the Committee of the International Electrotechnical Commission dealing with l.v. fuses (SC32B), for one set of time/current 'gates' within which the time/current characteristics of all fuses for general purpose applications must fall. This decision was the culmination of many years of intense activity in IEC and it is significant to note that the time/current

141

characteristics of the modern British hbc fuse-link fall within these
agreed 'gates', thus indicating that British practice with regard to
hbc fuse-link design has been the correct one. It is therefore an
opportune point in time to consider the modern hbc fuse from the view-
points of design and performance, application in general purpose
circuits and in motor circuits, and its effect on the design of associated fuse switchgear and motor starter combinations.

HBC FUSE-LINKS DESIGN AND PERFORMANCE

The performance requirements of hbc fuse-links for voltages up to
1000 V a.c. or 1500 V d.c. are covered by BS 88: 1975: Parts 1 and 2
'Fuses for use on industrial applications' and by BS 1361: 1971 'Fuses
for use in domestic and similar applications'. BS 88 defines a fuse
as consisting of a fuse-link and fuse-holder. The fuse-holder consists
of a fuse-base and in most cases a fuse-carrier. A diagrammatic
representation of a typical fuse is shown in fig. 14.1.

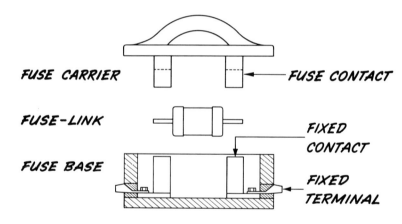

Figure 14.1 Component parts of a fuse

The minimum performance requirements which must be met by hbc fuses
complying with these standards are:

(a) A breaking capacity of not less than 80 kA at 415 V a.c. for fuses
    to BS 88, and 33 kA at 415 V a.c. or 16.5 kA at 250 V a.c. for
    fuses to BS 1361. Fuses to these standards can successfully
    interrupt any fault current from the minimum fusing current of the
    fuse up to the rated breaking capacity at the specified lagging

power factors, e.g. 0.2 for industrial fuses and 0.3 for fuses
for domestic applications.

(b) The temperature-rise of the fuse when carrying rated current must
not exceed 65°C at the fuse terminals. In addition, maximum permitted power losses are specified for each fuse-link size and
these are such that for the majority of fuse ratings the terminal
temperature-rises attained are very much less than the permitted
maximum of 65°C.

(c) The ability to protect PVC-insulated cables from damage due to
overload currents. The specification determines this by requiring
a fuse-link to operate within 4 hours at an overload of 150% rated
current. Fuse-links which meet this requirement are said to have
Class Q1 fusing factors and they are marked accordingly. However
the 15th Edition of the IEE Wiring Regulations (based on the
requirements of the IEC) specifies that for the protection of
PVC-insulated cables the overload protective device must operate
at 145% of the continuous rating of the cable for a given installation condition within a specified time known as Conventional
Time. This aspect is discussed in more detail later.

(d) The time/current characteristics of a fuse must fall within the
specified time/current zones given in the respective standards.
Here again it should be noted that the proposed revision of the
IEC Standard for fuses will introduce the time/current 'gates'
mentioned earlier which are narrower than the zones at present
included in BS 88.

Figure 14.2 illustrates the test requirements of BS 88 and it
can be seen that, for verification of breaking capacity, the fuse-
link is submitted to five test currents I_1, I_2, I_3, I_4 and I_5
covering a range of prospective currents from a breaking capacity
of 80 kA down to a current equal to 1.25 I_F (the conventional
fusing current). I_F is specified as being equal to 1.6 I_N (the
rated current of the fuse-link) and there is also specified a
conventional non-fusing current (I_{NF}) which for fuse-links to
BS 88 is equal to 1.2 I_N. This is the IEC way of expressing the
long time characteristics of fuse-links, and the minimum fusing
current of 1.5 I_N, which has been British practice for many years,
falls within these two zones. Thus BS 88 contains two methods of

expressing the long time characteristics of fuse-links but in the recent IEC agreement and in the next Edition of BS 88 the reference to minimum fusing current and fusing factor will be deleted leaving I_F and I_{NF} as the sole method of specifying the long time characteristics of all fuse-links.

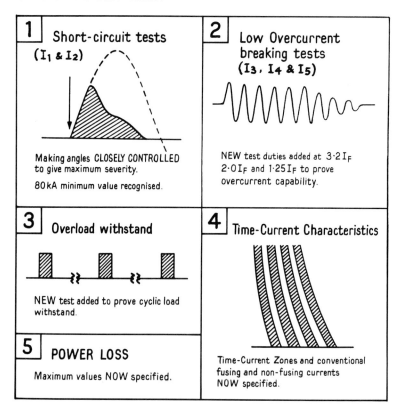

Figure 14.2 BS 88: 1975 Principal changes from earlier issue

With regard to the temperature-rise limit for terminals, the existing value of 65°C will, in the revision of BS 88 be increased to 70°C which is the standard value specified in all associated IEC standards for l.v. devices such as contactors, circuit-breakers, switches, etc., thus producing a uniform reference value for the temperature-rise requirements of all l.v. equipment.

Proof of compliance with (a) necessitates testing at a high power test laboratory under the closely controlled test conditions required by BS 88. If the high power laboratory is controlled by the

Association of Short Circuit Testing Authorities an ASTA Certificate
of rating can be issued as proof of compliance with the breaking
capacity clauses of the standard. Test conditions for breaking
capacity are, as indicated in fig. 14.2, arranged to ensure that the
fuse interrupts the worst possible combination of voltage, current and
inductance which could occur in practice on systems having fault
levels up to the breaking capacity of the fuse.

The pending revision of BS 88 does not contain any changes in the
breaking capacity requirements but it adds a number of verification
tests such as protection against heat, against abnormal heat and fire
and against corrosion. It also includes specified degrees of enclosures (IP numbers) and, with respect to fuse-holders, verification of
the ability of contacts to perform satisfactorily if (a) left
undisturbed for long periods and (b) after repeated engagement and
disengagement. Furthermore there is also a verification test to prove
cable overload protection.

The verification tests such as protection against corrosion and
abnormal heat and fire reflect the growing demands by the inspection
and test authorities of many countries that any performance claims in
a specification must have a test requirement which is deemed to verify
that claim.

DESIGN OF CARTRIDGE FUSE-LINKS
Although the fuse-link complying with BS 88 has a similar outward
appearance to a fuse-link complying with earlier editions of the
British standard, changes in element design and element configurations
within the fuse-link have achieved significant improvements in breaking capacity and time/current characteristics within existing
dimensions.

The modern cartridge fuse-link consists of a ceramic body, one or
more fuse elements depending upon the current rating, an inert arc
quenching filler such as granulated quartz, tin-plated copper or brass
endcaps and, usually, tin-plated copper tag terminations. A typical
fuse-link is shown in fig. 14.3. The fuse elements used in modern
l.v. fuse-links are made from a tape or strip. Different fuse manufacturers have different ideas on the precise form of the element but
all of them employ a number of reduced sections along the length of

the element in order to promote multiple arcing under short-circuit conditions (i.e. creating a number of arcs in series which burn simultaneously).

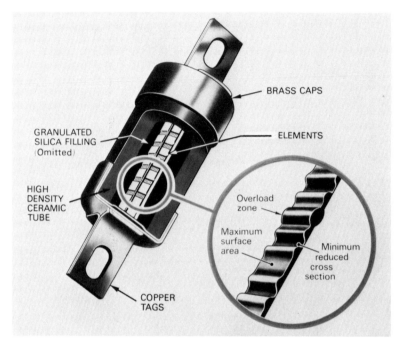

GRANULATED SILICA FILLING (Omitted)

HIGH DENSITY CERAMIC TUBE

BRASS CAPS

ELEMENTS

Overload zone

Maximum surface area

Minimum reduced cross section

COPPER TAGS

Figure 14.3 Sectioned view of typical hbc fuse-link

When arcing commences in a modern hbc fuse-link a high transient pressure is set up within the fuse body due to the vaporisation of parts of the element which can only expand to a limited extent in the interstices in the quartz filler. This high pressure, combined with the high temperature generated in the arc column, necessitates the use of special ceramic material for the body. The joints between endcaps and body must also be strong enough to withstand the stresses created. Granulated quartz is chosen as the filler because it is inert and has excellent heat-absorbing properties which make it an ideal arc quenching medium. Its purity and grain size are also very important factors in obtaining a high breaking capacity. The design of the fuse element controls both the mode of operation on short-circuit and the shape of the time/current characteristics of the fuse.

The number and lengths of the reduced sections of the element govern the arc voltage of the fuse. Arc voltage is the voltage which appears across the terminals of the fuse during the arcing time of the fuse-link and it is the resultant of four components:

(a) the voltage dropped across the arcs in series
(b) the resistive voltage drop of the rest of the circuit due to the passage of a large fault current
(c) the circuit emf
(d) the inductive voltage, $L(di/dt)$, produced in the circuit due to the dissipation of its inductive energy $(\frac{1}{2}Li^2)$ within the fuse arcs.

Components (a) and (b) tend to reduce the current while (c) and (d) try to maintain its flow. The generation of an adequate arc voltage ensures that current ceases to rise after the commencement of arcing and the subsequent variation in arc voltage controls the rate at which the current reduces to zero.

A major factor affecting the arc voltage is the grain size of the quartz filler because this in turn can affect the pressure generated within the fuse body when the element vaporises during the arcing period. An arc burning under pressure requires a higher voltage to maintain it than an arc in free air. It is therefore possible to design a fuse-link which will produce a predetermined maximum value of arc voltage. BS 88 stipulates an upper limit of 2.5 kV for the arc voltage produced by fuse-links rated up to 660 V but in a good design this value is never reached. The range of fuse-links using the type of element illustrated in fig. 14.4 produces arc voltages in the region of 1 kV.

An indication of the speed of operation and current limiting ability of the hbc fuse is given in the oscillogram shown in fig. 14.5. This is the record of a 400 A fuse interrupting a prospective current of 80 kA rms symmetrical at 415 V a.c. with a lagging power factor of 0.15. BS 88 specifies that the fault shall be initiated such that arcing commences in the fuse at not less than 65 degrees after voltage zero. This produces an asymmetrical fault current with a peak prospective value of 180 kA.

The limitation of thermal and electromagnetic stresses achieved by the fuse is better appreciated when it is remembered that both vary as the square of the current. An examination of the oscillogram serves to illustrate this point.

Figure 14.4 Fuse element manufactured from silver strip

The peak or cut-off current permitted to flow by the 400 A fuse is
40 kA, i.e. 22% of the possible peak current. The electromagnetic
force produced is therefore only about 5% of that which would otherwise
have occurred. Similarly the thermal stress has been reduced to less
than 1% of that which would have occurred if a circuit-breaker having
a speed of operation of 0.02 seconds had been the protective device.
The combination of current limitation and rapid operation enables this
high degree of protection to be obtained. Figure 14.6 shows the cut-
off currents of a range of fuses, having current ratings from 2 A to
800 A on a prospective current of 80 kA. This illustrates the reduction in electromagnetic stresses which can be achieved with hbc fuses.

On high short-circuit currents the energy required to melt a fuse
is a minimum and constant value because there is no time for heat to
be dissipated from it to its surroundings. The magnitude of this
energy, known as the pre-arcing energy of the fuse, can be determined
from the oscillograms of fuse operations on high short-circuit
currents. Similarly the arc energy, which is the energy liberated in
the fuse during its arcing time, can also be determined.

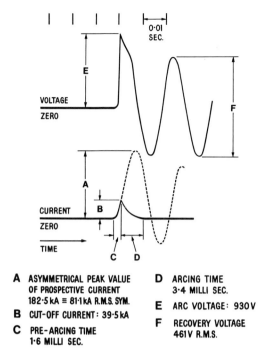

A ASYMMETRICAL PEAK VALUE OF PROSPECTIVE CURRENT 182·5 kA ≡ 81·1 kA R.M.S. SYM.	**D** ARCING TIME 3·4 MILLI SEC.
B CUT-OFF CURRENT: 39·5 kA	**E** ARC VOLTAGE: 930 V
C PRE-ARCING TIME 1·6 MILLI SEC.	**F** RECOVERY VOLTAGE 461 V R.M.S.

Figure 14.5   Oscillogram of the operation of a 400 A 415 V fuse on a large fault current

Unlike the pre-arcing energy, however, the arc energy can vary between wide limits depending upon the circuit conditions but the maximum value is obtained during the breaking capacity tests to BS 88. In effect the arc energy of a fuse is the energy stored in the circuit at the commencement of arcing which must be dissipated in the fuse before the circuit is finally opened. It must however be appreciated that the energy dissipated in the fuse is a function of $I^2t \times R_F$ where R_F is the resistance of the fuse during its pre-arcing and arcing periods.

When considering the short-circuit protection the fuse provides to equipment and cables in the circuit, the information of interest is the cut-off current and the I^2t value (A^2 sec). The cut-off current, as stated earlier, is a direct indication of the limitation of electromagnetic stresses achieved by the fuse. The thermal stresses in the circuit can be expressed in terms of I^2t because this is the common factor between the fuse and other components in the circuit.

149

Obviously in a cable the energy is a function of $I^2t \times R_C$ the resistance of the cable.

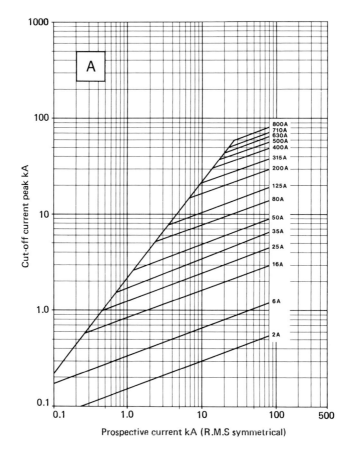

Figure 14.6   Relationship between prospective current and cut-off current for a range of fuses

It is common practice, however, for manufacturers and designers of associated apparatus such as fuse-switches, contactors, busbars and cables to express the short time thermal ratings of the equipment in terms of I^2t. This enables the manufacturers of such equipment to state in a simple manner the degree of thermal protection required by various items of equipment under short-circuit conditions. A fuse manufacturer can determine the I^2t of a fuse on large short-circuit currents from the relevant oscillograms and usually presents the minimum pre-arcing I^2t (i.e. the I^2t from the commencement of the fault

until the arcing commences) and the maximum arcing I^2t (from commencement of arcing until circuit interruption) under worst fault conditions
in the manner shown in fig. 14.7. This shows the pre-arcing and total
(pre-arcing plus arcing) I^2t values for a range of fuses from 2 A up
to 800 A under short-circuit conditions on prospective currents up to
80 kA. Figures 14.6 and 14.7 represent a comprehensive picture of the
short-circuit protection provided by this range of fuse-links.

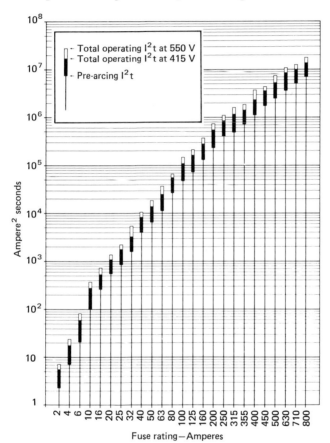

*Figure 14.7 I^2t characteristics for a range of fuses showing
pre-arcing and total values. (Discrimination
between fuse-links is achieved when the total I^2t
of the minor fuse-link does not exceed the pre-
arcing I^2t of the major fuse-link)*

OVERLOAD CHARACTERISTICS

The method of achieving compliance with the conventional fusing current or minimum fusing current mentioned earlier has traditionally been achieved by including an overload zone in the element. This is done by adding a precise amount of low melting point metal (tin) to the element, which is usually silver. Under overload conditions the temperature of the fuse element gradually increases until a temperature is reached at which the tin becomes molten and a metallurgical phenomenon, commonly known as 'M' effect, takes place. A eutectic alloy is formed at this temperature between the tin (melting temperature 230°C) and silver (melting temperature 860°C) and the alloy thus formed has the same melting temperature as that of tin (230°C). This ensures that the element will melt in the overload zone at the desired current of 1.6 I_N without excessive temperatures being reached. All modern designs of cartridge fuse utilise this 'M' effect in one form or another.

A recent trend, due to the high cost of silver, has been to utilise copper as an alternative material because the 'M' effect can be achieved between tin and copper although it occurs at a higher temperature (400°C) permitting higher temperatures to be reached by fuses under overload conditions which is not a desirable trend. A novel design of element which consists largely of copper, but still utilises silver in the overload zone, is shown in fig. 14.8.

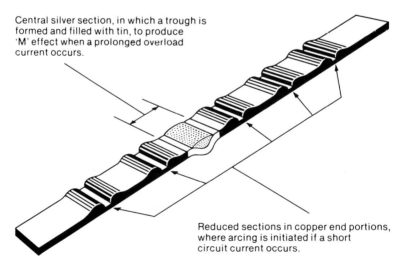

Central silver section, in which a trough is formed and filled with tin, to produce 'M' effect when a prolonged overload current occurs.

Reduced sections in copper end portions, where arcing is initiated if a short circuit current occurs.

Figure 14.8 Silverbond element, showing that the 'M' effect zone is placed at a full section

With this design the unequalled ability of the silver/tin eutectic is retained while economy is achieved in the use of copper for the majority of the element.

FUSE-HOLDER

The fuse-holder (i.e. the fuse-carrier and base) also plays an important part in the design of a cool running fuse. Robust contacts ensure a low temperature-rise by helping to dissipate the heat from the fuse-link when carrying rated current. The method chosen for connecting the cable to the fuse terminals must be carefully considered to avoid the danger of a bad connection which could nullify an otherwise satisfactory design. Most of the front-connected fuse-holders to BS 88 employ tunnel-type terminals which are ideally suited for the connection of unprepared stranded copper conductors. This form of terminal is however not normally suitable for the direct connection of aluminium conductors. When aluminium conductors are used, it is preferable to terminate the conductor with a suitable cable lug and utilise a back-connected fuse-holder which provides a stud connection suitable for connecting the cable lug. High quality moulding materials are widely used in modern designs of fuse-carriers and bases which permit compact dimensions and extensive shrouding of current-carrying parts. These features are highlighted in fig. 14.9 which illustrates a widely used design of fuse-holder.

Figure 14.9 Sectioned fuse-holder showing how extensive shrouding of live parts is achieved

APPLICATION OF HBC FUSES

The 15th Edition of the IEE Wiring Regulations clearly states the requirements which must be met when providing cables with both overload protection and short-circuit protection. These two terms are covered by a more general term overcurrent protection. With regard to protection against overload, the Wiring Regulations state that the protective device must operate within a stated conventional time when carrying a current equal to 1.45 I_Z (the current rating of the associated cable).

It has been stated earlier that fuses to BS 88 must have a fusing factor of 1.5 for type Q1 and, to the IEC requirements, fuses must have a conventional fusing current of 1.6 I_N. Both the IEE and the International Wiring Regulations recognise that because the fuse-links to BS 88 have their conventional fusing currents and minimum fusing currents determined in a standard test rig, the value of 1.5 reduces to 1.45 when they are mounted in enclosed fuse-holders due to the effect of enclosure. This means that if the current rating of a fuse to BS 88 or BS 1361 is not greater than I_Z, the rating of the associated cable, compliance with the requirements of the 15th Edition for overload protection of cables is achieved. This rule confirms a practice which has existed in the UK for many years and it is interesting to note that this practice is now internationally accepted.

With regard to the protection of cables against short-circuit (the other form of overcurrent), the hbc fuse is indisputably the best device for the purpose particularly if the fuse has a current rating not exceeding that of the cable. Even when the fuse has a greater rating than the cable it gives adequate short-circuit protection. The limiting parameter specified in the 15th Edition with regard to the maximum size of fuse which can give short-circuit protection to a cable, depends on the minimum value of the short-circuit current which can occur, see fig. 14.10.

There have previously never been any clear-cut guide lines for such a minimum value of short-circuit current and the only previous reference to a relationship between fuse and cable rating is given in Regulation A68 of the 14th Edition of the IEE Wiring Regulations. Here permission is given for the use of a fuse of up to twice the rating of the associated cable in a motor circuit when overload protection is provided by the motor starter. In the 15th Edition protection must be provided for cables for short-circuits of durations up to 5 seconds and Regulation 434-6 gives an adiabatic formula $t = k^2 S^2 / I^2$ (where S is the cross-sectional area of the conductor and k is a constant for each type of cable), which can be used to calculate the $I^2 t$ withstand capability of various types of cables at 5 seconds. It is therefore a relatively simple job to determine from the published information the maximum size of cable which can be protected by a given size of fuse on a short-circuit current of 5 seconds duration.

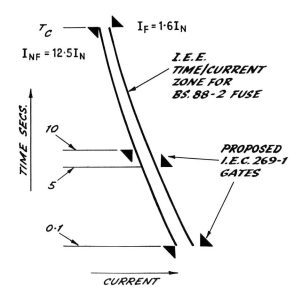

Figure 14.10 *Short-circuit protection of 10 mm^2 PVC-insulated cable by hbc fuses*

Table 14.1 shows, by utilising the formula mentioned above, the appropriate maximum size of cable which can be protected against short-circuit in a motor circuit for both open and enclosed installation conditions. It can be seen that the old rule of twice the cable rating still applies in the majority of cases. An important point to appreciate is that if a fuse protects a cable under short-circuit conditions at 5 seconds, it will, because of its unique current limiting ability, protect that cable on all fault currents in excess of the 5 second value up to the breaking capacity rating of the fuse-link. This cannot be assumed for other types of protective devices such as circuit-breakers of the non-current limiting type where it is necessary to check whether protection is afforded at the maximum prospective fault current likely to occur at that point in the circuit, see fig. 14.11.

Table 14.1 Short circuit protection of PVC-insulated cables in motor circuits

Conductor size (mm^2)	Maximum current rating (A)		Maximum associated type 'T' fuse (A)
	open conditions	enclosed conditions	
1.5	20	14	25*
4	36	29	50
10	61	51	100
25	106	87	200
50	160	125	355
70	200	160	500
120	280	220	750

Application of rule 434-6 in 15th Edition of IEE Regulations
*Rule interpreted to cover these sizes.

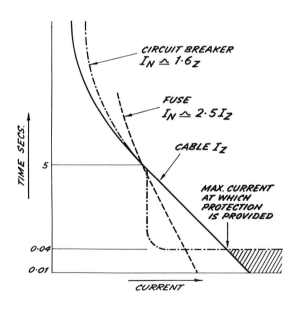

Figure 14.11 Comparison of protection provided to PVC-insulated cable by hbc fuses and circuit-breakers

This illustrates how effectively the modern hbc fuse can provide overload and short-circuit protection in accordance with the 15th Edition without sacrificing any of its ability to permit maximum utilisation of the other components of the circuit it is protecting, e.g. cable, motor starter, etc.

DISCRIMINATION AND BACK-UP PROTECTION

In any well-planned electrical system discrimination between over-current protective devices throughout the system is essential. Clause 533-6 of the 15th Edition states this as a requirement for compliance. Discrimination between any two protective devices in series is achieved when, on the occurrence of a fault in the circuit protected by the minor device, only that device operates leaving the major device intact. When hbc fuses are used as the protective device throughout a system the degree of discrimination which can be achieved is unequalled by any other forms of protective device.

To achieve discrimination on the worst conditions (i.e. on high prospective fault currents) it is simply a matter of ensuring that the pre-arcing I^2t of the major fuse is in excess of the total I^2t of the minor fuse and a reference to fig. 14.7 shows that this can readily be determined. In fact it has been established for many years that on 415 V systems discrimination can be achieved between fuses having a ratio of 2:1 in current rating under the worst possible fault conditions. This close degree of discrimination cannot be achieved with any other short-circuit protective device. If one takes a more practical view of fault conditions and assumes that the worst possible fault is so rare that discrimination under such conditions can be waived, a ratio as close as 1.6:1 can be achieved because under such conditions the arcing I^2t of the minor fuse is small.

In the modern electrical installation there are a number of devices such as miniature circuit-breakers (mcbs) and contactors which, although they are overcurrent protective devices, have a limited breaking capacity. In situations where the fault level exceeds their breaking capacity, it is necessary to provide back-up protection which will take over from the mcb or contactor at a fault current not exceeding the breaking capacity of these devices.

Such a back-up device must not only protect the circuit but

ideally it should not allow the mcb or contactor to be damaged by letting too much energy flow through them. This is expressed as the let-through I^2t and the unique ability of the hbc fuse under fault conditions to keep the let-through energy to very low values explains why it is the most effective means of back-up protection for these devices.

When selecting a fuse as the back-up device in a motor circuit, further objectives must be achieved. In addition to the ability to interrupt the fault current successfully and protect the associated contactor and cable, it must be capable of withstanding the motor starting current for the starting period. The generally accepted method of determining the capability of a fuse to withstand motor starting conditions is to refer to the 10 second withstand current. Usually it is assumed that the starting current is approximately six times the motor full load current and that such a current would exist for up to 10 seconds. Experience has shown that this is satisfactory for the popular ranges of starting times and currents.

Most fuse manufacturers give recommended sizes of fuse-links for standard sizes of motor in their catalogues and in the pending revision of BS 88 there is a specified value of current for each rating of fuse-link which that fuse-link must withstand for 10 seconds. This is a considerable step forward in harmonising the characteristics of different makes of fuse-link, but it is still not the complete answer because, in those applications where the motor is likely to be started at frequent intervals, further consideration should be given to the rating of the fuse-link. Here again most manufacturers give further advice on this particular aspect.

MOTOR CIRCUIT FUSE-LINKS

The 1975 Edition of BS 88 included, for the first time, the motor circuit fuse-link. This type of fuse-link provides the necessary degree of back-up protection but in a smaller physical package than that of the equivalent rating of standard fuse-link. Its inclusion in BS 88 recognises the fact that when a fuse is used as back-up protection to another protective device (motor starter) the same degree of short-circuit protection is provided by either a standard fuse-link or the physically smaller motor circuit fuse-link of the appropriate current rating. For example the 32M63 fuse-link in the A2 dimensions to BS 88 provides the same back-up protection as the 63 A fuse-link in the larger A3 dimensions for the same voltage rating and breaking capacity.

The dual rating on such fuse-links is explained as follows. The first rating denotes the continuous current rating of the fuse-holder or fuse-switch in which the fuse-link can be fitted and the second rating (after the letter M) indicates the time/current characteristic of the fuse-link. Therefore the 32M63 fuse-link has a continuous rating of 32 A because of the limitation of the fuse-holder or fuse-switch in which it is installed and has the same time/current characteristics as the standard 63 A fuse-link.

This type of fuse-link permits full utilisation of the make/break capabilities of the modern fuse-switch. For example, a 200 A fuse-switch with a 200M315 fuse-link fitted can be used on a motor circuit having a load current up to approximately 200 A whereas with a stand-ard 200 A fuse-link fitted it would be limited to a circuit of 125 A because of the reduced motor starting ability of the 200 A fuse-link. As will be discussed later, the make/break performance of the 200 A fuse-switch is such that it can safely break the stalled motor current of a motor having a 200 A full load current. Thus the motor circuit fuse-link has been an important contribution to the achievement of the compact dimensions of the modern fuse-switch.

It is important to note that the motor circuit fuse-link is a general purpose type and must be tested to the same breaking capacity requirements as that of the standard type (i.e. I_1 to I_5). The reduction in equipment dimensions which can be achieved by using motor circuit fuse-links, is appreciable and their international recognition is now assured because they have been included in the pending revision of IEC 269.

FUSES IN HIGH AMBIENT TEMPERATURES

A fuse can carry its rated current continuously in ambient temperat-ures up to 35°C but if it is required to carry its rated current at higher ambient temperatures or in enclosures where the inside air temperature is more than 15°C in excess of this value, it is necessary to apply a derating factor and most manufacturers give such information

in their publications. If however a fuse is providing back-up protection in a motor circuit employing direct-on-line starting, derating is
not usually required at these higher temperatures because in such an
application the fuse is only carrying approximately 50% of its rated
current producing only 25% of the temperature-rise normally achieved
at rated current. Therefore unless the local air temperature is
excessively high (above 60°C) there is no need to derate in such motor
circuit applications.

PROTECTION AGAINST ELECTRIC SHOCK
The biggest difference between the 14th and 15th Editions of the IEE
Wiring Regulations concerns the rules which are included in the 15th
Edition with regard to protection against electric shock. The implic-
ations of these new rules are at present the subject of considerable
discussion and it is not the intention here to endeavour to cover the
whole subject. But as fuses figure significantly in certain measures
of protection, it is opportune to comment on those aspects of the
Wiring Regulations where fuses can be used to good effect in achieving
protection against electric shock. The most popular measure of protection against indirect contact (contact with exposed conductive
parts made live by a fault) is 'earthed equipotential bonding and
automatic disconnection of supply'. The Regulations in the 15th
Edition, notably Regulations 413-2 and a number of Regulations in
Section 547, give details regarding the steps to be taken to achieve
the necessary earthed equipotential bonding which is the first part
of the requirement. The second part, automatic disconnection of
supply, is covered by Regulations 413-3 to 7 specifying the requirements for (a) final circuits supplying socekt-outlets and (b) final
circuits supplying only fixed equipment.

    Regulation 413-5 gives specific rules for the protection of
circuits having a nominal voltage to earth of 240 V rms a.c. when
protection is provided by means of an overcurrent protective device.
It states that in order to comply with the requirements for electric
shock the earth fault loop impedance Z_s shall not exceed values given
in Tables 41A1 for final circuits supplying socket-outlets, where the
disconnecting time of the protective device under fault conditions
must not exceed 0.4 seconds, and Table 41A2 for final circuits

supplying fixed equipment, where the appropriate disconnection time shall not exceed 5 seconds. Among the devices mentioned in the Tables are cartridge fuses to BS 88: Part 2, BS 1361 and BS 1362. The earth fault loop impedances given against each rating of fuse in each Table have been determined from the time/current characteristics of these fuses and Appendix 8 of the Regulations shows the upper limit of the time/current zone for the appropriate rating of fuse-link.

It follows from these disconnecting time requirements and those mentioned earlier for short-circuit protection, that the current to cause operation of the fuse in 5 seconds is now of great importance and the pending revision to the IEC fuse standard includes maximum values for the 5 second operating current for all rated currents of general purpose fuses. Furthermore, in order to provide information on currents causing the fuses to operate in 0.4 seconds the time/current characteristic must also comply with minimum and maximum values of current at 0.1 seconds.

Typical requirements are shown in table 14.2 and fig. 14.12 illustrates the time/current 'gates' which are to be included in the next revision of the IEC fuse standard and which should automatically be accepted as a revision to BS 88. It should be noted that in this revision the value of I_{NF} has been increased from $1.2I_N$ to $1.25I_N$.

Table 14.2   Gates for 'gG' fuses, extract from Table II of IEC 269-1 (Proposed). Limits of pre-arcing time of fuse-links

I_N (A)	I_5 sec max. (A)	I_{10} sec min. (A)	$I_{0.1}$ sec min. (A)	$I_{0.1}$ sec max. (A)
16	66	33	85	150
50	250	122	353	614
100	580	290	818	1450
200	1250	610	1910	3417
400	2840	1420	4504	8057
800	7000	3060	10620	19000

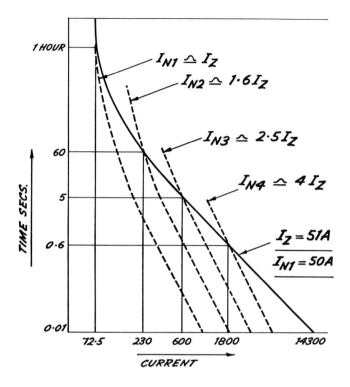

Figure 14.12 Time-current gates in IEC 269-1

Another important requirement of the 15th Edition and also the
14th Edition is the need for final circuits of an electrical installation to have a voltage drop not exceeding 2½% of the system voltage
when the phase conductors are carrying full load current. It has been
established by the IEE Wiring Regulations Committee during consideration of this particular problem, that in the vast majority of cases
compliance with the 2½% voltage drop limit automatically ensures, in
a TN system (an earthed neutral system), compliance with the values of
Z_s given in the appropriate Tables. In fact it can be shown that
where a fuse is giving complete overcurrent protection to a circuit
supplying fixed equipment installed in accordance with the requirements
of the 15th Edition, the disconnecting time in the event of a negligible fault to earth is considerably less than 5 seconds and in the vast
majority of applications less than 1 second. It can also be seen from
the values of earth loop impedance given in Table 41A1 (of the
Regulations) that in TN systems the hbc fuse is suitable for the

162

protection of all socket-outlet circuits except the socket-outlet
supplying equipment outside the equipotential bonding zone. Here the
Regulations make the fitting of a residual current device (rcd) of
30 mA sensitivity a mandatory requirement and forbid the use of an
overcurrent protective device for protection against electric shock
for this particular socket-outlet. It can still provide overcurrent
protection to this circuit and back-up protection to the rcd.

In addition to the foregoing, the energy limiting ability of the
hbc fuse can be used to good effect in achieving economies in the size
of the circuit protective conductor. Regulation 543-1 states two
methods of selecting the size of this conductor. The first method is
by calculation of the cross-sectional area using an adiabatic equation
$S = \sqrt{(I^2t/k^2)}$ which is applicable for disconnecting times not exceeding
5 seconds, and the second method relates the cross-sectional area of
the circuit protective conductor to the associated phase conductor, the
details of which are given in Table 54F of Regulation 543-3. The
values given in Table 54F, particularly for circuits of large current
rating, are considerably in excess of those specified in Table D2M of
the 14th Edition. For example for a 16 mm^2 copper phase conductor it
recommends a protective conductor of the same size, compared with one
of 6 mm^2 in the 14th Edition and a 240 mm^2 copper phase conductor
requires a protective conductor of 120 mm^2 instead of 70 mm^2 required
in the 14th Edition.

If the adiabatic equation is used, which takes into account the
I^2t let through by the fuse, a much smaller size of protective conductor can be used, particularly when account is taken of the foregoing
statement that in the vast majority of applications the fuse disconnects in times less than 1 second. The other important point is
that, if protection is afforded to the protective conductor by a fuse
under these conditions, it is assured on higher fault currents.

Even in motor circuits where the fuse is providing back-up
protection and is therefore usually about twice the rating of the
phase conductor, it can be shown that the use of the adiabatic formula
results in smaller sizes of protective conductor than those specified
in Table 54F.

One of the difficulties in applying the adiabatic formula is that
it requires a knowledge of Z_e which is the value of earth loop

impedance external to the installation. Where this value is known it is a simple matter to use the adiabatic formula. In those situations where the precise value of Z_e is not known, it can be shown that even where the value of Z_e is as high as 50% of Z_s, appreciable economies can be gained by using the adiabatic formula.

The foregoing confirms that on fuse-protected installations on TN systems existing practice usually achieves compliance with the new requirements for protection against electric shock by equipotential bonding and automatic disconnection of supply. This is applicable for fixed circuits, where the fuse is either giving complete overcurrent protection to a circuit or back-up protection to motor circuits, and also to circuits feeding socket-outlets, except those socket-outlets feeding equipment outside the equipotential bonded zone.

DOMESTIC FUSE APPLICATIONS

Mention has been made earlier of fuse-links to BS 1361 and 1362. These are also covered in the 15th Edition together with the semi-enclosed fuse to BS 3036. The fuse-links to BS 1362 are well established in the 13 A plug which is widely used both in this country and overseas, and the type II fuse-links of BS 1361 are the standard house service cut-out fuse-link used by all of the British Supply Authorities.

The BS 1361 fuse-link Type 1 range (5 A to 30 A) provides a non-interchangeable range of fuse-links for use in domestic consumer units. It was initially launched in 1947 but due to lack of availability of replacement fuse-links and the lack of effort in educating the general public, who had previously only been used to semi-enclosed fuses, the system was abused and the anticipated growth of this type of consumer unit was never achieved.

It is interesting to note, however, that the fuse-links to BS 1361 which are used in domestic consumer units, have a breaking capacity of 16.5 kA which is the maximum fault level specified for domestic installations in this country, and discriminates with the 100 A house service cut-out fuse. Furthermore, the BS 1362 fuse-link in a plug is apparently used without any noticeable abuse because the general public is now well educated in the use of cartridge fuse-links, and the requirements of the 15th Edition may well see an increase in the use of domestic consumer units incorporating cartridge fuse-links to BS 1361.

Although these fuse-links are referred to in IEC 269: Part 3, 'Fuse-links for domestic and similar purposes', the UK never adopted IEC 269: Part 3 because the test requirements for such fuses were inferior to BS 1361. However, the revision of IEC 269: Part 3, which is now under consideration, contains acceptable test requirements and when this IEC document is finalised, it will undoubtedly be published as BS 88: Part 3 thus replacing the existing BS 1361 and BS 1362.

The titles which have been agreed for the revised versions of the IEC 269 documents are Part 1 'Low voltage fuses - General applications', Part 2 'Fuses intended for use by authorised persons' (previously 'Fuses for industrial purposes'), Part 3 'Fuses for use by unskilled persons' (previously 'Fuses for domestic and similar applications').

SEMICONDUCTOR FUSE-LINKS

BS 88: Part 4 covers semiconductor fuse-links. The basic requirements for such fuse-links (breaking capacity, etc.) are similar to those specified for industrial fuses. Because the main attributes of semi-conductor fuse-links are the very low values of let-through I^2t and cut-off current, there are additional tests which must be made to ensure that the manufacturers' statements regarding such information as pre-arcing I^2t, total I^2t, cut-off current, arc voltage, etc., are verified.

The application of such fuse-links requires a knowledge of the semiconductor device and the type of circuit to be protected. Because of the precise nature of the application, more information is provided with regard to the performance of semiconductor fuse-links for the conventional industrial or domestic types. These include variation of pre-arcing I^2t with prospective current, variation of total I^2t with voltage and power factor and variation of arc voltage with applied voltage. This information is required in order to optimise the capability of the semiconductor devices.

FUSE-LINKS FOR SUPPLY AUTHORITY NETWORKS

The latest section of the BS 88 series of standards to date is Part 5 which covers the range of l.v. fuse-links used by the supply authorities. As these fuse-links are dimensionally standardised, the specification includes these dimensions together with standardised time/current characteristics. The breaking capacity of these fuse-links is 80 kA at 415 V a.c. and the method of short-circuit testing is similar to that for industrial fuse-links although the time/current characteristics are somewhat faster at the short time end of the characteristic than the equivalent rating of fuse-links to BS 88: Part 2. Electricity Supply Industry Standard ESI 12-8 also contains these characteristics as well as information on the co-ordination achieved between these fuse-links and the h.v. fuse-links used in the 11 kV and 6.6 kV ring main units.

A novel feature is the arrangement of the fuse tags. The fuse-links are accommodated in fuse-carriers which engage with the fixed contacts of the supply authority feeder pillar by means of a wedge action.

FUSE SWITCHGEAR

The combination of a switch and a fuse as a means of (a) providing short-circuit protection, (b) the switching of loads (both steady and fluctuating) and (c) means of isolation, dates back as far as the introduction of the fuse itself, but obviously the design of the modern types of such combinations meets the most onerous service conditions. These combinations fall into two categories, switch-fuses and the fuse-switches, and BS 5419 covers both types. However as BS 5419 is a reproduction of IEC 408 entitled 'Low voltage air break switches, air break disconnectors, air break switch-disconnectors and fuse combination units' it can be appreciated from such a cumbersome title that in IEC there was a definite need to differentiate between the switching function and the disconnecting function in such combinations. It is therefore worth examining the relevant definitions from these documents.

Switch (mechanical). A mechanical switching device capable of making, carrying and breaking currents under normal circuit conditions which may include specified operating overload conditions and also carrying, for a specified time, currents under specified abnormal circuit conditions such as those of short-circuit. It should be noted that a switch may also be capable of making but not breaking short-circuit currents.

<u>Disconnector (isolator)</u>.   A mechanical switching device which for reasons of safety provides in the open position an isolating distance in accordance with specified requirements. A disconnector is capable of opening and closing a circuit when either negligible current is broken or made or when no significant change in the voltage across the terminals of each of the poles of the disconnector occurs. It is also capable of carrying currents under normal circuit conditions and carrying for a specified time currents under abnormal conditions such as those of short-circuit.

<u>Switch-disconnector (switch-isolator)</u>.   A switch which in the open position satisfies the isolating requirements specified for a disconnector.

<u>Switch-fuse</u>.   A switch in which one or more poles have a fuse in series in a composite unit.

<u>Disconnector-fuse</u>.   A disconnector in which one or more poles have a fuse in series in a composite unit.

<u>Fuse-switch</u>.   A switch in which a fuse-link or a fuse-carrier with fuse-link forms the moving contact of the switch.

<u>Fuse-disconnector (fuse-isolator)</u>.   A disconnector in which a fuse-link or a fuse-carrier with a fuse-link forms the moving contact of the disconnector.
    All of the foregoing combinations of a fuse and switch or disconnector are covered by another definition.

<u>Fuse-combination unit</u>.   A combination of a switch, a disconnector or a switch disconnector and one or more fuses in a composite unit made by the manufacturer or in accordance with his instructions.
    A number of important points emerge from these definitions. There is a definite distinction drawn between a device which performs the functional switching, i.e. making and breaking the circuit, and one which provides isolation. The earlier types of fuse-combination units probably only provided overcurrent protection by the fuse combined

with an isolating function by the associated 'switch' but in more recent years, certainly in Britain, the popular combinations of either switch-fuse or fuse-switch have provided all of the functions mentioned earlier and the British user has come to expect that such combinations provide him with the isolating function.

Discussion in IEC has revealed that this assumption is not necessarily valid with respect to equipment made internationally because there are devices available which while performing the switching function do not have the necessary requirements for satisfying the safety aspects of an isolating function. This is highlighted in the 15th Edition in which Chapter 46 deals with Isolation and Switching, Section 476 of Chapter 47 describes the applications measures for isolation and switching and Section 537 of Chapter 53 specifies the type of devices to be used.

Chapter 46 considers separately the functions of isolation, switching off for mechanical maintenance, and emergency switching. Section 537 states that for isolators the isolating distances between contacts or other means of isolation when in the open position shall not be less than those specified for isolators according to BS 5419 and that the position of the contacts or other means of isolation shall either be externally visible or clearly and reliably indicated. An indication of the isolated position shall occur only when the specified isolating distance has been attained in each pole. The same requirements are specified for devices for switching off for mechanical maintenance. It is also necessary in order to comply with the requirements of the 15th Edition that such devices be provided with means for padlocking in the OFF position.

Section 463, Emergency Switching, requires that for every part of an installation which it may be necessary to disconnect rapidly from the supply in order to prevent or remove a hazard, a means of emergency switching shall be provided.

Regulation 537-12 states that the device shall be capable of cutting off the full load current on the relevant part of the installation. Where appropriate due account shall be taken of stalled motor conditions.

Regulation 476.1 includes a statement that when more than one of these functions, i.e. isolation, switching off for mechanical

maintenance or emergency switching, are to be performed by a common
device, the arrangement and characteristics of the device shall satisfy
all requirements of these Regulations for the various functions
concerned.

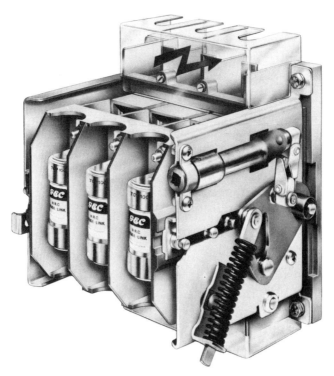

*Figure 14.13   100 A fuse-switch to BS 5419 suitable for use on system
voltages up to 660 V a.c.*

The modern combinations of fuse and switch are ideal for this
purpose. The most popular arrangement is undoubtedly the fuse-switch
although the switch-fuse is popular in circuits of small current
rating. The test requirements of BS 5419 for these combinations are
very rigorous. They include making on to a fault test where the switch
shall be capable of making on to prospective rms currents as high as
80 kA, the peak current and energy let-through being limited by the
fuse-link of maximum rating which can be associated with the switch.
The switch itself must be able to withstand twenty times its thermal
rating for 1 second. With regard to the overload make/break performance, there are various categories of duty, the most onerous of which

is AC23, and this requires the switch to make and break up to ten times rated current at a power factor of 0.35 at 110% rated voltage. There is also a requirement for mechanical and electrical endurance where the switch has to successfully withstand up to 10000 make/break operations with 5% of the operations being made at rated current and a power factor of 0.65.

There are many modern combinations of fuse and switch which can readily provide this performance up to 660 V a.c. having very compact dimensions. The full capability of the overload make/break performance of the fuse-switch can be utilised when motor circuit fuse-links are fitted. It can also provide all of the requirements for isolation by giving clear indication of the position of the contacts, adequate isolating distance and a padlocking-off facility. They are therefore ideal for use either adjacent to the equipment they are protecting or in a switchboard supplying a number of circuits. Figure 14.13 illustrates a very popular arrangement.

THERMAL RATINGS

One of the problems which has been encountered with fuse-switches is the fact that both the IEC and British Standards permit the thermal rating to be determined without an enclosure. This is known as a conventional temperature-rise test and can produce misleading results, particularly with the larger size of fuse-switch. British practice has always been based upon thermal tests conducted using the minimum size of enclosure normally associated with the fuse-switch and recent amendments to the IEC Specification make it mandatory for the manufacturer of the fuse-switch to state the enclosed current rating for his product. As this has been common practice in Britain the amendment will be welcomed by the user as it eliminates a misunderstanding which could create overheating problems in service. There is some safeguard in the requirements of BS 5486 which covers factory built assemblies (FBAs), where it is necessary for the manufacturer to ensure when designing his switchboard that no item of included equipment is subjected to a condition which could result in higher temperature-rises than those specified in its relevant specification. The above-mentioned amendment requiring a statement of the enclosed rating further emphasises the need for close attention to this particular aspect.

170

The fact that such a compact relatively simple device as the modern fuse-switch can offer such a range of protection firmly establishes its future role in the design, installation and utilisation of electrical systems.

Chapter 15
Motor Control Gear
C. Copestake
Simplex – GE Ltd

Motor control gear and associated circuitry are fundamental parts of electrical distribution and utilisation systems. As such electrical contractors, works and plant engineers, consulting engineers and electrical inspectors have long been employing control theory and equipment successfully but continuous updating in modern control systems and their installation procedures and techniques is necessary.

Motor control gear has two main functions. It must make and break the connections between the motor and the supply, with intermediate steps where necessary to limit the starting current surges. It must also automatically disconnect the motor (a) in the event of excessive current being passed which would overheat and ultimately destroy the windings or (b) if the supply fails.

In addition to the two main functions described above, motor control gear may also be required to: limit the starting current to the lowest value consistent with the requirements of the starting torque; bring the motor smoothly to rest when required; apply braking when rapid stopping, reverse rotation or varied speed are necessary; and carry out automatic operating cycles or sequences.

It follows that the control gear, if it is to carry out these duties efficiently and safely, must be appropriately designed, manufactured and selected with the utmost care to suit the characteristics of the motor and the drive.

Starters may be manually operated or activated by electromagnetic means. If operated electromagnetically there are two basic ways in which the control action may be initiated - manually or automatically. A pushbutton or a selector switch may be employed to initiate the magnetic operation of the starter manually. This is generally termed local control. Alternatively, remote control may be used where a limit switch or float switch may be connected to the starter to provide automatic initiation of the starter in response to predetermined conditions.

The rating of the motor and the starting torque, which is governed by the type of load, may require the starting of the motor at a voltage lower than that supplied by the line. This has the effect of limiting the starting current, thereby reducing voltage disturbances in the system. The maximum starting current permissible is generally limited by the supply authority's regulations, and sometimes by restrictions of other connected plant.

In some applications, the motor starter may be used to control the speed of the motor or its direction of rotation. The difference between a.c. and d.c. motors and the use of high voltage (h.v.) motor circuits also contribute to the extensive variety of construction and operating characteristics of motor starters.

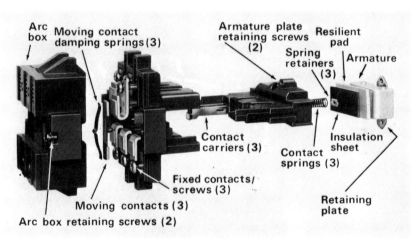

Figure 15.1 Exploded view of a typical air break contactor assembly

Before considering in detail the different types of motor starter available and the criteria for choice, it is worthwhile examining the various components utilised in motor control.

The most widespread device used in a starter is the a.c. magnetic contactor which consists of contact assemblies actuated by electromagnetic action. The operating coil when energised attracts an

173

armature to which is attached a set of moving contacts which make with a set of stationary contacts; fig. 15.1 shows a typical air break contactor assembly.

The contactor is magnetically held in position by maintaining the current flow through the coil. If the voltage to the coil fails or falls below a defined level, the contactor opens, thus disconnecting the motor from the supply. The coil must be constantly energised in order to keep the contactor closed.

CONTACTOR PERFORMANCE

To select the correct contactor for a given application the performance required of it must be clearly defined and the capabilities of the contactor known to ensure they are not exceeded.

The limiting capabilities of a contactor include: the making and breaking capabilities at different voltages; the thermal rating, I_{th}; the contact life for a given duty; and the short time current withstand capability. Any of these factors may determine the choice of contactor for a given application.

The relevant International and British Specifications are IEC 158-1 'Low voltage motor control gear for industrial use Part 1; contactors', and BS 5424: Part 1: 1977 'Contactors for voltage up to and including 1000 V a.c. and 1200 V d.c.' These specifications define utilisation categories, the performance expected of contactors when so used and the tests which contactors must pass to prove suitability for a given application, table 15.1.

All routine tests have to be carried out at supply voltage for normal operation except as indicated below, and at 110% supply voltage for proving operation. Full details of these tests and power factors at which they are carried out are given in IEC 158-1: 1970 and BS 5424: 1977.

Most manufacturers define the performance of their contactors with respect to the contactor utilisation categories shown in table 15.1. The performance normally relates to electrical endurance and is expressed as contact life curves for AC2, AC3 and AC4 duties as well as curves for mixed categories, e.g. 90% AC3 and 10% AC4 duty.

Table 15.1 Contactor utilisation categories

Utilisation category	Current as multiples of operational current			
	Normal operation		Proving operation	
	Make	Break	Make	Break
AC1 Non-inductive or slightly inductive loads such as furnaces and heating loads.	1	1	1.5	1.5
AC2 Starting of slip ring motors. Plugging with rotor resistance in circuit.	2.5	2.5	4	4
AC3 Starting of cage motors, switching of motors during running.	6	1*	10 / 8	8[†] / 6[‡]
AC4 Starting of cage motors, plugging, inching.	6	6	12 / 10	10[†] / 8[‡]

All tests carried out at supply voltage for normal operation except as indicated below and at 110% supply voltage for proving operations. For full details and power factors, etc. refer to specification IEC 158 and BS 5424.

*At 17% supply voltage.

[†]For rated currents up to and including 100 A.

[‡]For rated currents above 100 A.
With limiting values of 800 A, 1000 A and 1200 A for 6, 8 and 10 times the rated current.

SELECTING CONTACTORS

The following comments assist in correct selection with respect to different types of starting and motors. The characteristics of different methods of starting are discussed later in this chapter.

For direct switching starters, contactors should be selected on the basis of AC3 or AC4 rating. Ratings are generally based on the proving make/break figures of table 15.1 and infer that for normal operation the stalled motor current must not exceed six times the contactor AC3 rating. Many motors do in fact have starting currents in excess of this value and contactors used at their maximum listed ratings might be subjected to more than six times full load current.

This is generally acceptable provided that the actual stalled motor current does not exceed the proving break current of the contactor. Where only catalogue figures are available for motor stalled current, due allowance must be made for the tolerances permitted by the motor specification which may increase the listed figure by as much as 20%. If the motor accelerating time is greater than 15 seconds, contactor derating may be necessary. Actual cases should be referred to the manufacturer.

A reversing starter, by definition, is intended to cause the motor to reverse the direction of rotation by reversing the motor primary connections while it is running (IEC 292-1: 1969 'Low voltage motor starters', clause 2.3). In order to comply with the above definition AC4 ratings should be used; however where it is not intended that reversal shall take place when the motor is running AC3 rating is adequate.

Contactors connected in the delta loop of a star-delta starter, see fig. 15.2, can be uprated theoretically by a factor of $\sqrt{3}$, but it is considered preferable not to use the full uprating in order to cater for phase current unbalance which is of a higher order than that in the line. For starters using contactors in the line, AC3 rating should be used.

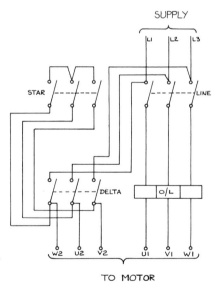

Figure 15.2 Wiring diagram for a star-delta starter

Contactors used in auto-transformer starters should be selected using AC3 ratings.

For stator-rotor starters, the stator contactors should be selected using AC2 ratings. Rotor contactor ratings are normally specified by the contactor manufacturer as enhanced ratings based on them being in circuit only during starting.

Another important consideration when selecting contactors is to ensure that the proposed cable conductor can be accommodated on the contactor. Most manufacturers supply this information in their catalogue together with the different types of termination that are available. A range of contactors is illustrated in fig. 15.3.

Figure 15.3 Range of Westmaster 2 a.c. contactors covering the range 4-360 kW

Vacuum contactors

Vacuum contactors are becoming increasingly popular for duties up to 11 kV contactors. These heavy duty contactors have been developed for use in the most arduous conditions, primarily for direct-on-line switching of cage induction motors. They are of course suitable for other applications including transformer and capacitor switching. Figure 15.4 shows a typical vacuum contactor, while a 3.3 kV board is shown in fig. 15.5.

177

Figure 15.4   Simplex-GE Vacutac vacuum contactor

The principle of operation is that interruption of the current takes place between two contacts housed in an evacuated ceramic envelope. The moving contact is attached to a metal bellow which provides movement and retains the vacuum.

Benefits of using a vacuum as an interrupting medium for a.c. work have been recognised since the early part of this century. However, it was not until improved vacuum technology and a better understanding of the mechanism of arc interruption in vacuum had been gained that practical interrupters became available on a commercial scale. It is one of the fundamental principles of vacuum interruption that the contact gap dielectric strength recovers extremely quickly after arc interruption. This property of a vacuum ensures that the current in the arc ceases to flow at the first current zero, thus reducing the arc energy considerably when compared with conventional devices using oil, air or air-blast techniques.

A vacuum contactor can produce current-chopping and associated voltage transients. This occurs when a low current in a highly inductive circuit is suddenly interrupted instead of continuing as a power

Figure 15.5 Typical multi-tier 3.3 kV vacuum contactor board with withdrawable units

frequency sine wave to zero. The chopping energy is stored in the inductance of the circuit and resonates with the circuit capacitance until dissipated in the circuit resistance. Voltage transients due to current-chopping are not a problem in capacitive or resistive circuits, because there is not sufficient inductance to provide chopping energy. Neither do the transients in inductive circuits present problems where the power factor is greater than 0.15, because the chopping energy is

179

very quickly dissipated in the circuit resistance. Where voltage transients generated by current-chopping produce problems, these can be overcome by circuit design.

Generally it is the lack of arc emission together with the resulting space saving of high current rated devices that give the vacuum contactor the following basic advantages over the air break design (see chapter 12).

(a) No by-products of arcing.

(b) No ionised gases after interruption.

(c) High breaking capacity.

(d) Short arcing time.

(e) Low contact wear and virtually weld free.

OVERLOAD PROTECTION

In conjunction with the contactor, the overload relay is a vital component of the motor starter. For many years motors have been manufactured with a more than adequate thermal capacity which has meant that the overload protection did not need to be highly accurate. The introduction of the continuous maximum rated (cmr) motor of today has been achieved by technical advances which have enabled the motor manufacturer to reduce the cost and the size to power ratio. This has resulted in a much more limited overload capacity and therefore modern cmr motors require much closer protection.

Types of overload protection available vary from the basic thermal overload relay to very sophisticated electronic protection relays which incorporate overload, earth leakage and short-circuit protection. The user needs to rely on his own judgement of what he can afford to pay for overload protection against the value he puts on the operation of the motor and the associated equipment. The cost of downtime and rewind or replacement of the motor are all factors which need to be considered.

Types available

Some of the more common types of overload protection available and their characteristics are indicated below.

Magnetic dashpot overload relay.   This relay employs a dashpot,

fitted with a piston which operates the overload trip mechanism. A
magnetic field set up by a coil surrounding the piston assembly is
proportional to the circuit current and the effect of the magnetic
field is to raise the piston out of the dashpot. The dashpot is
normally filled with oil, which slows down the movement of the piston
so that a transient overload, such as occurs under normal start conditions, will have ceased before the piston has moved sufficiently to
trip the mechanism. The characteristics of the overload relay may be
modified by the use of different viscosity oils which will control the
speed with which the piston will move. Figure 15.6 shows how the
operating characteristics may be varied. Note the inverse characteristics obtained.

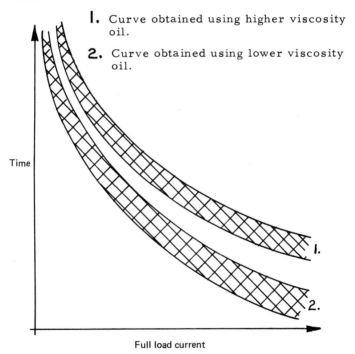

I. Curve obtained using higher viscosity oil.

2. Curve obtained using lower viscosity oil.

Time

Full load current

*Figure 15.6 Typical relay time/current curves for a magnetic (dashpot)
type overload relay*

Normally, silicone fluid is now used as it demonstrates a small
change in viscosity over a large temperature range. This type of
overload relay has little thermal memory and therefore offers little
protection against continuous inching or repeated attempts to start a

stalled machine. In this respect the magnetic overload relay is inferior to the thermal type. Magnetic overload relays are however particularly useful for stalled current protection as they offer a wide choice of time delays.

Thermal overload relay. This generally consists of a bimetal element whose coefficients of expansion differ. The bimetal element is heated by the motor current passing through it or through a heater coil adjacent to it. The element is secured at one end and bends when heated, causing the free end to operate some form of trip device. The inherent time delay in heating the element simulates the heating curve of the motor and is of the inverse time characteristic type.

A problem here is the fact that heating continues to have an effect even after the current has fallen to normal. This can cause tripping and it is advisable therefore to ensure that the trip characteristic is well above the starting current curve.

When a bimetal strip is used in each phase of a motor supply, a high degree of single-phasing protection is afforded by the differential trip system and a good response is achieved to small degrees of imbalance. Some form of ambient temperature compensation is necessary to avoid nuisance tripping at close protection levels. However this feature is not particularly accurate as it tends to compensate for the temperature in the starter enclosure, rather than that of the motor.

A thermal overload relay offers protection against incorrect operation because its cooling time prevents an immediate restart and the trip time from warm will be less than that from cold.

Conventional overload relays detect an overload by monitoring the supply current, but will not necessarily detect faults which could cause a critical increase in the temperature of the motor itself.

Thermistor protection. Thermistors are used to detect the temperature of the motor windings. A thermistor is a thermally sensitive semiconductor resistor, which exhibits a significant change in electrical resistance with a change in temperature. A detector monitors the sudden increase in resistance of the thermistor at the critical temperature. For the best results, thermistors should be fitted by the machine manufacturer who knows the positions where hot spots occur on the machine.

Thermistor protection has not been as widely accepted as might have been expected, especially in the UK. This is probably due to the fact that second to the power transformer, the induction motor is very reliable, in the majority of cases the extra expense is not warranted and the motors are special. They are more acceptable in larger machines. Also, auxiliary control cables are required between the detector and the machine.

Electronic relays. The application of electronics to protection systems has allowed a new breed of overload relays to be developed. In general the electronic overload relay models the time-current characteristic of the machine by means of solid state circuitry.

*Figure 15.7 Thermal, magnetic and electronic devices from typical
    overload relays*

The use of semiconductors allows devices to be set very close to the normal operating characteristic as the over-run can be made extremely small compared with the normal thermal type of overload. The time-current characteristics can be altered to suit the type of motor used.

In addition to overload protection, the electronic protection relay can provide earth leakage, single-phase, pre-overload alarm and short-circuit protection. Protective devices removed from typical overload relays are shown in fig. 15.7.

POPULAR STARTERS
A knowledge of starter types is required to enable one to select the correct unit for a specific application. Choice of the right starter is important because failure to do this can drastically reduce the working life of a drive and result in uneconomical operation. A modern range of starters is shown in fig. 15.8.

Figure 15.8 Typical range of motor starters available in the UK

Direct-on-line.   The simplest and least expensive form of starting
is direct-on-line (dol) and this is generally the standard choice for
motors up to 7.5 kW.

The switch-on current is quite high, up to five or six times the
motor full load current, falling off as the motor accelerates to
normal running speed. As well as the current, the initial torque is
also high, of the order of 125 percent of the full load torque. This
high level of starting torque can produce rapid acceleration and may
be detrimental with belt or chain driven loads or if starting is
frequent.

At low voltage, most supply authorities limit the maximum permissible starting current by restricting the allowable public supply
voltage drop caused by motor starting unless all details are given to
the supply authority. Typically the limits are 7.5% of nominal voltage
for frequent starts and 10% for infrequent starts. If full details are
supplied, sometimes larger machines are allowed depending upon local
circumstances.

At high voltage, much larger machines can be dol started and up to
100 kW is not unreasonable.

Star-delta.   If direct switching is not allowed, a method of reduced
voltage starting must be used in order to reduce the motor starting
current. The most popular method of reduced voltage starting is star-
delta due to its economy. The starting current is approximately one
third the value of dol starting current (about twice full load current)
and the starting torque is one third of that with dol starting. A six-
terminal motor must be used to enable the winding connections to be
changed during the starting procedure.

It is possible that switching transients on the change from star
to delta can cause problems.

The connection of the overload relay in star-delta starting is
important. Consider the relationship of currents during starting and
running of a typical motor, having a full load current of say 10 A and
taking twice full load current (flc) in star at start.

An overload relay connected in the line and selected on a basis of
10 A flc would experience a current of 20 A during starting. However,
the motor windings are rated at only 5.8 A and are subjected to a

current of around 350%. It follows that for correct motor protection during starting the overload should be connected in series with the motor windings and selected on the basis of three times motor flc.

Occasionally, tripping times may prove to be too short at start with the overload relay phase connected as recommended above; reverting to line connected often solves this problem. If very long accelerating times are experienced, the use of saturable current transformers may be necessary. As an alternative, the overload relay can be connected in series with the delta contactor, but this will provide no protection during starting. This disadvantage can be overcome by fitting a second overload relay in series with the line contactor, but rated at the higher current.

Any deviation from the theoretically correct method of protection should only be undertaken if it has been established that the motor can withstand the more onerous conditions placed on it.

Auto-transformer. Another reduced voltage starting method is that of an auto-transformer starter, which has significant benefits but is relatively expensive. It is particularly useful where progressive control of accelerating torque is required, for example with large fans or mixers, and is often used with submersible borehole pumps.

The starting voltage at the motor terminals (and therefore the starting torque) can be selected to suit the load by means of tappings on the auto-transformer - the usual values being 50, 65 and 80%. By using the Korndorfer system, the motor is not disconnected from the supply during the transition period in which the auto-transformer winding acts as a choke, thus eliminating the high induced currents that would otherwise occur.

Therefore, to a method of starting giving an adjustable starting torque are added the advantages of smooth starting, reduced current demands on the supply and acceleration with peaks and transients minimised.

The above starting methods are summarised in table 15.2 and are the most popular for cage motors.

Stator-rotor. The slip ring motor has the advantage that, while developing approximately the same starting torque as an equivalent

Table 15.2 Summary of starting methods for cage motors

Method	Starting torque % of dol value	Starting current % of dol value	Nature of start	Adjustment of torque	Advantage	Disadvantage
Direct-on-line	100	100	Quick starting at max. torque	Fixed (max.)	Cheapest, simplest, most reliable	Heavy current, heavy torque
Star-delta	$33\frac{1}{3}$	$33\frac{1}{3}$	Light starting heavy running torque	Fixed	Low cost and simple. Reduced starting current	Fixed torque, six terminal motors
Auto-transformer (Korndorfer)						
Tap - 50%	25	25	Light	Tappings selected to suit load	Smooth starting. Transient peaks reduced	Costly
65%	42	42	Normal			
80%	64	64	Heavy			

cage machine, the starting current is much lower. This type of motor is therefore largely used for applications where starting current restriction is essential and a relatively long time is taken to reach full speed due to the high inertia of the load. A stator-rotor starter is used with a slip ring motor. With this method the starter is switched direct to the full supply voltage but the current drawn from the supply is limited to usually between 125 and 200% of full load current by external resistors connected to the rotor windings. In addition to limiting the starting current, the resistors improve the power factor so that the current values given above produce starting torques of between 100 and 175% of full load value. As the motor accelerates, resistor sections are progressively cut out by rotor contactors closing in sequence under time control. The more rotor contactors, the lower the demand on the power supply and the smoother the acceleration.

Variable speed drives.   In many industrial processes it is necessary to continually vary the speed of the machine depending upon the conditions prevailing at a specific time. Traditionally this has been achieved by running the mains connected motor at a fixed speed and interposing some device such as a slipping clutch, variable belt, or gearbox between the motor and the load. Today this can be achieved using a variable speed drive which can provide an optimum process speed, an adjustable speed for different materials/end products, a stable speed, fast speed changes and introduce an element of energy saving.

The more popular types of drive are a.c. and d.c. thyristor systems. The basic principle of operation is the use of a thyristor, which like a rectifier diode has the property of allowing current to flow in one direction only. Unlike the rectifier diode, however, the thyristor contains a 'gate' which must be operated by a trigger pulse before it will allow current to flow in the forward direction. Having been triggered, the thyristor will conduct until the current flowing through it falls to zero, when it will revert to a non-conducting state and only conduct again when a further trigger pulse is applied to the gate. So with an a.c. supply applied to the thyristor, the gate can be triggered at any point in the positive half cycle, enabling the amplitude of the output direct voltage to be controlled between a maximum and zero. Thyristors can be connected in various converter configurations providing control of a.c. or d.c. drives.

When connected to an electrical network, a thyristor loads the system in a manner that is different from conventional loads such as motors and lighting circuits. This difference is primarily associated with the following two characteristics of these converters.

(a) High reactive power consumption in conjunction with a low direct voltage output, which results in, for example, voltage drops at the feeding point.

(b) Harmonic currents arising owing to the non-linear characteristic of the converter.

Providing that the converter load connected to a busbar is low, in relation to the other loads, it is frequently unnecessary to adopt any special measures. With large converter power ratings, however, both the nature of the supply network and the duty of the converter must be thoroughly studied so that the most suitable type of power factor correction or harmonic filtering can be selected.

Other factors affecting choice.   It is quite clear therefore that many factors need to be considered when choosing the method of starting, but this is only part of the process of selecting a motor starter. Other factors to be taken into consideration include control of the starter, the enclosure, cabling, environment and maintenance after installation.

In the majority of cases, the starter is controlled by pushbuttons on the starter housing. However, when selecting the starter it is necessary to consider whether remote control will be required, or if extra stop buttons are called for to effect remote stopping in an emergency. In some cases a pilot switch may be needed for automatic control by float and pressure switches, limit switches or thermostats. When remote control such as this is required, some slight and very simple modifications are sometimes necessary - such as the removal of internal links which may be carried out by the qualified installer.

The type of enclosure in which the starter is to be housed should be chosen carefully to suit the conditions under which the equipment will be operating. The most common classification of enclosure protection is defined by the IP numbers of IEC 144. The more general enclosures are listed below. Failure to select the correct type of enclosure for the conditions of use can be dangerous.

Open. No enclosing case. Suitable for installation in switch houses and similar special situations where the absence of moisture or dust can be ensured.

General purpose. (IP 40) This is the standard enclosure for contactor equipment for normal use.

Dust and damp protecting. (IP 51) For use in dirty surroundings where dust or moisture might cause mal-operation of control gear.

Weatherproof. (IP 54) For use in the open without further protection from the weather.

Hoseproof. (IP 65) For use in dairies, garages, etc. where equipment is liable to be splashed when hosing down.

Watertight. (IP 66) For shipboard service when mounted on an open deck. They are constructed to exclude all moisture.

Flameproof. For use in coal mines, petroleum installations and certain chemical plant applications where compliance with BS 4683 is required.

The positioning of the starter is largely governed by the location of the controlled equipment and its operator, but regard must also be paid to the IEE Wiring Regulations and to local regulations.

Motor control centres

Modern installations and process plant require many motor starters and it is therefore often convenient to group these together in a single cubicle switchboard known as a motor control centre (mcc); typically shown in fig. 15.9.

Many different designs of mccs are available and it is not possible to discuss the various features of every type. However some of the more important features are described below.

*Figure 15.9   Motor control centres form a compact means of housing
many starters*

The general arrangement of most mccs consists of a horizontal,
air-insulated, copper (or possibly aluminium) busbar system with
vertical droppers to the various components. Cable entry should be
available from the top, or bottom with front and rear access.

Incoming supply cables may be connected directly to the busbar
system via a set of line lugs or alternative arrangements such as air
circuit-breakers (acbs), moulded case circuit-breakers (mccbs) or
switch-fuses may be used. In association with any of these devices,
mccs sometimes include bus-section switchgear, key interlocks and
metering systems to meet specific customer requirements.

The selected starter units are contained in standard sized cubicles
which may be of a fixed pattern, particularly for larger drives or
withdrawable for drives up to around 160 kW.

A withdrawable starter has the advantage of being readily removed
from service and replaced by another starter of suitable type and
rating, thus ensuring minimum shutdown time on vital drives in the
event of a failure. A further feature of the withdrawable starter is
that the make up of the mcc (depending on the design) can be readily
modified to suit changing process requirements.

The motor isolator handle mechanism is usually mechanically

interlocked to ensure that the door cannot be opened when the isolator is 'on'. As an alternative to the very common isolator and fuses arrangement, the starter may accommodate an mccb having integral magnetic trips to provide starter isolation and short-circuit protection. When the prospective fault current of the supply system exceeds the breaking capacity of the standard mccb, current limiting devices integral with the breaker, are fitted to protect against high level short-circuit faults.

TRANSPORT AND INSTALLATION

Before leaving the manufacturer, an mcc is given final mechanical and electrical inspection and packed in keeping with practices for electrical equipment undergoing transport. Upon receipt of any apparatus an immediate inspection should be made for any damage or loss of equipment in transit. Should damage or missing material be noted, a claim should be filed with the carrier immediately. Any packing wedges in relays, meters or other protective devices should be removed.

Equipment is normally shipped in an upright position either complete or in handleable sections. Sections should be maintained in an upright position during handling. No attempt should ever be made to jack, lift or move the equipment at points other than the lifting eyes or floor sills. Two or more lifting ropes or cables should be used to distribute weight more evenly. Crowbars, pipe rollers or slings are useful implements for moving equipment, but care must be taken to maintain distributed loading and always to apply leverage at the floor sills and lifting points.

If it is necessary to store equipment for any length of time the following precautions should be taken:

(a) Uncrate equipment.

(b) Store in a clean dry area at moderate temperature. Cover with a suitable canvas or heavy duty plastics covers to prevent the entrance of foreign material.

(c) If it is necessary for equipment to be stored in cool or damp areas, as is often the case on site, not only should the equipment be completely covered, but heat should be provided to prevent condensation of moisture in the equipment. Space heaters (if furnished in the equipment) should be energised or a 150 W

192

standard tungsten filament lamp could be placed in the bottom of each enclosure.

Before any installation work is done, all drawings furnished by the manufacturer should be consulted as well as all applicable contract drawings for the particular installation.

Attention should always be given to the physical location of equipment and its relation to existing or planned cable runs. Care should be taken to plan for any future cable entries before the equipment is installed.

If the equipment is to be floor mounted, attention should be given to providing a level, even foundation. The purchaser may elect to install steel members in the floor, properly levelled and grouted, although these are not normally required.

The overall height of equipment should be considered with respect to head room, top cable entry space, and line up with other equipment.

The positioning of motor control gear needs to be carefully evaluated. Ventilation is important, as it allows equipment to run at a lower temperature and reduces condensation. In order to ease routine maintenance and to facilitate investigation of possible faults, accessibility should always be taken into account when siting the equipment.

Motor control gear should always be mounted where there is least vibration. When a suitable site has been located, mount the equipment firmly and vertically, otherwise operation of overload relays may be affected. Occasionally, nuts, bolts, screws and connections can be loosened in transit and should always be checked for tightness before commissioning.

When cabling up, it is important to check that the details on the rating plates of motor and starter correspond, particularly as regards kilowatt rating. The size of the cable selected should be adequate for the normal rated full load current of the motor. Due allowance should also be made for voltage drop, particularly where heavy starting currents will be drawn from the line, or where long cable runs are involved.

In order to facilitate connection, all terminals for external cables are normally marked in accordance with the diagrams provided by the manufacturer. Where these markings are on removable cable clamps, these must not be interchanged.

Care should be taken to ensure that cables do not touch parts likely to attain a high temperature, such as grids or units of resistance banks. Where a cable is in close proximity to such parts it should be of heat-resisting type.

Standard arrangements for connections are cable clamps, sweating sockets or socket-type terminals for crimping or fitted with clamping screws. The arrangements provided should always be used in the manner for which they were designed; the practice of making 'temporary' connections by twisting the bared ends of the cable beneath sweating sockets for example is strongly deprecated.

With cable clamps the stranded conductors should be evenly divided and compressed efficiently by the clamps. The bared cable should fit the sweating socket, any slight discrepancy in size being made up by packing with copper wire before sweating. A similar technique should also be employed for the socket-type terminal. Where crimped terminations are employed the correct tool should be used for the size of the cable involved.

When installing cables, care should be taken to avoid the possibility of cable insulation being damaged by any sharp edges (steelwork, screws, etc.). Excessive amounts of cable within the enclosure should also be avoided as this will lead to unnecessary heating. All safety shrouds, shields, warning labels and cover plates should be properly repositioned after installation.

All control gear should be efficiently earthed and normally a terminal is provided for this purpose.

In addition to the normal circuit checking after wiring is completed, the following specific actions should be taken before energising the equipment.

(a) Carry out an insulation resistance test on all terminals and bus-bars. Instruments or control devices sensitive to the high voltage should be isolated from the circuit.

(b) Operate each magnetic device by hand to see that all moving parts operate freely. Check all electrical interlock contacts for proper operation.

(c) Current transformers are often shipped with a shunt across the secondary if the circuit is not complete. Remove the shunt after completing connections to the transformer secondary.

(d) Check each overload heater against the full load current listed on each motor nameplate.

(e) Check motor-driven time switches for correct time interval settings.

(f) The interior of equipment should be thoroughly cleaned with a clean brush, soft cloth or vacuum cleaner. The use of compressed air is not recommended as this often contains moisture.

(g) Competent and trained personnel should check electrically the operation of all control circuit safety devices (with outgoing main circuits disconnected), e.g. stop pushbuttons, safety trips, relays and protection, etc.

Chapter 16

Lighting

R. L. C. Tate, FCIBS
formerly of Thorn EMI Lighting Ltd

THE NATURE OF LIGHT

The electromagnetic spectrum

Light is a form of electromagnetic radiation. It is basically the
same thing as the radiations used in radio and television, as radiant
heat and as ultraviolet radiation and the still shorter X-rays, gamma
rays, etc. Visible light is radiation in that part of the spectrum
between 380 and 760 nm, to which the human eye is sensitive. A nano-
metre is a wavelength of one millionth (10^{-6}) of a millimetre.
Within these limits, differences of wavelength produce the effect of
colour, blue light being at the short-wave and red at the long-wave
ends of the visible spectrum. Because the human eye is more sensitive
to the yellow and green light in the middle of the spectrum, more
power must be expended to produce the same effect from colours at the
ends of it. This is why the monochromatic low-pressure sodium lamps
which emit all their visible energy in two narrow bands in the yellow
region are more efficient in terms of light output than 'Northlight'
fluorescent tubes that imitate natural daylight pretty closely and
emit approximately equal packets of energy in each spectral band.

The areas of radiation on either side of the visible spectrum are
important to the lamp maker. Wavelengths shorter than those of violet
light are designated 'ultraviolet' or UV and have the property of
exciting fluorescence in certain phosphors. That is, when irradiated
with UV, they themselves produce visible light. Infrared radiation,
at the other end of the spectrum, produces heating effects and may be
considered simply as radiant heat. Where, as in the case of a

filament lamp, light is produced by heating a coil of wire to incandescence, far more infrared radiation is produced than visible light,
and this is radiated and may be reflected with the light.

Reflection

Light is reflected from a polished surface at the same angle to the
normal that it strikes the surface. A truly matt surface scatters
light in all directions, while a semi-matt surface behaves in a manner
in between the two. It must not be forgotten that all reflectors
absorb some of the light that falls upon them, transforming it into
heat. Even super-purity polished aluminium absorbs about 5% of the
light, while a white-painted semi-matt reflector will absorb as much
as 20% or more.

Concentrating specular reflectors are usually parabolic or elliptical in cross section. If a compact light-source is placed at the
focal point of a parabola, its light will be reflected as a parallel
beam, that from a source placed at one focus of an ellipse will be
reflected through the second focus, while a hemispherical reflector
will reflect light back through its own centre. These principles are
made use of in the design of various types of spotlights, film projectors and high-bay industrial reflectors, fig. 16.1.

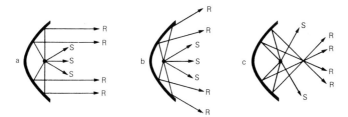

Light (R) reflected from a reflector of parabolic cross section will
produce a parallel beam when the source is at the focus of the
parabola (a), a divergent beam is behind the focal position (b), and
a crossing beam if it is in front of it (c). Spill light (S) is not
controlled by the reflector.

*Figure 16.1 Concentrating specular reflectors are used in the design
of various types of spotlights, film projectors and
high-bay industrial reflectors*

Refraction

When light passes from one clear translucent medium to another, e.g. from air to water, or air to glass, it is 'bent' or refracted at the surface. This can be observed by dipping a straight rod into water, which will appear to be bent at the point of entry. This property is made use of in lenses and refracting panels in lighting fittings. Again, it is important to remember that some light will be lost in passing through the medium and some will be reflected from its upper surface, in a greater or lesser degree according to the angle at which it strikes that surface.

Diffusion

If light passes through a surface that is partially opaque, it will be scattered or diffused in all directions. Typical diffusers are sand-blasted or acid-etched glass, flashed opal glass or opal acrylic sheet. The distance the light-source is mounted from the diffuser, the opacity of the latter and the nature of the background or reflecting surface will determine whether the light-source appears as a bright spot of light or its light is evenly diffused over the surface. Light losses in a 'near perfect' diffuser are greater than those in a partial diffuser or a prismatic panel.

UNITS OF LIGHT MEASUREMENT

The unit of luminous intensity is the candela. This is the amount of light emitted in a given direction by a source of one candle power. From it is derived the lumen, the unit of light flux. This is quite simply defined as the amount of light contained in one steradian from a source of one candela at its focus, fig. 16.2. The light output of all electric lamps is measured in lumens and their luminous efficiency (efficacy) is expressed in lumens per watt.

The unit of illuminance (measured illumination) is the lux. This is the illumination produced over an area of one square metre by one lumen. The 'foot-candle' or lumen per square foot has long been an obsolete term in the United Kingdom, but is still used in America.

Measured brightness is termed 'luminance' and should not be confused with 'illuminance'. Its units are the candela per square metre and the apostilb, the lumens emitted by a luminous surface of one

square metre. Imperial units, now obsolete, but still occasionally
quoted, are the candela per square foot and the foot lambert.

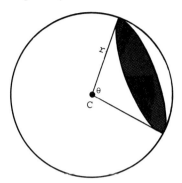

If the shaded area = r^2 and a source of one candela is at the
centre C, the light contained within the solid angle θ is one lumen.

*Figure 16.2 The relationship between the candela and the lumen is
shown by this diagram*

Two other terms that are easily confused are 'luminance' and
'luminosity'. The first is measured brightness expressed in apostilbs
or candelas per square metre, the second the apparent brightness as
seen by the eye. A simple example is the appearance of motor-car
headlamps by day and by night. Their luminance is the same in both
conditions but their luminosity is far greater at night than when they
are seen in daylight.

ELECTRIC LAMPS
Lamps produce light in three ways: by incandescence, by the excitation
of metallic vapours in an electrical discharge, and by fluorescence
initiated by a discharge in mercury vapour causing radiation in the
ultraviolet region of the spectrum.

All modern filament lamps consist basically of a coil of tungsten
wire enclosed in a glass bulb generally filled with an inert gas.
Tungsten is used because of its high melting-point; most filaments
operate at temperatures in the region of 2700°C. At this temperature
the surface of the filament evaporates slowly, until a point is
reached where it cannot support its own weight and fractures. The
rate of evaporation is controlled by the gas filling, usually a
mixture of argon and nitrogen, which in general service (GLS) lamps

exerts a pressure of about half an atmosphere on the surface of the filament. Evaporated tungsten settles on the inner surface of the glass bulb, discolouring it and reducing the amount of light emitted by the lamp throughout its life. The filament is coiled to reduce heat losses by convection currents in the gas; coiling substantially reduces the area exposed to them.

In the case of all standard mains voltage lamps made to BS 161: 1968, the life of the filament is 1000 hours. Some manufacturers make a 'double-life' lamp in which the filament is run at a slightly reduced temperature, giving a 2000 hour life at the cost of reduced light output. Lamps made for special purposes, such as projector lamps often have a shorter life.

Table 16.1 shows the lumen output of standard GLS lamps. Initial figures and 'lighting design lumens' are quoted. The latter takes care of the loss of light due to the deposition of evaporated tungsten on the bulb referred to above. Some manufacturers may quote the initial figures only, which can be misleading.

It will be noted that the lower voltage lamps have a higher light output than the 240 V types. This is because the filament is thicker and consequently has a larger surface area.

Reflector lamps

Blown glass reflector lamps were first introduced in the late '40s and are now made in sizes ranging from 40 to 150 W. Pressed glass lamps with a more accurately profiled reflecting surface followed in the mid-50s. The greater efficiency of the reflector allowed the filaments to be slightly underrun without loss of light in the beam so that these lamps have a rated life of 2000 h. Lamps are available with a dichroic reflecting surface which reduces radiant heat in the beam, but care should be exercised not to mount them in enclosed luminaires, which would overheat.

Tungsten halogen lamps

The use of a small quartz bulb allows the gas pressure to be substantially increased, thus lengthening the life of the lamp by reducing the rate of evaporation of the filament. Heavy blackening of the bulb by the tungsten deposited on it is avoided by the application of

the tungsten halogen principle. The addition of a small amount of a
halogen, usually iodine, to the gas filling results in an unstable
compound being formed with the evaporated tungsten, which is maintained at temperatures between about 200 and 2500°C. Since the bulb
wall temperature is in excess of 250°C, no tungsten is deposited on it.

Table 16.1 Lumen outputs of standard tungsten filament (GLS) lamps[*]

Watts	Volts	Initial light output	Lighting design lumens
Coiled coil lamps			
40	240	410	390
60	240	700	665
75	240	930	885
100	240	1330	1260
150	240	2160	2075
Coiled coil double-life lamps			
40	240	370	350
60	240	630	595
100	240	1200	1140
150	240	1940	1840
Single coil lamps			
15	240	112	105
25	240	215	200
40	240	340	325
60	240	610	575
100	240	1230	1160
150	240	2060	1960
200	240	2880	2720
300	240	4500	4300
500	240	8200	7700
750	240	13100	12400
1000	240	18400	17300
Single coil lamps			
40	110	445	410
60	110	770	710
100	110	1420	1300
150	110	2360	2160
200	110	3250	2980
300	110	5050	4710
500	110	8900	8270

[*] All the lamps quoted, except 'double life' have a 'life' of 1000 h.

The tungsten halide is carried into the filament by the convection
currents in the gas, where it separates into its original components,
the tungsten being deposited on the cooler parts of the filament and

the halogen being released to repeat the cycle. Note that the longer
life and higher light-output of these lamps is entirely dependent on
the increase of gas pressure and has nothing to do with the redeposit-
ion of the tungsten on the filament.

Mains voltage tungsten halogen lamps have from double to four
times the life of GLS lamps of equivalent type and give up to 20% more
light.

Discharge lamps

When an arc is struck in a gas or metallic vapour it radiates energy
in characteristic wave-bands. For example, neon gives red light,
sodium yellow and mercury vapour four distinct lines in the visible
and two in the ultraviolet region of the spectrum.

All modern discharge lamps operate in a translucent enclosure
(fig. 16.3), containing the appropriate metals or metal halides, the
initial discharge is usually struck in argon or neon. As the metal or
metal halide evaporates, it takes over the discharge from the starter
gas and emits light at its characteristic wavelengths.

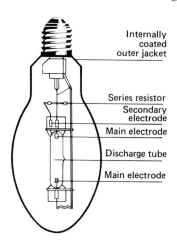

Internally
coated
outer jacket

Series resistor
Secondary
electrode
Main electrode

Discharge tube

Main electrode

A typical discharge lamp. (In this case an MBF lamp.)

*Figure 16.3 All modern discharge lamps operate in a translucent
enclosure containing the appropriate metals or metal
halides*

Because more light and less heat is radiated by these lamps, they
are more efficient in terms of lumens per watt than filament lamps,

but where a line spectrum is emitted there is a marked distortion of colours seen under their light.

Low-pressure sodium lamps

These are the most efficient lamps in terms of lumens per watt, because the monochromatic yellow light they produce is in the area near the peak of the eye sensitivity curve. Because only yellow light is emitted, however, objects are seen in tones of black and yellow only and colours cannot be perceived. They are extensively used for highway lighting and in situations where no colour discrimination is necessary.

High-pressure sodium lamps

If the internal vapour pressure of a sodium vapour lamp is increased, the sodium spectrum will broaden to include colours on either side of the original yellow lines. Although this will result in a slight reduction of efficacy, it allows colours to be discriminated. High-pressure sodium lamps are rated in sizes from 1 kW down to 50 W and are rapidly taking over from mercury discharge lamps in side streets and some industrial and increasingly in commercial applications. The efficacy of these lamps is in the order of 100 lm/W compared to 150 lm/W for low-pressure sodium and 45 lm/W for mercury lamps. A deluxe type, very similar in colour appearance and colour rendering to a filament lamp but with nearly ten times the light output is already available.

Mercury vapour lamps

Mercury vapour lamps emit a considerable amount of energy in two wave-bands in the UV region, the proportion of visible to invisible radiation being closely related to the gas pressure in the discharge tube. This is used to excite fluorescence in phosphors coating the inside of the outer bulb to add some of the missing red to their spectrum.

Metal halide lamps

Metal halide lamps use mercury vapour and the halides of a number of chemically active metals which are released as the temperature in the arc tube increases, producing a virtually continuous spectrum in which colours can readily be distinguished and seen with very little distortion. Their main advantage is that they provide a compact source of light with good colour-rendering properties at efficacies in the order of 80 1m/W, but they are only available in 250 W ratings and above because of inherent difficulties in the manufacture of the arc tube.

Compact-source iodide lamps

Two types of metal halide lamps are specially made for floodlighting and are extensively used for lighting football and sports stadia. One is a double-ended tubular lamp, with no outer jacket, designed to be used in an enclosed parabolic floodlighting projector and the other a very compact discharge capsule enclosed in a parabolic sealed glass reflector. This lamp, made only in the UK, is rapidly superseding the giant carbon arc projectors used in television studios and, because of its light weight and small size is specially suited to outside broadcasts. It is available in a 'hot restrike' version.

The main characteristics of discharge lamps are summarised in table 16.2.

Run-up time

All the discharge lamps so far referred to have a 'run-up' period varying from a few minutes to a quarter of an hour. They also require time for the vapour to cool and its pressure to drop before they will restrike after they have been extinguished, except for low-pressure sodium lamps which restrike immediately current is restored. High-pressure sodium lamps recover a great deal more quickly than other types.

Fluorescent tubes

A fluorescent tube is a low-pressure mercury discharge lamp. At this pressure, the mercury arc emits very little visible light and a considerable amount of UV radiation in two distinct wave-bands one in the harmless near-visible region and the other in the shorter-wave therapeutic area. This emission is used to excite fluorescence in the phosphors coating the inner surface of the tube, which may be up to

Table 16.2 Basic characteristics of discharge lamps

Lamp type	Lumens per watt		Colour		Power range (W)
	initial	design	appearance	rendering	
Mercury (MB)	56	50	Green	Poor	80 – 400
Mercury fluorescent (MBF)	62	58	Bluish white	Fair	50 – 1000
Mercury tungsten (MBTF)	25	23	White	Good	160 – 500*
Metal halide (MBIL)	92	85	White	Good	250 – 1000
Linear metal halide (MBIL)	80	75	White	Good	750 – 1600
Compact-source iodide (CSI)	90	81	White	Very good	400 and 1000
CSI reflector (CSI/PAR)	90	81	White	Very good	1000 only†
Low-pressure sodium (SOX)	–	140	Yellow	Monochromatic	35 – 180
Linear low-pressure sodium (SLI)	–	140	Yellow	Monochromatic	60, 140, 200
High-pressure sodium (SON)	120	110	Orange	Fair	50 – 1000
Deluxe high-pressure sodium (SONDL)	96	90	Golden	Good, resembles tungsten	150 and 250 only‡

*Requires no ballast, can be substituted directly for a filament lamp.

†Also available as hot restrike with dichroic reflector.

‡Designed for use in interiors where colour rendering is important.

Note – No manufacturer quotes a life for discharge lamps in his catalogue, but it may be taken that mercury and metal halide lamps have a life of about 5000 h and high-pressure sodium more than 10000 h.

Table 16.3 Lighting design lumens for fluorescent tubes

Length in mm	2400	2400	1800	1800	1500	1500	1500
Watts	125	100	85	75	75	80	65*
Lighting design lumens (Philips)							
Colour 84	9400	–	7000	6300	–	4900	–
White 35	8800	–	6800	6100	–	4700	–
Natural 25	7000	–	5300	4700	–	3600	–
Softone 32	5000	–	4000	3400	–	2800	–
Warmwhite 29	8800	–	6700	6100	–	4800	–
Daylight 33	8800	–	6500	5800	–	4700	–
Trucolor 37	–	–	–	–	–	2500	–
Northlight	5600	–	–	3800	–	3000	–
Lighting design lumens (GEC)							
White	8900	8000	6800	6000	5400	5100	4550
Warmwhite	9000	–	6750	6050	5400	5100	4600
Daylight	8600	–	6500	5800	5200	5000	4400
Natural	6250	–	4800	4100	3700	3800	3400
Colour-matching	5800	–	–	3900	3500	3400	3000
Deluxe natural	8000	–	3600	3200	2875	2600	2400
Deluxe warmwhite	–	–	–	–	–	3730	3500
Lighting design lumens (Thorn EMI)							
White	8800	8000	6850	5750	5200	–	4750
Warmwhite	8700	7900	6750	5650	5100	–	4600
Coolwhite	8400	7600	6500	5450	4950	–	4450
Natural	6500	5990	5000	4350	4000	3900	3400
Kolor-rite	5700	5200	4400	3850	3500	3400	3000
Northlight	5300	4100	4100	3600	3200	3100	2700

*
 Not available in the UK.

2400 mm long and either 38 mm, 26 mm or 16 mm in diameter according
to the power rating.

For the reasons already explained lamps, such as the 'colour-
matching' or 'Northlight' type, which give a close approximation to
north-sky daylight, are inherently less efficient than 'white', 'warm-
white' or 'natural' tubes, with less satisfactory colour-rendering
properties. Data for the majority of types of tube are shown in
table 16.3.

Two recent developments are the introduction of high efficacy
fluorescent tubes of 26 mm cross section (T8 and T12) utilising the
rare earths developed for colour television as well as the conventional

| 1500 | 1200 | 1050 | 900 | 900+ | 600 | 600 | 450 | 450+ |
50	40	40	30	30	40	40	15	15
–	3000	–	–	2350	–	1200	–	–
–	2800	–	–	2200	1700	1106	–	800
–	2300	–	–	1700	1400	850	–	700
–	1800	–	–	1200	–	700	–	500
–	2800	–	–	2150	1700	1100	–	800
–	2800	–	–	2150	1700	1100	–	800
–	1500	–	–	–	–	600	–	–
–	1900	–	–	2300	1200	–	–	–
–	2800	–	–	–	1850	1090	–	700
–	2850	–	–	–	1800	1120	–	700
–	2700	–	–	–	1750	1100	–	700
–	1900	–	–	–	–	770	–	500
–	1800	–	–	–	–	–	–	–
–	1500	–	–	–	–	–	–	–
–	2250	–	–	–	–	890	–	–
3600	2170	2800*	1850	2150	1700	1100	750	800
3550	2180	2700*	1850	2050	1700	1000	750	800
–	–	2650*	1750	2050	1600	1050	700	750
–	2100	–	1400	1600	1200	800	600	280
–	1800	–	–	1300	1100	750	–	–
–	1700	–	–	1250	1050	700	450	500

halophosphates, and krypton gas to facilitate starting. Because the
light from the phosphors is mainly produced in the three areas of the
spectrum, blue, red and green, which combine to give the effect of
white light, instead of having a virtually continuous spectrum like
the conventional type of tube, they may occasionally give rise to the
effect of 'metametric mismatching' of colours. In situations where
accurate colour-matching is essential, therefore, the standard halo-
phosphate tubes should be used. Table 16.4 gives technical details of
these lamps. They must always be operated on a starter-switch circuit
and consume fractionally less current than their conventional equiv-
alents when operated on the same chokes.

207

Table 16.4 Comparison of lumen characteristics of T8 and T12
          fluorescent tubes

Tube size (mm)		Lamp watts (W)	Type	Lighting design lumens at 2000 h
600	T12	20	Standard white	1100
	T8	18	Polylux*	1325
	T8	18	Pluslux*	1100
1200	T12	40	Standard white	2800
	T8	36	Polylux	3200
	T8	36	Pluslux	2800
1500	T12	65	Standard white	4750
	T8	58	Polylux	5100
	T8	58	Pluslux	4700
1800	T12	75	Standard white	5750
	T8	70	Polylux	6300
	T8	70	Pluslux	5700
2400	T12	125	Standard white	8900
	T8	100	Polylux	9000

*
'Polylux' and 'Pluslux' are the Thorn trade names for the colour-
matching and white types of these tubes. Pluslux is also made in
'white' and 'coolwhite'. Philips call their lamps 'Powerslimmers'
and GEC merely refer to their diameter.

CONTROLGEAR AND STARTING

All arc lamps require a current limiting device to prevent them taking
more and more current until they destroy themselves. In most cases a
starting device is also necessary to strike the arc.

A high-pressure mercury lamp is operated in series with a choke
having a laminated iron core. The starting device consists of a
secondary electrode within the arc tube, connected through a resistor
to one electrode and in close proximity to the other. When the lamp
is switched on an arc is struck between the adjacent electrodes, ion-
ising the argon filling of the arc tube so that the main discharge is
struck between the cathodes. The secondary electrode then ceases to
function because of the resistor in series with it.

Metal halide and high-pressure sodium lamps require an external
ignitor in addition to the choke, although some manufacturers sell SON
lamps with an internal starter like that of a mercury lamp, so that
they can be operated from a choke designed for approximately the same
sized mercury lamp. The separate ignitor, however, is more reliable.

It must be placed as close to the lamp as possible to avoid voltage drop in the lead to the lamp; the position of the choke is not critical.

Fluorescent tubes, being essentially low-pressure mercury lamps, also need a current limiting and starting device. The former usually takes the form of a choke, but occasionally a resistor is used. Some of the earlier domestic luminaires made use of a filament lamp wired in series with the tube and there are luminaires housing two 20 W 600 mm tubes controlled by a resistance wire available for domestic use. It will be appreciated that such devices largely offset the advantage of the low current consumption of the tubes. A starter switch, wired in parallel with the tube, is commonly installed, but transformer starters are also used.

In all cases where an inductive current limiting device is used a capacitor is included in the circuit for power factor correction. This is usually housed in the luminaire with the rest of the control gear, but bulk power factor correction at a central point is occasionally used. Starters are always housed in the luminaire, but in some cases, as for example street-lighting lanterns and floodlights using CSI or metal halide lamps, the choke may be mounted elsewhere. This type of choke is very bulky and heavy and for outside television is usually mounted on a truck. Chokes for street-lighting lanterns are often housed in a cupboard at the foot of the column.

LUMINAIRES (LIGHTING FITTINGS)

Most of the light from a bare lamp is likely to be wasted; in addition, a bare, unshielded lamp gives rise to glare which can hinder vision, so the use of a luminaire to house the lamp(s) and direct or diffuse its light is essential. The detailed design of luminaires is outside the scope of this book, but some knowledge of the principles involved is needed if satisfactory lighting schemes are to be produced. Luminaires may be classified by their light distributing qualities and their choice governed by the quality of light required. It may also be influenced by special safety considerations, such as where lamps are used in explosive or corrosive atmospheres or are liable to mechanical damage or excessive vibration.

Display lighting equipment

Luminaires designed for display purposes fall into four main categories; simple housings for blown-glass or pressed glass reflector-lamps;
polished aluminium reflectors, usually of approximately parabolic
cross section to accept mains voltage GLS lamps; reflectors of more
accurate profile for use with extra low-voltage half-silvered lamps,
giving a more concentrated beam than the mains voltage type; and
reflectors for use with tungsten halogen lamps of the lower power
ratings. These may be more accurately described as 'floodlights'
rather than 'spotlights' and their use is largely confined to the shop
window, because of the problem of radiant heat in the beam.

Where spotlights used for internal displays cause discomfort to
customers, the use of PAR 38 lamps with dichroic reflectors is
recommended, as this reduces the heat in the beam. In such cases,
well-ventilated fittings are needed to avoid overheating of the lamp-
holder and wiring; a simple swivel mounting is the usual solution.
Luminaires unsuitable for these lamps are marked as fig. 16.4.

Figure 16.4 Luminaires unsuitable for PAR 38 lamps are clearly marked

'Black-hole' fittings, in which the spill light from the reflector
is either absorbed by a system of matt-black painted baffles or redir-
ected downwards by a specular skirt have become very popular with some
architects. It is important to space them closely together if an
uneven illumination is to be avoided, so that their use is rather
uneconomical.

Luminaires for general lighting

In commerce and industry, the choice of luminaires for the general
illumination of a room is governed by a number of considerations, the
most important being the visual task to be performed and the dimensions
of the room. In rooms of normal ceiling height, fluorescent luminaires

are likely to be used, but where, as in some industrial situations, they have to be mounted high up, to clear a travelling gantry for example, concentrating luminaires using metal halide or high-pressure sodium lamps are more likely to be found.

Fluorescent luminaires

The design of fluorescent luminaires has become largely stereotyped. Most surface-mounted or pendant types are based on a common backspine, carrying the tubes and control gear, to which are attached simple reflectors, for industrial use or plastics enclosures designed to diffuse or control the light in commercial interiors. Recessed modular luminaires, usually housing three or four tubes are also made and there are surface-mounted versions of this type of luminaire as well.

Although bare 'batten fittings', (the backspine without any attachments), are commonly used in washrooms, corridors, stores and similar locations their use is not recommended where exacting visual tasks are performed. Both bare tube and diffusing luminaires can give rise to cumulative glare if mounted at right angles to the normal direction of view in a large room. It is usually best to mount them parallel to the main axis of the room, or better still, to use recessed luminaires, preferably with low-brightness reflectors or controllers.

High-bay luminaires

High-bay luminaires fall generally into two categories; those designed for conventional single-ended discharge lamps and those intended for linear light-sources such as the double-ended SON lamp.

Those accommodating conventional discharge lamps usually consist of a ventilated lamp-holder assembly attached to a housing containing the control gear to which is attached a deep spun anodised aluminium reflector of approximately parabolic or elliptical cross section. Since the lamp is mounted vertically only a part of the arc tube can be at the exact focal point of the reflector, so it is mounted as high up as possible to reduce spill light.

This type of luminaire is used in situations such as foundries, steel rolling mills and heavy engineering shops where considerable head-room is available. They are often fixed on walkways to facilitate maintenance and in such cases the control gear may be mounted separately from the reflector.

Where greater accuracy of beam spread is required, or in situations where luminaires are mounted above a travelling gantry, leaving little space between it and the structural ceiling, floodlighting projectors housing linear high-pressure sodium lamps have been used. The much more accurate placing of the tube in the parabolic reflector gives excellent light control with less spill light. Control gear may be mounted at the end of the luminaire to conserve space or, if it is placed on a walkway, mounted remotely from it.

Methods of facilitating fixing
Luminaires that contain two or more fluorescent tubes or high-pressure discharge lamps with their control gear are of necessity heavy and less easily fixed than those using filament lamps. A number of solutions to this problem have been put forward by the manufacturers. One range of standard fluorescent luminaires is so made that a simple backplate can first be fixed on the ceiling to accept the mains wiring, and the backspine containing the control gear and lamp-holders, can be latched on to it and plugged in to the supply. This method has the added advantage that if a single-tube luminaire is needed where a twin-tube one was originally installed, it can simply be substituted without disturbing the wiring or fixing. Faulty luminaires can also be replaced and examined at bench level.

An alternative to the individual ceiling plate is to mount the luminaires on trunking. This is almost standard practice in industrial installations where the trunking also carries other services. In the case of the luminaire described above, it must be designed to suit the latching arrangement, but mounting ordinary fluorescent luminaires on trunking also solves some installation problems.

Where heavy high-bay fittings are concerned a similar arrangement is used. The container for the control gear is latched or otherwise attached to a backplate and the lamp and reflector added later. The device of a ceiling-mounted backplate has also been applied to lumin-aires designed to take 70 W SON lamps, but in such cases the whole luminaire is hooked on to the backplate, although alternative types of light controller are added as required.

The provision of heat-resisting wiring outside the luminaire is seldom necessary, although manufacturers use it where necessary, especially where filament lamps are concerned. It is important to avoid using dichroic reflector-lamps in luminaires designed for the normal type of pressed glass lamp. In very dusty atmospheres, chokes may overheat due to a layer of dust reducing their heat radiation. It is important to use sealed luminaires in such situations, but in the case of fluorescent luminaires, this may introduce a further complication.

Ventilated and air-handling luminaires

Because a fluorescent tube is essentially a low-pressure mercury discharge lamp, an increase in the vapour pressure in the tube due to a rise in the ambient temperature can reduce the proportion of UV in the arc and so lower the tube's light output and distort the colour of its light.

Most surface-mounted luminaires are sufficiently ventilated to overcome this, although in the case of the sealed types referred to above, it has to be accepted. Recessed ceiling luminaires can however become 'heat pockets'. This has led to the design of air-handling luminaires which are also used as heat extractors in an air-conditioned system. In most cases air is injected into the room space through separately constructed vents, but sometimes these are integrated with the support system for the luminaires, which may also provide support for ceiling tiles.

It will be obvious that in such cases careful alignment and accurate levelling of the luminaires is essential, and the 'bodies' are provided with adjustable suspensions. Gear trays, lamps and diffusers or louvres are added after the ceiling has been installed.

OUTDOOR LIGHTING EQUIPMENT

Floodlights

Until quite recently, the use of high-powered tungsten filament or discharge lamps in outdoor floodlighting equipment led to very bulky equipment. The diameter of a floodlight for a 1 kW incandescent or a 400 W mercury, metal halide or high-pressure sodium lamp is about 600 mm and its weight, exclusive of control gear, about 13 kg.

The introduction of tungsten halogen lamps has resulted in two 'families' of floodlights both much smaller than the conventional types. One, originally produced under the name 'Sunflood' by Thorn, and extensively copied, is a very simple open housing with a parabolic reflector for the linear type of lamp and is much used in car parks and domestic situations. The other, an enclosed floodlight, is found in a number of industrial and commercial situations, especially where an immediate flood of light is needed. Narrow-beam floodlights for single-ended mains voltage tungsten halogen lamps are also available.

The use of linear high-pressure sodium and metal halide lamps in similar floodlights followed almost immediately and this type of projector soon became very popular for such applications as the floodlighting of minor football fields and sports grounds, including trotting tracks and for the lighting of the yards and loading bays of industrial premises. In addition to the longer life and higher light output of these sources, the type of floodlight described has much less weight and windage than the conventional types; for example a 1000 W fitting of this type weighs approximately 9.5 kg and is approximately 450 mm square.

Specialised floodlights for football stadia

Floodlights using metal halide (MBIL) linear lamps specially designed for football stadia in which matches are covered by coloured TV are usually intended for comparatively low mounting heights, on the roofs of the stadia or just above them. The 1500 W type is very compact and weighs only 7.5 kg. It may be fitted with an internal baffle to prevent direct light from the arc tube dazzling spectators on the opposite side of the pitch. All the weights quoted are exclusive of control gear, which is housed separately from the floodlight.

An even more specialised floodlight, mounted on high masts for lighting stadia and also for general television work incorporates the 1000 W CSI lamp which is itself housed in a PAR 64 reflector. This housing is designed to take either the ordinary CSI lamp or the hot restrike type and sufficient ventilation is provided to take care of the heat passing through the dichroic reflector used with the hot restrike lamp. The ignitor is mounted on the lamp housing, but the chokes and power factor correction capacitors are separately housed.

FLOODLIGHTING CALCULATIONS

Floodlights mounted on poles are extensively used for lighting areas
such as loading docks, parking lots and so forth. The calculation of
the illuminance is not difficult, but it varies from the method used
in the interior of buildings in certain respects.

Instead of the usual 'utilance factor' a 'waste-light factor' is
used. This is usually taken as about 0.9, but in awkward shaped areas
may be as high as 0.5. It is influenced by the width of the floodlight
beam.

Beam angle

This is the width or spread of the beam and is defined as the total
angle over which the intensity drops to 1% of its peak value. A single
figure is given for a floodlight with a symmetrical distribution, two
for a unit with an asymmetric distribution.

Beam flux and beam factor

Beam flux is the total flux contained within the beam angle and is
usually expressed as the proportion of lamp lumens contained within
the beam (beam factor). It is usually presented in tabular form by
the manufacturers.

Illuminance diagrams

A number of manufacturers publish illuminance diagrams which provide
an easy method of calculating the illuminance over an area from a
specific floodlight at a known mounting height and aiming angle. These
can be superimposed to calculate the illuminance from an array of
floodlights. A typical diagram is shown in fig. 16.5. Conversion
factors are used to adapt the figure for different mounting heights.

Zonal flux diagrams

Another method, which is very adaptable is the use of 'zonal flux
diagrams', a typical example of which is shown in fig. 16.6. It is
divided through the plane of symmetry with isocandela lines plotted on
the angular grid and figures denoting the flux per 1000 lamp lumens in
each angular zone on the right. It can either be used to calculate
point values of illuminance or the flux intercepted by the area to be

lit, which can be drawn as an overlay using the same angular scale. Elevation of the floodlight can be shown by moving the diagram up and down the vertical grid line, but a fresh diagram must be drawn for adjustments in azimuth. The beam factor of the floodlight is expressed by the dotted line on the diagram. The beam lumens per 1000 lamp lumens is twice the value of the flux values enclosed within it.

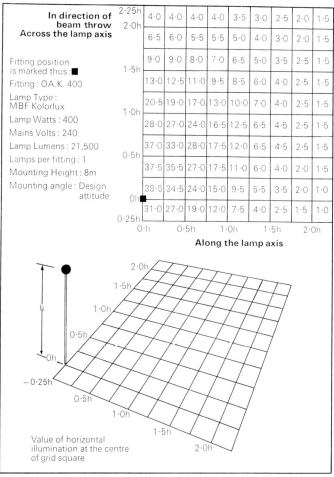

Illuminance diagram shows illuminance over an area lit by a floodlight mounted at a specific height. (Note: use current data for design work).

Figure 16.5 An illuminance diagram provides an easy method of calculating the illuminance over an area from a floodlight at known mounting height and aiming angle

OAKG 400/400W MBF

Description	Area Flood (glass visor) with 400W MBF lamp
Report Number	500/EL/4301/2

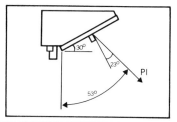

Lamp Type	Lamp Watts	Beam angles to ⅟₁₀ peak (degrees)			Beam angles to ½ peak (degrees)			Beam Factor	Peak Candelas Per 1000 Lumens	Angles to ⅟₁₀₀ peak (degrees)		
		Horiz	Vertical Above Peak	Below Peak	Horiz	Vertical Above Peak	Below Peak			Horiz	Vertical Above Peak	Below Peak
MBF	400	154	51	94	104	29	49	0.54	256	164	65	113

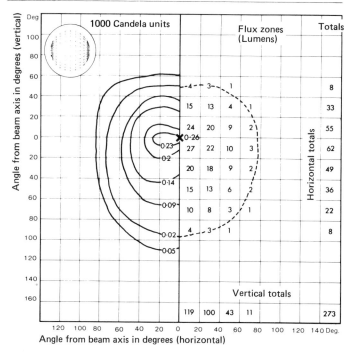

Figure 16.6 *Typical example of a 'Zonal flux diagram' for calculating the illuminance from a floodlight*

Street lighting lanterns

In Great Britain the basic principle of highway lighting is to achieve a bright road surface against which vehicles can be seen in silhouette.

217

The non-specialist lighting engineer can usually ignore highway lighting techniques since he is only likely to be concerned with lighting roadways and parking areas within a factory complex or similar location. A number of lanterns consisting of a lamp in a diffuser mounted on top of a pole are available for this purpose. They are usually designed to take any suitable light-source and the control gear may be mounted in the housing or in a chamber at the foot of the pole.

LIGHTING DESIGN FOR INTERIORS

Recommended task illuminance

The amount of light needed to perform a visual task satisfactorily varies according to the size of the object being handled and the contrast between it and the background, either in terms of brightness or of colour or both. For example fine assembly, as in watch-making may require an illuminance of about 1000 lux. Insufficient light may lead to eye-strain and slow down production, causing mistakes to be made or faulty workmanship to be overlooked. For example a fuzzy third or fourth copy of a typed invoice may easily be misread if the lighting level is too low; increasing the illuminance improves the contrast between the type and its background and thus facilitates the reading of the document.

These considerations have led to the CIBS Lighting Division, (formerly the Illuminating Engineering Society), to publish detailed recommendations for specific tasks. These recommendations are summarised in table 16.5 but engineers are recommended to study the full list in the IES Code.

IES Code

The IES Code for Interior Lighting, published by the CIBS Lighting Division, is the recognised authoritative document on lighting in the United Kingdom. It deals both with daylighting and artificial lighting and lays down standards of lighting for almost every visual task. It is an essential tool for the lighting engineer and indeed, for anyone concerned with lighting design.

Table 16.5 Recommended standard service illuminations (IES Code 1977)

Task group and typical task or interior	Standard service illuminance (lux)
Storage areas and plant rooms with no continuous work	150
Casual work	200
Rough work; rough machining and assembly	300
Routine work; offices, control rooms, medium machining and assembly	500
Demanding work; deep plan, drawing or business offices; machine offices, inspection of medium machining	750
Fine work; colour discrimination, textile processing, fine machining and assembly	1000
Very fine work; hand engraving, inspection of fine machinery or assembly	1500
Minute work inspection of very fine assembly	3000

Note - The visual task, not the importance of the operator determines the recommended illuminance. For example, a managing director, reading top copies of typescripts, does not need as much light as a filing clerk, sorting out sixth carbon copies.

Visual acuity also decreases with age, due to the onset of presbiopia (long sight). Elderly people may therefore need rather more light.

Photometric data

To plan a lighting installation to give a specified illuminance on a working surface or plane, the engineer must know how to use photometric data published by reputable fittings manufacturers, and be familiar with such terms as 'light-output ratio' (LOR) of luminaires and in some cases understand how to use polar diagrams. The significance of the utilisation factor in calculating the illuminance from an array of luminaires by the 'lumen-method' of design must also be understood. Such matters as the relationship between the spacing to mounting-height ratio of luminaires, the evenness of the illumination on the working plane, and the use of British Zonal (BZ) ratings to control direct glare from the luminaires, must also be borne in mind.

Light-output ratio

The LOR of a luminaire is the proportion of the total lumen output of the lamp that is emitted. It must be understood that all reflecting and diffusing media absorb a certain amount of light; what matters, is the amount of light delivered where it is wanted: light falling on walls and ceilings may not be entirely wasted, but less will be reflected from such surfaces than from a well-designed reflector forming part of the luminaire.

For this reason, the LOR of a luminaire is of little use by itself. For example, a bare fluorescent single 'batten fitting' may have an LOR as high as 95%, but in most cases will be less effective than one fitted with a reflector with a total LOR of 84%. It is normal to specify upwards and downwards LOR. For example a bare tube might have an upwards LOR of 29% and downwards of 66%, and the reflector unit 2% upward but 82% downward, an obvious improvement where light delivered on the working plane is concerned. This is especially important where luminaires are mounted under a glass or dark-coloured roof, a common situation in industrial interiors.

Luminous intensity and polar curves

Most manufacturers publish luminous intensity tables, giving the intensity in candelas per 1000 lamp lumens on a single vertical plane for symmetrical (tungsten or discharge lamp luminaires) or on a transverse and axial plane for fluorescent luminaires and those using line sources. All the illumination data for the luminaires are derived from these measurements, although, in some cases more than two planes are measured.

From the table of luminous intensities the 'polar curve' for the luminaire can be derived, fig. 16.7, which may also be printed in the data. Polar curves are a useful indication of the general light distribution of a luminaire and are also valuable if accurate calculations of the intensity of illumination in a given direction or the illuminance at a given point are required. It must be clearly understood that the area enclosed in a polar curve does not give an indication of the amount of light emitted by the luminaire in that direction. Figure 16.8 shows that although the downward component of the polar curve illustrated covers a greater area than the horizontal one, the actual lumens contained in the latter, which represents a circular zone of light around the luminaire, is considerably greater.

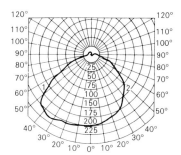

1. Transverse curve.
2. Axial curve.

Figure 16.7 Polar curves are a useful indication of the general light distribution of a luminaire

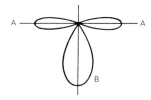

A. All light in equatorial area.
B. All light in polar area.
Actual lumens delivered at A is considerably in excess of B.

Figure 16.8 A polar diagram must not be misread in that the amount of lumens contained in the horizontal plane may be greater than in the vertical plane

Utilisation factors and room indices

Where an area has to be lighted evenly over the working plane, as opposed to situations where a considerable variation in illuminance may be permissible or desirable, it is simpler to use the 'lumen method of design' than to work out the illuminance from an array of luminaires from their individual polar curves. In order to do this, a 'room index' based on the proportions of the room has to be used.

Figure 16.9 makes it clear that in a tall, narrow room more light is absorbed by the walls, assuming the same mounting height for the luminaires than in one of more generous proportions. It must also be borne in mind that a glass roof can be considered as a black area, reflecting no appreciable light into the room and that uncurtained windows must be regarded as absorbing areas too.

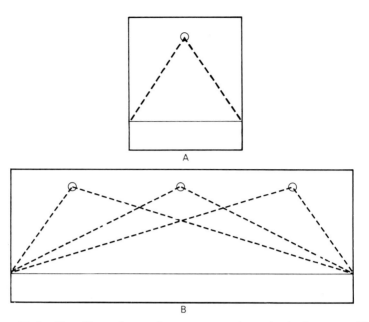

Figure 16.9 The dimensions of a room are important when considering absorption and other factors

The formula for obtaining the room index is

$$Ri = \frac{L.W}{Hm \ (L + W)}$$

where L = length of the room in metres

   W = width of the room in metres

   Hm = mounting height of luminaires.

The utilisation factor can then be obtained by reference to the photo-metric tables published by the manufacturer.

Spacing to mounting-height ratios

Where an array of luminaires is designed to give an even illuminance on the 'working plane', usually assumed to be 0.85 m above the floor, the recommended spacing to mounting-height ratio shown in the data must not be exceeded. This is S/Hm where S is the distance between fittings, (in the case of fluorescent luminaires measured in the trans-verse axis), and Hm their mounting height above the working plane. Too wide a spacing will result in a serious falling off in illuminance between the luminaires. The recommendations are based on an illuminance of 70% of that directly below the luminaires at the mid-point between them. The tables of utilisation factors usually show three values of Hs/Hm, Hs being the distance the luminaires are suspended from the ceiling (0, 0.3 and 1.0).

In practice, the number and spacing of the luminaires are often determined by the ceiling height or the beam structure. The recommended spacing can be exceeded if the luminaires are mounted above work-benches or rows of desks, but this presupposes a permanent layout which may not be considered when the lighting scheme is designed.

BZ system

Luminaires in a large room can be a serious source of direct glare, especially if they contain fluorescent tubes and are mounted at right-angles to the principal line of view. Some are now made with specular plastics low-brightness louvres to overcome this difficulty. They may be classified by the BZ (British Zonal) method according to their light distribution. A BZ1 luminaire gives concentrated downward light as in the case of a high-bay reflector with a parabolic specular reflector. Low-brightness fluorescent luminaires of the type described above seldom exceed BZ2; those with prismatic controllers are usually BZ4 while ordinary diffusers are likely to be in the order of BZ5 or 6.

The IES Code gives approximate glare ratings as well as recommended illuminance figures for the situations listed in it; to apply these recourse should be made to the tables in the CIBS Lighting Division (IES) Publication No 10.

Designing an installation

Lumen method of design.   The lumen method of design is still the simplest available and is always recommended where the precise use of a room and dispositions of work-benches or desks are not known. It provides for an even and virtually shadowless illuminance over the whole of the working area and is generally employed in planning the lighting of speculative office blocks or factories where future requirements are not known.

After the task illuminance has been settled and the type of lamp and luminaires decided upon, the method starts with a simple

calculation of the number of luminaires required, based on the
formula:

$$N = \frac{Eav.A}{C.M.F}$$

where F   = lumen output of the lamp or tube(s)

     Eav = the average illuminance in lux

     A   = the area to be lighted in square metres

     C   = the utilisation factor

     M   = the maintenance factor.

If the work to be performed is not known or specified an average
task illuminance of 100 lux should be aimed at. The utilisation
factor is derived from the photometric data provided by the luminaire
manufacturer and a maintenance factor of 0.8 is usually taken, although
in very dirty locations this would have to be changed to 0.6 (see the
remarks on maintenance below).

The value of N seldom comes out as a whole number and may produce
difficulties in the arrangement of the luminaires. In such a case,
the smallest whole number of these that can be installed at adequate
spacing can be calculated from the formula:

$$\frac{L.W}{MS.MS}$$

where L = length of the room in metres

     W = width of the room in metres

     MS = maximum permitted spacing between luminaires.

Further modifications may be imposed by the beam structure of the
room and by such considerations as wholly glazed walls, where a row
may have to be mounted closer to the wall than usual to take account
of light losses through the glass. The spacing to mounting-height
ratio of the luminaires should not be exceeded.

The final scheme must be checked for glare rating, and, if it
falls outside the recommended limits, a type of luminaire with a better
glare rating must be substituted and the calculations repeated.

Low energy installations.   The need to conserve electrical energy
has led to a reconsideration of lighting methods in offices and work-
shops. For many years draughtsmen have tended to prefer localised

lighting on their drawingboards, often using the heat from the filament lamps to dry the ink on their drawings. But it has long been the practice to provide a high level of uniform lighting at the working plane of offices and factories by means of a general lighting system. This has been much assisted by the use of fluorescent tubes.

Today, although general lighting of such places must still be provided, if only to avoid heavy shadows under desks or benches with consequent untidiness, and to facilitate movement, there is a tendency to keep it at a fairly low level and supplement it with local lighting at the work-point.

Considerable impetus has been given to this by the introduction of smaller diameter high-efficacy fluorescent tubes and to a lesser degree, by the use of tungsten halogen lamps. Both have led to the design of small, compact reflectors, taking up comparatively little space on a desk or above a work-bench.

The calculation of a general lighting system has already been described but that of the lighting from localised luminaires is less obvious. A useful rough guide to the illuminance that can be provided by such a light-source is the 'halving law', in which the intensity in the desired direction is divided by twice the distance in metres from the object to be lighted. The inverse square law really only applies to point sources and consequently may be used with compact filament or discharge lamps. A more accurate method of calculation of the illuminance from line sources is the use of aspect factors described in the CIBS/IES Report No 11. The aspect factors of fluorescent luminaires are usually shown in the photometric data published by the manufacturers. If they are not one assumes a LOR of 50% from the luminaire and calculates the lumens falling on the area to be lighted according to the mounting height of the luminaire. Most localised luminaires are designed to be mounted about 600 mm above the working plane. Note that the local luminaire is usually mounted on the left-hand side of the desk to reduce the possibility of reflected glare, a common hazard with this type of lighting.

EMERGENCY LIGHTING

There are two basic types of emergency lighting; standby lighting and escape lighting. The former is designed to provide adequate task lighting in the event of mains failure. Chapter 6 discusses standby supplies. It should be noted that where high-pressure discharge lamps are used, a period of darkness occurs before the lamps restrike. It is recommended therefore that in places such as hospitals and factories, where so long a break in the lighting is dangerous, fluorescent or filament lamps are used. In some industries, it is necessary to make sure that machinery is safe before quitting the building; in such cases a limited standby system may be installed.

For most people, however, emergency lighting means 'escape lighting' and for this all that is necessary is to provide a lighted path from the occupied parts of the building to the open. This is the system to which BS 5266: Part 1 refers. A summary of the statutory requirements of this standard appears below.

Requirements of BS 5266

Minimum illuminance.   A minimum illuminance of 0.2 lux is recommended on the escape route. This must be measured at the end of the specified duration period and take account for depreciating performance at the end of battery life. A maximum diversity in illuminance of 40:1 is recommended. Positions of maximum importance, such as exits, staircases, etc., can be lighted to forty times the minimum illuminance by luminaires, often in the form of signs, positioned over them.

Positioning of luminaires.   Emergency lighting points must be placed to indicate the escape route and to emphasise hazards such as change in direction, steps, changes in floor level and the position of exit doors. The illuminance on the centre line of the escape route must not fall below 0.2 lux.

Legal responsibility.   Fire officers are responsible for the issue of fire certificates for most premises, but HM Factory Inspectorate deals with government offices, schools and local council property.

Apart from those areas where luminaires must be installed over exits, stairways, etc., the inspector will demand a written guarantee from the contractor that the installation conforms with local standards, usually to BS 5266.

The final legal responsibility lies with the owner or occupier.

Safety precautions.   The BS also warns that in certain circumstances high voltages may be generated and points out that electrolytic capacitors may explode if the polarity is reversed. Recommendations for the disposal of run-down batteries are included and it is stated that guidance may be obtained from local authority Health and Safety Officers.

The importance of regular maintenance and testing is also emphasised.

Alternative systems

Slave luminaires.   In this system the luminaires are fed from a central battery and may be located in existing mains-operated luminaires. This reduces the cost of the individual luminaire but is offset by the need to provide wiring to each and a central battery and control room. The system is simple to operate but suffers from the disability that, if the wiring system is itself damaged, the emergency lighting may not work, or a part of it only may be energised. Consequently, most people are turning their attention to the systems of self-contained luminaires that make use of the miniature fluorescent tubes and nickel cadmium cells.

Self-contained luminaires.   Since these can be operated from existing wiring, they may be added to an existing installation. They operate independently on the interruption of the supply and can be tested simply by the removal of the fuse governing the circuit into which they have been introduced. Illumination is provided within 5 seconds of the interruption of supply and the battery pack has sufficient capacity to provide the required statutory illuminance of the escape route for a period of at least 3 hours. Upon the resumption of supply, the emergency lighting is switched out and the batteries become fully recharged within 24 hours.

Exit and emergency exit signs are provided with two lighting systems, one which is in constant use while the mains supply is available and the other operating on the emergency circuit as described above.

Planning procedure

It is important to remember that emergency lighting is designed only to provide lighted escape routes and not as an auxiliary lighting system. Escape routes should be marked on a floor plan of the premises, making sure that they are as direct as possible and that they avoid congested areas and those where fire is likely to spread. Danger points should then be marked and an emergency luminaire or warning sign located at each of them. Isolux diagrams or spacing/mounting height graphs provided by the manufacturer should then be used to determine points between these luminaires where the illuminance falls below 0.2 lux, and extra luminaires installed at these positions. It will be clear that in most cases the actual illuminance on the escape route will be somewhat in excess of the statutory minimum.

Exit signs should be mounted where possible between 2.0 and 2.5 m above floor level and positioned close to the points to which they refer. Subsidiary signs may be needed to point people in the right direction in places where the main sign is not visible. It is important that the intermediate luminaires should be mounted on the centre line of the escape route, so that if the rooms are filled with smoke, they will act as beacons to direct movement.

Chapter 17

Mains and Submains Cables

G. A. Bowie, DFH, CEng, FIEE
Consultant

Mains cables are used to supply electricity to complete electrical
installations and since the electrical loadings of such cables must
take account of the total loading of the electrical installation,
mains cables are generally of larger sizes than the wiring cables
dealt with in chapter 18.

From the main intake position it is often desirable to divide the
installation into a number of sections, the individual sections being
fed by submains cables.

For most installations mains cables operate on low voltage, that
is about 440 V, but for very large installations, particularly where
the site is extensive and large loads are carried over long distances,
mains cables operating at higher voltages are used. In these cases
the h.v. source might be provided from the public electricity supply
or from a private generating station on the site. In some industries,
such as paper-making, large quantities of process steam are needed and
it is often convenient for the company to generate electricity at the
same time as producing steam.

This chapter deals with cables for operating at voltages up to and
including 11 kV and in conductor size larger than about 25 mm^2.

CABLE SPECIFICATIONS
All cables are fundamentally similar in that they contain conductors
for carrying current, insulation for surrounding the conductors and
some form of overall covering to provide mechanical and possible
corrosion protection to ensure that the insulation may continue to
operate satisfactorily throughout the life of the cable once the cable
has been installed.

229

The majority of mains and submains cables used in United Kingdom installations comply with British Standards Specifications (BS) while the few others which are not yet covered by such standards are closely defined in Electricity Supply Industry Standards which are prepared for use by electricity boards.

Table 17.1 lists the more important BS types dealt with in this chapter. All these standards make reference to other BSs for the various materials and components used in the construction of the cables.

Table 17.1   British Standard types of cables used for mains and submains

Specification	Title	Voltage ranges for mains uses
BS 4553	PVC-insulated split concentric cables with copper conductors for electricity supply	600/1000
BS 5467	Armoured cables with thermo-setting insulation for electricity supply	600/1000 1900/3300
BS 5593	Impregnated-paper insulated cables with aluminium sheath/ neutral conductor and three shaped solid aluminium phase conductors (CONSAC) for electricity supply	600/1000
BS 6346	PVC-insulated cables for electricity supply	600/1000 1900/3300
BS 6480	Impregnated-paper insulated cables for electricity supply Part 1. Lead or lead alloy sheathed for working voltages up to and including 33 kV	600/1000 1900/3300 3800/6600 6350/11000

British standards for electric cables are expressed in metric terms and wherever possible they align with applicable internationally agreed standards. Such international standardisation includes Harmonisation Documents agreed by the European Committee for Electrotechnical Standardisation (CENELEC) and Publications prepared by the International Electrotechnical Commission (IEC). UK manufacturers, users and the electricity supply industry take an active part in the work of international standardisation.

CABLE CONDUCTORS

Conductors for all voltage ranges of cables covered may be of copper or aluminium. Because of its better conductivity copper is the preferable material but economic considerations usually require that aluminium conductors shall be used. Since aluminium has a poorer conductivity than copper it is necessary for carrying a given current to employ a larger aluminium conductor (see Current Ratings) which also results in a larger cable but in certain circumstances the use of aluminium conductors may be considered where weight savings are important.

BS 6360 'Conductors in insulated cables and cords', specifies the sizes and constructions of standard conductors used in a wide variety of cables but the individual cable specifications lay down particular requirements for each type of cable.

Copper conductors

Circular copper conductors can be of solid or stranded construction. The solid conductor is used in the annealed condition, otherwise it would be too stiff and springy for easy handling, but in the range of cables covered here it is used only in mineral-insulated (MI) cables which are employed as submains.

Stranded circular conductors are made up from a number of smaller circular copper wires twisted together in concentric layers. All individual wires in a conductor are of the same nominal size before stranding and are in the annealed condition to provide adequate flexibility to the cable to allow for handling during installation.

Some stranded circular copper conductors are compacted, that is, the wires in the outer layers are somewhat flattened so that the outer interstices between the wires become reduced and the outside surface of the stranded conductor becomes smoother and smaller in diameter. This is of benefit with some types of cable where the insulation is applied by extrusion techniques since the insulation does not tend to penetrate between the wires, making stripping easier, and reducing the overall dimensions of the cable.

For multicore power cables, except in the case of very small conductor sizes, stranded copper conductors are shaped to result in the overall cable dimensions being reduced, thus saving on materials and

231

weight.   Figure 17.1 illustrates how cable dimensions are reduced by
the use of shaped conductors.

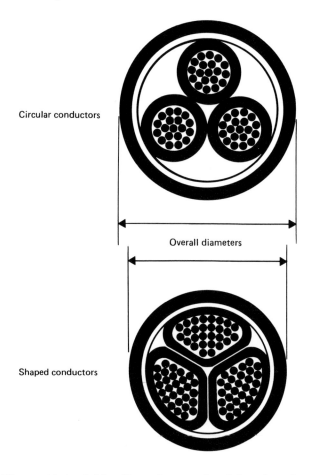

Circular conductors

Overall diameters

Shaped conductors

Figure 17.1   Cable dimensions reduced by shaped conductors

Copper conductors are sometimes composed of tinned wires; the thin
coating of tin on each wire serving as a barrier to prevent chemical
interaction between certain constituents of elastomeric insulation
materials and the copper of the conductor.   Tinned copper conductors
have a slightly higher electrical resistance than plain copper wires.

Aluminium conductors

Solid circular aluminium conductors, because of the rather more
ductile nature of aluminium, can be used in sizes considerably greater

232

than with solid copper but in sizes larger than 300 mm^2 the circular cross section is made up from four solid segments, as shown in fig. 17.2. This form of construction provides a conductor which can be bent by normal cable handling techniques and is also within the handling capabilities of cable manufacturing plant.

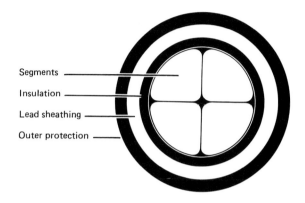

Segments
Insulation
Lead sheathing
Outer protection

Figure 17.2 Large solid circular aluminium conductor made from four segments

Where greater ease of bending is required use is made of stranded circular aluminium conductors which are generally available in sizes up to 1000 mm^2.

Solid shaped aluminium conductors provide a compact form of conductor for multicore cables and are generally used in larger sizes up to and including 300 mm^2.

Stranded shaped aluminium conductors provide rather more flexibility for easier handling than solid shapes but produce a cable having slightly larger dimensions because small spaces exist between the wires of the stranded construction.

While copper conductors for mains cables are produced from annealed copper wire it is normal for aluminium conductors to have their individual wires in the semi-hard condition before stranding. While fully annealed aluminium provides good conductivity it is very soft and can create problems at conductor terminations of the mechanical clamping type.

INSULATION

Conductor insulating materials used in cables operating at system voltages up to and including 11 kV include impregnated paper, thermo-setting synthetic insulation and thermoplastic synthetic insulation.

Impregnated-paper insulation

Cables with impregnated paper have been used successfully since towards the end of the 19th century and this form of insulation can provide a cable service life of upwards of 50 years, some of the earliest power cables still being in service. BS 6480 gives constructional details and test requirements for cables having this form of insulation.

Cable conductors are lapped with layers of thin narrow paper tapes to the required total radial thickness. Cables for 11 kV operation have two layers of semi-conducting carbon paper tape applied first to the conductor; this is known as conductor screening and its purpose is to reduce electrical stresses at the interface between the outside surface of the conductor and the insulation.

Multicore belted cables have their cores laid up together, any spaces between the cores being filled with paper or jute strings, with the whole assembly being lapped with further paper tapes to provide the belt insulation. Cables for 11 kV operation include a semiconducting carbon paper tape in the outer layer of belt papers for the purpose of providing an equipotential screen for controlling electrical stresses.

Single-core cables for 11 kV operation have the outer surface of the core insulation lapped with a screening tape, which may be semi-conducting carbon paper or metallised paper, or even thin copper or aluminium tape. This screening is for the purpose of controlling electrical stress distribution. Three-core 11 kV cables can be of the 'screened' type where each individual insulated core is screened with metallised paper or non-ferrous metal tape and the whole assembly of laid-up three cores is lapped with a binder of fabric tape incorporating interwoven copper wire in order to ensure electrical contact between the screens of all cores and the overall metal sheath. These copper-woven fabric tapes are also applied over the screening of large single-core screened cables for the same purpose of maintaining good electrical contact between screen and metal sheath.

The paper tape insulation is dried under vacuum and heat to remove moisture and is then impregnated with a special insulating compound based upon oil. Conventional impregnating compounds were based upon mineral oil containing about 20% of rosin, the rosin making the compound viscous. Cables impregnated with such compounds are entirely suitable in situations where the cable is laid in virtually horizontal runs but they have the disadvantage of tending to drain to lower points in runs where cables are laid vertically or on gradients. This results in higher parts of the cable becoming partially drained of impregnated compound with a resultant lowering of dielectric strength. Also, oil at lower levels tends to leak out of terminations or, at worst, can burst the metal sheath at the bottom of long vertical runs.

To overcome these problems cables have been manufactured from paper tapes which are already dried and impregnated with oil/rosin compound before their application by lapping to the conductors. Such cables are known as being pre-impregnated but do not have such good dielectric strength as fully impregnated insulation.

The most satisfactory solution for overcoming the drainage problems is to employ compounds composed of mixtures of oils and microcrystalline waxes with other substances which result in impregnating compounds which are virtually solid at the normal operating temperatures of cables, yet are sufficiently fluid at the impregnating temperature during manufacture to allow the paper tapes to become properly saturated. Cables having this type of insulating compound are known as mass-impregnated non-draining (MIND) types. While such cables present no drainage problems over their range of normal operating temperatures it has to be appreciated that at excessive temperatures due to overloads the compound may become sufficiently fluid to drain from higher to lower levels. The majority of mains and submains cables with impregnated paper insulation are of the MIND type.

Impregnated-paper insulation must be enclosed within a metal sheathing to ensure that the insulation remains free from moisture. Ends must also be sealed from the atmosphere.

Thermosetting synthetic insulation

These insulations include ethylene propylene rubbers (EPR) and cross linked polyethylene (XLPE). Such materials are applied to cable

conductors by extrusion techniques while in a hot thermoplastic state
and once on the conductor the materials are subjected to a curing process which causes cross linking of the molecules, resulting in a tough
elastic material which does not soften again over the normal range of
operating temperatures of the cable conductor.

Earlier power cables having thermosetting insulation used butyl
rubber but this had limited mechanical strength properties, although
it is still used for some wiring cables.

BS 6899 'Rubber insulation and sheath of electric cables', includes
requirements applicable to ordinary EPR but a tougher material is
specified in BS 5469 'Hard ethylene propylene rubber insulation of
electric cables'. This is known as HEPR and is suitable for use in
cables having conductor operating temperatures as high as 90°C.

Ethylene propylene rubbers have excellent electrical properties;
their good ozone resistance making them suitable for high voltages.
Like natural rubber, the material burns and is not particularly oil
resistant, therefore the insulated cable cores must be provided with
some form of external protection.

BS 5468 'Cross linked polyethylene insulation of electric cables',
covers requirements for XLPE for use in cables having continuous operating conductor temperatures up to 90°C. Before it is cross linked,
ordinary polyethylene has a somewhat sharp melting point of around
110°C so one of the important tests in BS 5468 ensures that the material removed from the finished cable is properly cross linked and is
thus capable of withstanding high temperatures resulting from short-
circuit conditions where the cable conductors might reach about 250°C
for short periods.

Ethylene propylene rubbers and XLPE burn and continue to burn when
ignited; EPR tends to burn in much the same way as natural rubber
compounds.

Lower voltage cables have the insulation applied by extrusion
which is followed by the passage of the insulated core through the
section of the manufacturing machine where the material is subjected
to the cross linking, or curing, operation. Afterwards the insulated
cores are assembled into complete cables of the required design.

For h.v. cables it is necessary for the electrical stresses at the
inside surface of the insulation adjacent to the conductor and at the

outside surface of the core to be carefully controlled so that no points of concentrated high stresses develop during the operation of the cable. This screening is achieved by the use of layers of semi-conducting materials immediately over the conductor and over the outside surface of the insulated core; both layers being in intimate contact with the insulation. It is possible, by careful manufacturing control, to achieve this screening by applying lappings of semiconducting tapes over the conductor and over the core. More positive and efficient screening is achieved by extruding a thin layer of semiconducting rubber-like material over the conductor and also over the outside surface of the core. These materials are applied on the same machine and at the same time as the main insulation is extruded on to the cable conductor.

Thermoplastic synthetic insulation

For power cables polyvinylchloride (PVC) is the most widely used thermoplastic insulation; polyethylene being used infrequently and then only for high voltages. As already stated, polyethylene has a sharp melting point around 110°C and is thus prone to cause failures where cable conductors exceed this temperature due to overloads or short-circuits.

PVC compounds are composed of mixtures of the basic resin and plasticisers together with small amounts of other compounding ingredients, such as, fillers, stabilisers, lubricants and pigments. The plastics technologist, by selection of varying quantities of different ingredients, can produce a very wide range of PVC compounds having an extremely wide range of physical and electrical properties but BS 6746 'PVC insulation and sheath of electric cables', closely specifies the requirements for compounds used in cables.

PVC insulating compounds have excellent electrical properties suited to power cables used up to and including 3.3 kV but at higher voltages the material is not so suitable, mainly because it has a relatively high dielectric constant and dielectric losses become high. One electrical characteristic of PVC which is often not appreciated is the fact that its insulation resistance varies quite considerably with temperature. At 70°C a PVC-insulated cable has an insulation resistance some 700 to 1000 times lower than the value at 20°C.

Being a thermoplastic material, PVC is harder at lower temperatures and becomes progressively softer with increasing temperature. Unless PVC compounds are specially formulated for low temperatures (it is possible to produce compounds which can be bent at -40°C) it is usual to limit the temperature at which PVC cables are bent during installation to about 0°C otherwise there is a risk of the PVC compound cracking.

The grades of PVC used for mains cables are designed for conductor continuous operating temperatures of 70°C and under short-circuit conditions the conductor temperature should never exceed 160°C, otherwise the core insulation would flow and the cable would become permanently damaged.

When PVC is excessively heated the polymer suffers chemical degradation and at continuous temperatures above about 115°C serious chemical breakdown begins to occur with corrosive hydrochloric acid forming in association with damp conditions. Standard PVC compounds are self-extinguishing when the source of ignition is removed but the material will continue to burn when subjected to fire from adjacent burning material and toxic and corrosive gases are produced. Special PVC compounds are available which have less tendency to burn and which produce lower levels of toxicity.

While polyethylene is little used for power cables it may be noted that it burns exceedingly well and, while burning, has the undesirable characteristics of dripping burning molten material which can easily cause spread of fire. By incorporating special additives into polyethylene the material can be made more flame retardant but these additives seriously affect the electrical properties, resulting in an insulation not much better than PVC.

PVC insulation is applied to cable conductors by means of extrusion at elevated temperature and upon leaving the extrusion die the hot material in a soft plastic state is run through cooling water so that by the time the insulated core is wound on to the collection drum the PVC has become sufficiently hard.

CABLE CONSTRUCTION

The manufacture of cable is carried out under carefully controlled conditions which include quality control procedures on the individual

constituents. All manufacturing lengths are subjected to the
electrical tests required by the specification.

Impregnated-paper insulated cables with lead sheathing

Paper insulated cables to BS 6480 have a continuous sheathing of lead
or lead alloy applied over the assembled cores. Lead alloys have
their compositions specified in BS 801 'Lead and lead alloy sheaths of
electric cables', and for unarmoured cables Alloy E or Alloy B are
generally used. Both alloys are more resistant than lead to the
effects of vibration, Alloy B being used in cases where severe conditions of vibration are to be experienced. It may be noted that lead
can develop a crystalline structure when subjected to vibration and
cracks can then develop through the wall of the sheath on the cable
with the ultimate result that moisture or water can enter and cause
electrical breakdown of the insulation. Armoured cables often have
lead or Alloy E.

The lead or alloy sheathing is generally provided with some form
of outer protection. Single-core cables are normally given an oversheath of extruded PVC. Unarmoured multicore cables can also have an
oversheath of extruded PVC but the majority of multicore cables are
of the armoured type. Armour, for mechanical protection of the lead
sheath, can be in the form of double steel tape armour or wire armour.
Steel tape armour provides a certain degree of mechanical protection
against sharp objects penetrating the cable from outside and consists
of two helical lappings of tape, applied with gaps between convolut-
ions, the outer tape covering centrally the gaps in the underlying
tape. The tapes are applied with gaps to allow bending of the cable.

For protection giving longitudinal mechanical strength and a
certain degree of protection from penetrating objects, single-wire
armouring is used, consisting of a helical layer of galvanised steel
wires. For additional longitudinal strength, for example for cables
which need to be suspended vertically, double-wire armouring, consisting of two layers of galvanised steel wires, is applied, the outer
layer of wires being applied in the reverse direction from the inner
layer. A separator of waterproof compounded textile tape is applied
between the two layers of wires to allow the wires a certain free
movement in relation to one another when the cable is bent.

Armoured cables have a bedding applied first to the lead or lead alloy sheath and this may consist of lappings of compounded paper and textile tapes, all adequately coated with waterproof compound, or if the cable is to have an overall extruded PVC sheath the bedding may consist of an extruded PVC covering or lappings of PVC tapes.

Unless cables are to be left with the wire armour in the bright condition, it is usual for the armouring to have an overall protection in the form of serving applied in the form of compounded textile tapes or as an extruded PVC sheathing.

If single-core lead sheathed cables are required to be armoured for mechanical reasons, the armouring must be composed of wires of non-magnetic material, such as aluminium alloy, otherwise considerable electrical losses and heating effects occur due to magnetic hysteresis in steel wires with alternating current loads of more than about 50 A.

Impregnated-paper insulated cables with aluminium sheathing

Instead of a lead or lead alloy sheath for providing the moisture-proof covering for protecting the impregnated-paper insulation an alternative design uses aluminium sheathing. Aluminium sheathing is mechanically tougher than lead therefore aluminium sheathed cables generally do not require any further armouring for mechanical protection.

Aluminium sheathing is also more rigid than lead sheathing and cables having smooth aluminium sheaths are more difficult to handle during laying, especially at bends. To overcome this problem corrugated sheathing is used, the annular corrugations being formed after the sheathing has been extruded on to the cable cores in smooth form. The result is a cable having equivalent bending performance to that of lead covered wire armoured cable. Figure 17.3 illustrates the design.

Should the corrugated sheath become damaged there could be the possibility of moisture movement from the local damage moving along under the sheath, resulting in a long length of cable becoming unserviceable, so to avoid this possibility the annular corrugations are substantially filled with a suitable compound. The quantity of compound has to be carefully controlled so that when the cable is operating at its full load temperature the internal pressure within the sheath due to thermal expansion does not create undue pressure.

Aluminium sheathing, whether smooth or corrugated, must be adequately protected from corrosion when laid in the ground and the usual protection consists of a good coating of bitumen compound applied directly to the aluminium sheath followed by an extrusion of PVC.

The above types of aluminium sheathed cables are generally used only on 11 kV systems.

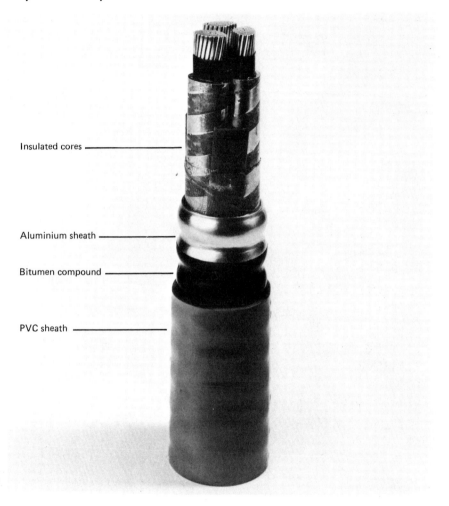

Insulated cores

Aluminium sheath

Bitumen compound

PVC sheath

Figure 17.3 Paper insulated cable with corrugated aluminium sheath (courtesy Pirelli General Cable Works plc)

CONSAC cables

Because aluminium sheathing provides a good electrical conductor there is one type of cable which makes use of this sheathing as the neutral

conductor. This is CONSAC cable in accordance with BS 5593 which has
been used by some UK electricity boards for l.v. mains. The word
CONSAC is derived from 'concentric aluminium cable'. Figure 17.4
shows the general construction which consists of three shaped aluminium conductors for the three phases, each paper insulated and then
having an overall belt, the whole insulation being impregnated with
non-draining compound, then encased in a smooth aluminium sheath which
is liberally coated with bitumen compound and finally sheathed overall
with PVC. A requirement of the specification is that the bitumen compound shall adhere to both the aluminium and the PVC sheaths.

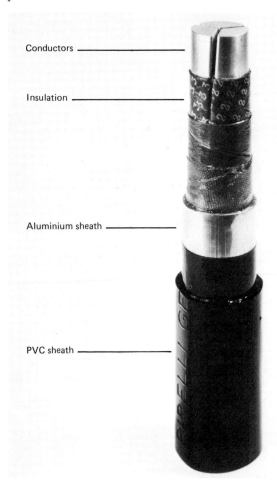

Conductors

Insulation

Aluminium sheath

PVC sheath

Figure 17.4 CONSAC cable (courtesy Pirelli General Cable Works plc)

CONSAC cables are used in systems where it is permitted to employ combined protective and neutral conductors (PEN). One advantage claimed for CONSAC cables over other PEN types having extruded synthetic insulation is that should the aluminium sheath become corroded there is every possibility that the cable insulation would fail because of ingress of moisture through the corroded sheath and the circuit protection would isolate the cable long before the neutral conductor became completely corroded away with the loss of the earthing connection. Other types of PEN cables could lose their neutral and earth continuity yet would still provide the phase voltage and thus could present a hazard to the electricity consumer.

CONSAC cables can be made in sizes up to and including 300 mm^2.

Thermosetting elastomeric insulated cables

Cables with EPR and XLPE insulation are gradually tending to replace impregnated-paper insulated cables because of easier handling and terminating techniques. This applies particularly at higher voltages.

A typical 11 kV three-core cable is shown in fig. 17.5. This has heavily compacted stranded aluminium conductors with semiconducting screening and extruded EPR insulation. The insulated cores are covered with semiconducting screening material which are in turn lapped with metal tapes in order to ensure longitudinal electrical continuity. The three screened cores are laid-up together, filled circular, then wire armoured and sheathed overall with PVC. Similar 11 kV single-core has armouring of non-magnetic material.

BS 5467 provides requirements for wire armoured cables having HEPR or XLPE insulation for operating at voltages up to 3.3 kV. The specification covers a wide range of conductor sizes in both copper and aluminium conductors. As well as wire armouring composed of circular wires the specification also includes aluminium strip armour consisting of a layer of strips of fairly hard aluminium.

Because the insulation of these cables can operate up to 90°C it is not always suitable for the bedding under the armour or the overall sheathing to be of PVC and the specification allows the use of other synthetic materials. Such sheathing material could be chlorosulphonated polyethylene, known as CSP or Hypalon. This provides an oil-resisting and flame-retardant covering to the core insulation.

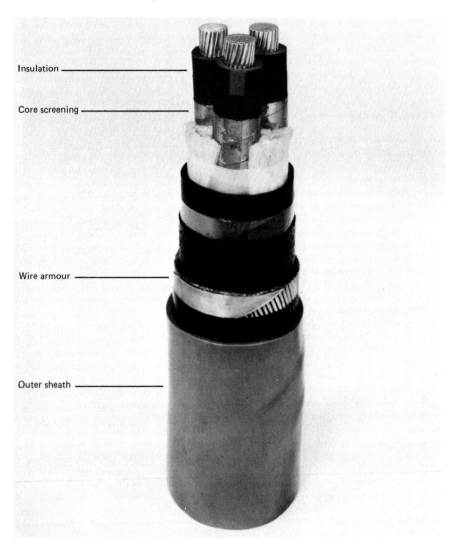

Insulation

Core screening

Wire armour

Outer sheath

*Figure 17.5   Elastomeric insulated cable for 6350/11000 V operation
(courtesy Pirelli General Cable Works plc)*

Waveconal cables

As an alternative to CONSAC cables extensive use is made in electricity
distribution at low voltages of Waveconal cables which have solid
shaped aluminium conductors insulated with either XLPE or HEPR. The
three-phase cores are laid up together and lapped with an open spiral
of clear plastic tape. The assembled cores are then covered with an
extrusion of rubber-like material which acts as a bedding for the

concentric neutral conductor and the same material also completely covers the wires of the neutral conductor.

The aluminium wires forming the neutral conductor, which may be seen in fig. 17.6, are applied in an oscillatory manner instead of in a helical form and this enables the cores to be exposed when making tee-joints under live conditions without the need to cut the neutral wires, and thus break the return path of the combined protective and neutral conductor of a TN-C-S system.

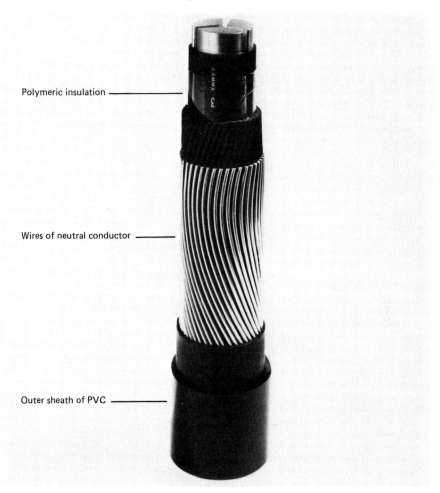

Polymeric insulation

Wires of neutral conductor

Outer sheath of PVC

Figure 17.6   600/1000 V Waveconal cable (courtesy Pirelli General Cable Works plc)

The aluminium neutral wires are carefully segregated so that they are individually surrounded by the rubber-like filling material in order to prevent moisture transference around the neutral in the event of mechanical damage.

The cable is finally sheathed with PVC to provide mechanical protection to the rubber-like covering around the neutral wires.

Cables with synthetic thermoplastic insulation

The most widely used l.v. cables in and around buildings have PVC insulation and BS 6346 'PVC-insulated cables for electricity supply', fully specifies a large range of cables having both copper and aluminium conductors, with and without armouring.

For vertical risers and some submains single-core unarmoured designs would be used but in general it is more normal to employ wire armoured or aluminium strip armoured cables for the mains supply where PVC cables are required.

All the cables in BS 6346 have their PVC insulation applied to the copper or aluminium conductors by extrusion; multicore cables with shaped conductors have their insulation applied in sectoral shape so that the complete cable is compact and thus overall dimensions are kept to a minimum. Figure 17.7 shows examples of cross sections of typical solid sector-shaped aluminium conductor cables.

Cables have a bedding for the armour of either an extruded covering of PVC or a lapping of two or more plastics tapes.

Armouring on copper conductor and some aluminium conductor cables consists of a conventional layer of galvanised steel wires, although single-core cables, requiring armouring, have wires of non-magnetic material if the cables are to be used in a.c. circuits.

Aluminium conductor cables can also have aluminium strip armouring, consisting of a single layer of aluminium strips of the sizes specified in BS 6346. This form of armouring is useful where low armour resistances are required; aluminium strip armouring has a much lower resistance than galvanised steel wire armouring. For smaller cables the strip armouring resistance is approximately half that of steel wire while for larger sizes the aluminium strip has only one quarter of the resistance.

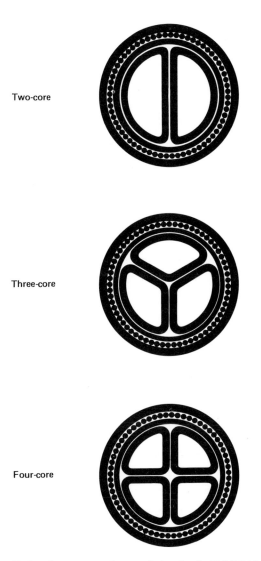

Two-core

Three-core

Four-core

Figure 17.7   Cross sections of typical 600/1000 V solid aluminium conductor PVC-insulated cables

All BS 6346 cables have an overall extruded sheathing of PVC.

Cables to the above specification are also available for operation on 3.3 kV circuits. Such cables are similar to those for use at l.v. but the thickness of core insulation is somewhat greater. At 3.3 kV there is no necessity for conductor or core screening as is required

247

for higher voltage elastomeric cables since PVC is able to withstand adequately the electrical stresses involved.

Concentric neutral-and-earth service cables having PVC insulation are made in a variety of combinations having copper or aluminium phase conductors and concentric neutral conductors of aluminium or copper wires. These cables are generally not used in sizes greater than 35 mm^2 and can have one or three phase conductors.

Where a concentric cable is required with separate neutral and earth-continuity conductors, there is a design available in accordance with BS 4553 'PVC-insulated split concentric cables with copper conductors for electricity supply'. These cables, in sizes up to and including 35 mm^2, have the central circular stranded copper phase conductor insulated with PVC. The neutral conductor is made from a number of single copper wires, each covered by an extruded layer of PVC to a diameter the same as the wires forming the earth-continuity conductor.

The earth-continuity conductor wires are bare and not individually covered with PVC.

The covered neutral wires and the bare earth-continuity wires are applied around the central phase core as a concentric layer, the neutral wires being together as a band and the earth-continuity wires as a separate band. PVC string separators, about the same diameter as the bare copper wires, are laid either side of the group of earth-continuity wires to separate the group from the covered wires forming the neutral conductor.

A binder of non-hygroscopic tape is applied immediately over the concentric layer and the whole assembly is sheathed with PVC.

Cables with mineral insulation

Chapter 18 deals with mineral-insulated cables for general building wiring but large single-core cables are used as submains, particularly as risers in buildings. Copper sheathed cables are available with or without an overall covering of PVC but mineral-insulated cables with aluminium sheathing have an overall extruded PVC covering to protect the metal sheathing from corrosion.

BS 6207, which is in two parts dealing with copper sheathed and aluminium sheathed cables, respectively, provides full constructional

details and gives a range of single-core conductor sizes up to
150 mm^2.

INSTALLATION

A number of precautions are necessary when installing cables not only
as to handling but also when terminating and fixing them in position.

General care in handling

Cables can be perfectly manufactured and meet all the required specification tests at the cable factory and then be easily ruined and made
unfit for service if not handled with care during installation.

Unlike building wiring cables, mains cables are generally large
and are on heavy drums, so in designing an installation careful thought
must be given to the method by which the drum of cable is to be delivered to site and removed from the delivery vehicle. Dropping a drum
of cable from a lorry tail board not only causes possible damage to
the cable but can cause collapse of the wooden drum and subsequent
severe damage to the cable when attempting to remove the tangled turns
from the broken drum.

If drums of cables have to be rolled any distance over the ground
the battens should be left in their fixed position so that some protection can be given to the outside turns on the drum. Many cables
have been damaged by rolling over a removed batten on the ground with
the sharp ends of the nails pointing upwards and penetrating the cable
passing over it.

Where drums are rolled it is important that the direction of
rotation should be in accordance with the arrow on the side of the
drum. If this is not observed the turns of cable on the drum can work
loose and very large longitudinal forces set up which either push the
inner end out of the flange or, if it is rigidly secured, may damage
the cable itself.

When pulling cables off drums a spindle of adequate size and
strength should pass through the central holes in the flanges and
proper drum jacks should be used to support the spindle. A person
should be stationed at the drum position to stop the drum unwinding as
soon as cable pulling is stopped, otherwise the drum can over run and
a damaging kink form in the cable when it becomes bent too sharply.

With long pulls, especially with heavy cable and also where straight-pulls are not possible, cable rollers should be placed at frequent intervals to support and guide the cable. Care should be taken to ensure that the cable runs in the centre of each roller and does not become wedged at roller edges.

Where cables are cut or where factory seals are removed during the laying operation the exposed ends should be quickly sealed. This applies not only to impregnated-paper insulated cables which are quickly destroyed by ingress of moisture but to all types of insulation. If cut ends are left exposed to the elements, or worse, left in the ground, water can penetrate even along elastomeric and thermoplastic cables, leading to untold problems later during jointing or terminating operations.

Methods of installation

The method of installing a cable obviously depends upon where the cable has to run but the shortest route is not necessarily the most economic route. Rocky ground can be expensive to excavate and corrosive ground can call for expensive anti-corrosion finishes to the cable.

Conventional methods of installing mains cables are: laid direct in the ground; pulled through ducts in the ground; laid in troughs; or installed in the air on supports such as cable trays or cable ladders.

Laying directly in the ground involves expensive excavation and cables must be laid at a sufficient depth to ensure that no disturbance or damage to the cable can take place under normal circumstances. The soil immediately around the cable should contain no sharp stones or similar objects, ideally it should be sifted. In order to comply with the 15th Edition of the IEE Wiring Regulations cables buried in the ground should be marked with tiles or by some other suitable means so that persons excavating the ground later have some warning of the presence of the cable before reaching it.

If several cables are laid side by side in the trench the spacing between them should be carefully maintained otherwise their current carrying capacities may be seriously affected.

Cable trenches should be filled in again as quickly as possible after cables have been laid in order to reduce possible damage to the cable at the bottom of the trench.

Where cables pass under busy roads it is useful for ducts to be used, spare ways being left so that additional cables can be later drawn through without the need to excavate the road again.

Where cables are laid in troughs thought has to be given to the possible effects of adding more cables at a later date, since these can adversely affect the current ratings of all the cables.

Cables installed in air must be supported at intervals sufficiently close so that no mechanical strain is exerted on them. Appendix 11 of the IEE Wiring Regulations gives guidance. Where cables are run on trays or cable ladders the positioning of the trays or ladders requires careful consideration since they are often used by other trades for walking upon to gain access to adjacent areas and the cables can become damaged.

For all methods of installation, cables should not be bent in radii close to terminations less than those shown in Table 52C of the IEE Regulations but during the actual operation of pulling the cables into position every effort should be made to ensure that cables are only bent into somewhat large radii.

In cold weather conditions cables having PVC components should not be installed when the cable or ambient temperatures are at 0°C or lower. Installation should not commence until the temperature has been above 0°C for at least 24 hours unless the cable can be stored in a warm atmosphere to ensure that it is well above freezing point and it can be taken out and laid quickly. In freezing conditions there is every chance that the PVC material may shatter. The same care must be taken with any cables having bituminous compounded coverings since these also can crack.

Precautions against spread of fire

In all installations precautions should be taken to ensure that cables cannot spread fire. Where cables pass through walls or partitions the holes should be made good with fire-resisting material.

Where vertical risers pass upwards through floors fire barriers must be fitted at each floor. Not only does this restrict spread of fire but alleviates a build-up of heat at the top of the cable run which would otherwise affect the current rating of the cable.

Where cables run together in large groups there is always a risk that one burning cable may ignite adjacent cables and eventually the whole group can be involved in a major cable fire. Special PVC compounds having better flame-retardant properties than standard grades are available for cables in fire risk areas but wherever possible cables in large groups should be avoided.

Cables without metal sheathing should not be run in ground liable to be saturated with hydrocarbons, such as from the petrochemical industry, because some liquids, while not attacking PVC and some other elastomers, are able to penetrate through cable coverings and insulation and flow along the cables into switchgear and apparatus to which the cables are connected, thus creating a dangerous fire and explosion risk. Where cables have to be run through such ground the cable design should include a lead sheathing since this is impermeable to such liquids. Precautions might have to be taken to protect the lead sheath from corrosion.

JOINTING AND TERMINATING

Jointing and terminating mains cables of any type involves making adequate electrical connections to conductors, ensuring continued satisfactory functioning of the cable insulation and providing adequate electrical continuity to the metal sheath, armouring or other metallic covering.

Conductor connections

Any joints or terminations in conductors must be capable of carrying any load current to be expected during the life of the cable and also very heavy currents which may occur as a result of faults and short-circuits. All conductors expand when they become heated by the passage of currents and contract when the current is reduced or removed. This expansion and contraction is both longitudinal and radial, thus, cable conductors become longer when hot from the passage of the normal load current and much longer from the passage of short-circuit currents. On cooling, the conductor tries to return to its original length. These longitudinal movements can create considerable forces which must be taken into account in joint and termination design.

The radial expansion and contraction has to be accommodated in the device for making the electrical connection to the conductor; the

electrical resistance of the connection must remain very low throughout the life of the connection and this requires that the conductor
metal must remain in constant intimate contact with the connecting
device at all times. The passage of current through any increased
resistance will result in the generation of additional heat which may
lead to the ultimate failure of the connection and its insulation.

For copper conductors soft-soldering into lugs or ferrules has
been the traditional method for terminating or jointing for many years
and is still considered the most reliable method when properly carried
out but it involves the use of heat and certain skills. The alternative is to use crimping methods where lugs or ferrules having
sufficient wall thickness are compressed, usually by hydraulic means,
on to the conductor. Many designs of compression-type joints are
available but the user should always first ensure that the one selected
has been fully type tested under all conditions. The most reliable
tools for undertaking the compression operation are those which cannot
be removed from the joint until the pressure device has travelled the
whole distance of its compression stroke.

Smaller conductors can be terminated in devices having pinching
screws or clamping bolts but great care must be taken to ensure that
all the screws or bolts are tightened with sufficient torque and
remain tight. There are many cases of fires resulting from the
development of high resistance contacts in terminations of the pinching
screw type where the screws have not been sufficiently tight.

Aluminium conductors can be soldered; there are satisfactory
solders and fluxes available from a large number of sources, but such
soldering requires more skill than for copper conductors. It is well
known that aluminium develops a thin oxide layer on its surface which
is difficult to break down and therefore special techniques are
necessary in order to obtain satisfactory alloying between the
aluminium and the solder. In the case of stranded conductors it is
not only necessary to make a good electrical cónnection to the outside
layer of wires but the inner layers in large strands must also be
jointed so that they may carry their full share of the load current.

The jointing of solid aluminium conductors is more usefully
undertaken by crimping methods, using specially designed hydraulically
operated tools. Again, only systems which have satisfactorily

withstood type tests, involving long-term cyclic testing, should be used.

Because of the presence of the oxide layer on the surface of aluminium wire, connections made with pinching screws are prone to failure unless the screws are tightened with sufficient torque and remain at this tightness throughout the life of the installation. Failures of such connections can result in fires.

Insulation at joints and terminations

Impregnated-paper insulated cables must have their insulation protected from ingress of moisture and conventional joints involve making good the insulation over the conductor joints by lapping with impregnated-paper tapes then enclosing the whole joint in a metal sleeve which is plumbed or soldered to the ends of the existing metal sheathing, the whole sleeve then being filled carefully with special compound which is generally poured in hot. Conventional terminations are dealt with in a similar manner, the end of the cable being enclosed in a suitable case which is filled with special compound to maintain it air and moisture tight.

These conventional methods have stood the test of time but are being replaced by newer methods which are said to involve less skills and are quicker. For through-joints paper insulated cables can be encapsulated in synthetic resin, such as polyester, which contains a hardener. The resin is poured as a cold liquid into a mould placed around the joint and once the resin has become hard there is no further need for the mould. While simple in basic principle, such joints have to be made with great care. The resin must be mixed and poured carefully so that no air bubbles remain, otherwise these can develop into paths for moisture penetration, also corona discharge at higher voltages. Great care is necessary to ensure that the resin adheres to the ends of the cable sheathing for the same reasons.

Terminations for paper insulated cables can also be encapsulated in resin but more modern techniques involve the use of heat-shrink seals over the ends of the cable cores. The heat-shrink material in the form of tubes is slid over the cable cores and a heat-shrink glove fits over the crutch of the cable and the end of the metal sheath. By careful heating of the cable end the seals shrink down tightly on to

254

the cores and sheath and provide a waterproof seal. Stranded conductors must have their ends completely sealed otherwise there is a
possibility of moisture travelling along between the wires of the
strand and causing failure of the insulation. Although basically a
simple terminating method, skills are still needed to ensure that the
heat-shrink materials are adequately heated and also that they are of
the correct size for the cable size. Only designs which have been
fully type tested should be contemplated.

Low voltage polymeric cables having EPR, XLPE and PVC insulation
can have their outer coverings just trimmed back for sufficient distance to ensure no surface tracking at terminations and there is no
need for the ends of the cores to be enclosed in any sort of compound
in normal dry situations. At joints for these l.v. cables it is
necessary to seal the jointed cores from ingress of moisture from the
ground in the case of buried joints and the usual manner is to enclose
the whole joint in compound or resin. In pouring hot compound into
PVC cable joints the temperature of the compound must not, of course,
be so high as to cause softening of the insulation. As with paper
insulated cables, polyester and similar resins must be mixed and poured
so that no air bubbles remain after the material has hardened.

High voltage polymeric cables require rather special attention.
Because of the manner in which the semiconducting screen material is
applied to the outside surface of the core insulation great care has
to be taken to ensure that all traces of this are removed for a
sufficient distance at ends for jointing or terminating, otherwise
tracking along the surface of the core can result, with complete
failure of the cable end. Since the semiconducting material is
generally very adherent to the core insulation some form of mechanical
removal of the layer is necessary; special tools are available for the
purpose.

Where the screens of h.v. cable cores are terminated on being
trimmed back for jointing there can be points of high electrical stress
when the cable is operating and at these points the core insulation
can eventually fail unless special precautions are taken. To overcome
these problems proprietary stress relieving devices are available which
slip over the cores and are used in association with heat-shrink seals.
These devices must be carefully fitted in accordance with manufacturers'
instructions.

Continuity of metal sheath or armouring

The metal sheath, armouring or other metallic covering of any cable
must be capable of carrying fault currents which may flow through it
and where such metal is relied upon as an earth-continuity conductor
it must provide a low resistance path at all times. This means that
at any joints or terminations the continuity must be efficiently maintained throughout the life of the installation.

Over the years conventional joints and terminations with paper
insulation have proved satisfactory because the metal sheathing has
been plumbed or soldered to whatever it is connected and armour wires
have been adequately connected into massive metal joint box enclosures
or glands. With the advent of more modern jointing techniques the
continuity of metal sheathings and armouring has depended more upon
various forms of metal clamps. Tests with overload and fault currents
and with cyclic loadings, also under damp corrosive conditions, have
been conducted on many new designs of jointing methods for metal
sheaths and armour wires and many have been found to be unreliable,
developing into high resistance connections with passage of time.

Before any jointing or terminating methods are selected for use in
a particular cable installation the suppliers of the system should be
requested to produce evidence to show that the technique for providing
continuity has satisfactorily withstood appropriate tests when used in
conjunction with the particular type of cable to be installed.

In general, for resin-type joints, armour wires are best connected
from one side of the joint to the other by means of crimped joints, a
bunch of wires from one side being carried over and joined by a crimped
ferrule to a bunch of wires from the other side.

At terminations the wire armouring or metal strips of polymeric
cables are most efficiently secured in glands to BS 6121 'Mechanical
cable glands for elastomer and plastics insulated cables'. This
standard covers a wide range of glands and the correct type for a
particular cable must be selected. It is important that full details
of the cable to be accommodated are stated at the time of ordering.

In corrosive conditions all types of metal sheath, armour and
metal strip connections should be well encased in suitable material to
reduce risk of corrosion of the electrical connection.

CABLE RATINGS

The passage of current through a cable conductor raises its temperature. In the case of sustained current an equilibrium is eventually established and the heat generated is equal to the heat dissipated through the insulation, sheathing and other coverings and finally into the surrounding ground or air. The highest value of current a cable can carry continuously depends upon the highest safe operating temperature applicable to the insulation or other parts of the cable. Table 17.2 gives the maximum temperatures for continuous operation for a range of insulants and these values are used for the calculation of sustained current ratings.

Table 17.2 Temperature limits of mains cable insulants

Insulating material	Maximum conductor temperature (°C)
Impregnated paper below 6350/11000 V	80*
Impregnated paper 6350/11000 V other than belted	70†
Impregnated paper 6350/11000 V belted	65†
Polyvinylchloride (PVC)	70
Hard ethylene propylene rubber (HEPR)	90
Cross-linked polyethylene (XLPE)	90

*60°C for unarmoured lead sheathed cables laid in ducts.
†50°C for unarmoured lead sheathed cables laid in ducts.

Current ratings may be determined from practical field tests for any size and type of cable installed in a particular manner by making sufficient temperature measurements at appropriate values of current in association with relevant ambient temperature conditions. Alternatively, ratings may be calculated from first principles or may be more easily obtained from published tables.

Methods for calculating ratings have been standardised on a world-wide basis and are given in IEC Publication 287 'Calculation of the continuous current rating of cables (100% load factor)'. In order to calculate current ratings one must have detailed information of the cable construction since dimensions and properties of the components enter into the calculations.

The usual method is to obtain ratings from published tables which cover standard cable types and cater for a variety of installation conditions. For l.v. cables it will be found that the tables of current ratings included in the IEE Wiring Regulations relate generally to cables installed above ground and mostly in air. These ratings are based on an ambient air temperature of 30°C. Ratings for power cables are provided in more detail in the 69-30 series of reports issued by ERA Technology Ltd and cover installation methods for cables in the ground, in underground ducts and in air.

These ratings are tabulated for a standard ground temperature of 15°C and an ambient air temperature of 25°C; the different air temperature results in slightly different tabulated current ratings from the IEE values. Factors in both documents allow adjustments to be made for particular ambient temperatures.

Current rating tables are also included in catalogues of many cable makers.

In using published ratings tables it is most important to take cognizance of all the notes and footnotes in order that the correct factors are applied to the standard ratings to take account of the actual installation conditions. In particular, attention must be paid to the temperature of the surroundings in which the cable is to be installed, the precise method of installation and the effects of grouping.

If the temperature of the air or the ground surrounding the cable is higher than the standard value appropriate to the published rating the temperature-rise applicable to that rating would result in the cable conductor temperature exceeding the maximum permitted operating temperature for the conductor insulation. For this reason the rating must be reduced by the application of the appropriate factor. Only in cases where it can safely be assumed that the surrounding temperature will always be lower than the standard value is it possible to take advantage of a slight increase in rating.

The manner in which a cable is installed in relation to its surroundings and any other cables affects its ability to dissipate heat. For this reason the factors appropriate to such matters as depth of laying, grouping, type of soil, must be applied to the published ratings.

For cables laid in the ground the ERA reports provide tabulated ratings based upon a solid thermal resistivity of 1.2 deg C m/W which can be a fair average value for much of the UK but the type of soil affects its thermal resistivity considerably and it is strongly recommended that the information regarding different types of soil provided by ERA is studied. In some areas of the world very dry conditions for long periods can result in high values of soil resistivity which can reduce the safe ratings of cables.

Impregnated-paper insulated cables are well standardised and their current ratings in all sizes up to high voltages are provided in the ERA reports. Standardisation of polymeric cables is less advanced at higher voltages and current ratings for 11 kV types are not yet available in published form, although electric cable makers can provide current ratings values on request. At lower voltages the ratings for polymeric insulated cables are included in the ERA reports.

TESTING AND FAULT FINDING

After mains cables have been installed, jointed and terminated they should be subjected to electrical tests to ensure that they have not become damaged and that joints and terminations have been properly made.

The essential test is a h.v. test which is more conveniently carried out with d.c. than a.c. since long lengths of cables having high capacitances would require an unacceptably large size of testing transformer for a.c. tests (due to the high charging currents involved).

Table 17.3 shows the values of applied voltages which should be increased gradually to the full value and maintained continuously for 15 minutes between conductors and between each conductor and sheath. No breakdown should occur.

If switchgear or other apparatus cannot be disconnected from the ends of the cable during the test the value of test voltage must be the subject of agreement with all parties concerned.

During the testing period special precautions must be taken to keep all persons away from any exposed parts which may be charged at the high voltage.

If cables with special anti-corrosion sheathing have been used and it is thought that the sheathing could have become damaged during cable

laying operations it is sometimes beneficial to apply a voltage test
between the cable sheath and the ground before the cable is terminated. The value of test voltage should be agreed with the cable maker
or designer of the installation.

Table 17.3 Test voltages for cables after installation

Cable voltage designation (V)	Test voltage d.c.	
	between conductors (V)	between all conductors and sheath or armour (V)
600/1000	3500*	3500*
1900/3300	10000	7000
3800/6600	20000	15000
6300/11000	34000	25000

*2000 V for 1000 V class mineral-insulated cables.

If a cable should break down as a result of h.v. testing the position of the breakdown must obviously be found so that a repair or
replacement can be made. If the test set can provide sufficient power
the fault can often develop into a low resistance path which may be
located after the removal of the h.v. by conventional methods using
resistance bridge techniques. More often than not, the fault remains
of high resistance which can involve problems of location. Sometimes
the position of the fault can easily be detected by ear if the test
voltage is left connected, preferably at a lower value than the full
test value.

Various makes of sophisticated fault location gear are available
for finding high resistance faults and most cable manufacturers offer
a fault location service.

One quite effective method is to charge a large capacitance by the
h.v. test set through a resistance and then discharge it into the
faulty cable core through a spark gap. The voltage and size of spark
gap are arranged so that the capacitor discharges every few seconds.
By walking along the cable the position of the fault can usually be
heard as the insulation breaks down each time the capacitor discharges.
A stethoscope, consisting of a microphone, amplifier and earphone, is
useful for detecting the fault position in buried cables.

Chapter 18

Wiring Cables

R. G. Parr, BSc(Eng), ACGI, CEng, MIEE
D. W. M. Latimer, MA(Cantab), CEng, MIEE
ERA Technology Ltd and Deritend Electrical Services Ltd

Wiring cables are used to distribute electricity through those sections
of an installation which operate at voltages not greater than 1 kV,
going to the individual points of utilisation from distribution boards
which are fed by mains or submains. The term is usually restricted to
cables having conductor cross sections not greater than 25 mm². Some
types of cable are suitable for use in either mains or wiring circuits
(e.g. the 1 kV cables in BS 6346), while others are used almost
exclusively in final distribution circuits and are regarded as wiring
types. Popular examples of the latter are cables containing a protective conductor and the insulated conductors used with conduit or
trunking. On the other hand, mineral insulated cable, while being
generally regarded as a wiring type, can be used in the larger sizes
for submains circuits, as may the larger sizes of BS 6004 cables run
in trunking.

Table 18.1 lists the types of cables available for wiring purposes
and gives brief indications of the main features of their applications.
More detail is given later and there are useful guides on the applications of the various types in the relevant British Standard
specifications and in Appendix 10 of the 15th Edition of the IEE
Wiring Regulations.

Table 18.1 Types of cable and flexibles

BS No.	Insulation	Construction	Conductor	Application
6004	PVC	Unsheathed single-core	Copper, solid, stranded or flexible	In conduit, trunking or similar enclosures where mechanical protection is provided. Above ground. Cable should not be immersed in water. Not directly in plaster, etc.
6004	PVC	Sheathed single and multicore	Copper, solid, stranded or flexible	On trays, ladder supports, cleats, wiring surface where mechanical damage is unlikely. Single-core cables without armour for a.c. circuits. In the ground if provided with additional mechanical protection. Can be embedded in plaster.
6346	PVC	Steel wire or aluminium strip armour with PVC covering, single and multicore	Copper and aluminium, solid and stranded	No restrictions except in cases where severe mechanical impact is expected. Can be used directly in the ground without additional mechanical protection provided it has PVC covering. Single-core cables must have aluminium armour when used on a.c.

262

4553	PVC	Split concentric single-phase + earth	Copper, stranded	General use including underground without further protection. Should not be installed where mechanical damage is a likely hazard.
5467	Elastomeric: cross-linked polyethylene or EP rubber	Armoured	Copper and aluminium, stranded	As for BS 6346 cables. Caution should be exercised where these higher temperature cables are run together with PVC-insulated cables.
6007	Elastomeric: vulcanised rubber, butyl or EP rubber, silicone rubber	Unarmoured single-core with various coverings. Multicore, flat or circular with elastomeric sheath	Copper, aluminium as an alternative, stranded and flexible	Butyl, EP rubber and silicone insulated cables used for high ambient temperatures. Braided coverings in dry situations only. Entry to luminaires. Sheathed cables resistant to some oils and solvents. Can be obtained with a lead sheath where pollution is severe.

263

Table 18.1 (contd)

BS No.	Insulation	Construction	Conductor	Application
6141	Rubber or PVC, capable of operating at high temperatures up to 150°C	Non-sheathed single-core cables. Sheathed two- and three-core flexible cords	Copper plain, tinned or plated, stranded or flexible, only small sizes	Zones having high ambient temperatures, such as in the vicinity of hot process plant, boiler houses. Non-sheathed versions must be protected mechanically by being enclosed. Wiring inside and into (high temperature tails) hot equipment such as luminaires and immersion heaters. Considerable variety of types, see BS for details.
6207	Mineral	Plain copper sheathed or with additional PVC covering	Copper (solid), rigid	General wiring but especially where continuously high temperatures are expected. Excellent fire resistance (alarm and safety circuits). Looks well as surface wiring, not affected by most contaminants. Unlikely to need further mechanical protection.

				Excellent for use in very low temperatures. Weather resistance excellent. Limitations depend on seals at terminations and joints and on material used to insulate conductor tails.
Pirelli FP 200 ANTS Cert. No. 79/6	Silicone rubber	Multicore, PVC/ metallic sheath	Copper solid and stranded, small sizes only	General, especially where high ambients are expected. Good fire resistance. Where full capabilities of mineral insulated cable are not needed.
Pirelli PX ANTS Cert. No. 80/2	PVC	Multicore, PVC/ metallic sheath	Copper solid and stranded, small sizes only	General. Looks well as surface wiring, does not need seals.
Simplex ANTS Cert. No. 79/8	PVC	Similar to BS 6004 flat twin but has steel-tape armour	Copper solid or stranded	General wiring, especially where extra mechanical protection is needed, otherwise identical to BS 6004 sheathed flat twin cables.

Table 18.1 (contd)

BS No.	Insulation	Construction	Conductor	Application
6005 (flex- ible cords)	Rubber, PVC or glass fibre	Multicore, unsheathed and sheathed	Copper flexible or tinsel	Large variety of types of flexible cords with work-ing temperatures up to 150°C. Some types are similar to those in BS 6141. Includes all general purpose flexibles and the high temperature varieties for use in or into hot equipment. Rubber or PVC sheathed varieties can be used out of doors or for indust-rial applications. See extensive guide in Appendix of Specification.

CONSTRUCTION OF WIRING CABLES AND FLEXIBLES

When selecting a wiring cable there are three components that must be considered, conductor material, insulation and protective covering.

Conductors

Conductors of wiring cables are made of annealed copper, and for sizes of 16 mm^2 and above, also of aluminium. Apart from solid, or single-wire conductors, which are available up to 2.5 mm^2 in copper and for all sizes in aluminium, conductors are built up from several wires twisted together to impart various degrees of flexibility to the conductor. (Note - All sizes of conductor in mineral-insulated cables are of solid annealed copper.) The wires used in ordinary cables are of such a diameter that the cable is sufficiently pliable for convenient installation, but in no case should they be subjected to continuous movement. Excessive vibration can cause breakage of the wires, usually at or near terminations. Flexible conductors are built up of fine wires and are available for applications where continuous movement or vibration occurs.

Insulation

PVC compounds provide the most economical choice of insulating material for all normal uses and special grades are available where ambient temperatures exceed the normal limits. For much higher temperatures, materials such as ethylene propylene rubber (EP rubber), cross-linked polyethylene (XLPE) and mineral insulation (MI) are available. Where flexibility is important, the various types of rubber can be more appropriate.

Mechanical properties are usually the most important ones for insulation of cables up to 1 kV, and loss of strength and brittleness are the best signs to look for when judging the state of a cable. This applies also to the insulation on the tails of mineral-insulated cables, but not of course to the insulation of the cable itself.

Sheaths and coverings

Cable and cord insulation have been designed and tested to provide adequate electrical strength and any additional coverings are required only in order to protect the insulation against environmental hazards.

PVC insulation is tough enough to withstand pulling into conduits without further protection.

Coverings can consist of a simple sheath of PVC or rubber which provides good protection against abrasion and liquids and modest resistance to impact. Because some hydrocarbon solvents leach out the plasticiser of PVC compounds and creosote softens and destroys them it is best to avoid routes where such contaminants are likely. Otherwise a lead sheath is generally used, but the type of metal/polymeric laminate used on cables such as the Pirelli FP 200 could be suitable. Mineral-insulated cables have a solid-drawn copper sheath and are resistant to water and oils. However it is attacked by some chemicals and a covering of PVC is advisable.

Where a cable is likely to be subject to impact, or installation conditions are difficult, a cable having steel wire or aluminium strip armour incorporated in the protective coverings should be chosen. The cable can be used without further mechanical protection but it is general practice, particularly for outdoors or below ground use, to prevent corrosion of the armour by adding a further covering of PVC.

TEMPERATURE LIMITS

Insulating materials must be used within certain temperature limits if a satisfactory performance and an adequate service life are to be obtained. Upper limits of temperature are determined by the thermal sensitivity of each material, the higher the temperature the shorter the period for which the necessary electrical and mechanical properties are retained. The values in table 18.2 are based on extensive experimental work and field experience and are recognised internationally.

Temperature limits for MI cables are the exception in table 18.2 in that they are not based on insulation performance. Their limits are related to the temperature capability of the over-sheath material, or to a maximum cable surface temperature where they are exposed to touch, or can be in contact with thermally sensitive materials. Where neither of these limitations applies the temperature at which MI cables operate is not critical except that it must not exceed the maximum value set by the end seals.

Table 18.2 Temperature limits of wiring cable materials

Insulating material	Maximum conductor temperature (°C)	
	continuous operation	short-circuits
Polyvinylchloride compounds (PVC)	70	160
60°C rubber	60	170
85°C rubber	85	220
Ethylene propylene (EP) rubber	90	250
Silicone rubber	150	250
Cross-linked polyethylene (XLPE)	90	250
Mineral insulation (MI) (see text)	70	*
Glass fibre	185	*

*
Refer to manufacturers.

CABLE RATINGS

The size of conductor used must be large enough for it to carry the
expected load current without exceeding the temperature limit appropriate to the insulating material involved. Factors affecting the
current that a cable can carry are discussed below.

Sustained current carrying capacities

The highest value of current a cable can carry continuously without
exceeding its maximum insulation temperature given in table 18.2 is
referred to as its 'current rating' and can be derived either by calculation or by experiment. This current is dependent on the rate at
which heat can be dissipated from a cable. Clearly a cable mounted by
itself on a wall can dissipate much more heat than one which is in a
bunch of cables or is enclosed in conduit. As a consequence the
rating depends on the installation conditions. UK cables are made to
internationally accepted specifications and as a consequence their
ratings are comparable with those used in other countries. Methods
for calculating ratings have now been standardised on a world-wide
basis.

Ratings are usually given in tabular form, such as those in the
IEE Regulations and those in the 69-30 series of reports issued by ERA
Technology Ltd. (The major differences between these two documents

are in the types of installations provided for and in the ambient temperatures for which ratings are tabulated. The 69-30 reports include ratings for cables in the ground.) To keep the individual tables within reasonable limits of size, ratings are given for single-circuits only (i.e. two single-core cables or one twin cable in a single-phase or d.c. circuit and three or four single-core cables or one multicore cable in a three-phase circuit). Where more than one circuit is installed close together or in the same enclosure, thus forming a group, mutual heating occurs between the cables and their rating must be reduced by multiplying by an appropriate group factor.

Ambient temperature

The rating of a cable is derived directly from the amount of heat it can liberate when it is running at its maximum operating temperature and dissipating that heat into surroundings which are at a stated ambient temperature. Given that the installation conditions are the same as those assumed for the determination of the ratings, there is no margin on the conductor temperature-rise. If anything changes to reduce the amount of heat which can be dissipated then the cable will become overheated and its expected life reduced. The most likely causes of overheating in practice are high ambient temperatures and installation of cables in groups.

Tables of cable ratings for wiring installations are generally based on an ambient temperature of 30°C. This is sufficiently high to include most general installations, so that it is possible in many cases to use the values in the tables directly without correction.

However, there are situations where the ambient temperature does exceed 30°C, such as in boiler houses, in the vicinity of industrial processes and in domestic airing cupboards. Unless there is an accepted value of ambient temperature for the particular situation, an estimate or a measurement must be made, if necessary referring to a similar type of installation. The measurement can be made using any suitable type of thermometer and appropriate instructions are given in the IEE Regulations. It is important to observe that the measurement must take into account all sources of heat, but should not be influenced by heat from the cable under consideration, that is if the cable is in place then it should not be loaded or the thermometer should be appropriately shielded.

Ambient temperature correction factors are given with tables of
cable ratings and the correct rating is obtained by multiplying the
tabulated rating by the appropriate correction factor. Where it is
known that ambient temperatures will be consistently lower than 30°C,
it is possible to take advantage of this fact and to increase a rating.
Here again appropriate factors are usually provided.

Groups of cables

Where more than one circuit or cable run together in conduit, trunking,
or on the surface the mutual heating between them reduces their current
carrying capacities. For most arrangements of cables in general use
factors are issued with the rating tables whereby the maximum current
carrying capacity of cables in groups can be calculated.

Because they have to deal with the subject in a general way, these
factors must be derived on the assumption that all the cables in a
group are of the same size and are equally loaded. This situation
does not often arise in practice, but it is usually assumed that the
application of such factors to a practical group of mixed sizes of
cables would be on the safe side. This is not necessarily so, and
situations can arise where it results in the smaller cables being
overloaded and the larger ones being under utilised. Continuing
investigation has made it possible to give much more attention to the
performance of specific grouping arrangements and rating factors for
groups on racks, ladder supports and trays can be obtained from
information given in suitable sources such as ERA Technology reports
in the 69-30 series and reports 74-27,28 and 29.

A point worth making here is that, except for MI cable, a wiring
cable which is continuously loaded to even 10% more than its maximum
value has its expectation of life reduced by about 50%. Where a large
number of simultaneously loaded cables must be accommodated it can be
preferable to split them into several small groups so as to avoid the
economic penalties of the low ratings required for large groups.

Overcurrent protection and selection of cable size

One of the functions of circuit protection is to prevent currents
greater than the rating of a cable flowing for a duration long enough
to cause damage. There are two types of such overcurrents; those

which arise in a healthy circuit because of an excessive load and those resulting from a faulty condition such as a short-circuit.

Overloads. A properly designed circuit will be capable of safely carrying the highest expected load. In general, however, there will be a small unquantifiable risk that, under exceptional and unpredictable circumstances, the design load could be exceeded. It is a general requirement, therefore, that all circuits (apart from a few exceptions noted in the IEE Regulations) must have overload protection, chosen so that an excess current cannot persist long enough to cause damage.

As a result of considerable experimental work and field experience it has been concluded that a PVC-insulated cable can safely withstand overload currents up to 1.45 times its continuous rating. However, it is essential to realise that such currents can only be tolerated if they occur for a strictly limited duration and only very occasionally, say not more often than a few times during the life of the installation. If it is expected that such currents might persist more frequently then the circuit should be designed accordingly. Most other cable materials can withstand this treatment, so the rule limiting overload to not more than 1.45 times the cable rating has been adopted generally for all wiring.

Selection of an appropriate combination of protective device and cable is illustrated in fig. 18.1. Having estimated the maximum sustained load (design value) I_B, a circuit protection device is chosen which has a rating of I_n, equal to or greater than I_B. A cable size is then chosen so that its rating, corrected for ambient temperature and for grouping, I_z is equal to or greater than I_B, and furthermore 1.45 times I_z is equal to or greater than the long duration operating current of the device, I_2. The cable will then be capable of carrying the design load safely and can also withstand infrequent overloads which will not be cut off by the protective device. This selection process is a requirement of Clause 433 of the IEE Regulations.

Recognising the need for devices which can provide suitable overload protection, fuses to BS 88 or to BS 1361 and circuit-breakers to BS 3871: Part 1 or to BS 4752: Part 1 are made with characteristics such that under practical installation conditions their long duration

272

operating currents are not greater than 1.45 times their rating I_n.
This greatly simplifies the process of selection since it is then only
necessary to follow the simple rule given in the IEE Regulations, that:

$$I_B \leqslant I_n \leqslant I_z$$

A.

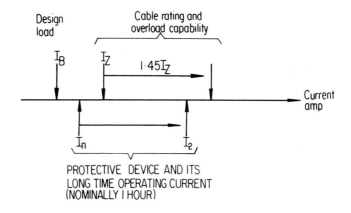

B.

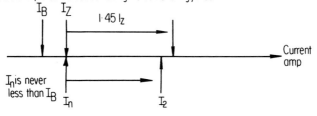

C.

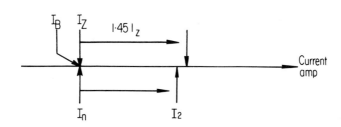

*Figure 18.1   Overload protection. (A) General situation; (B) Situation
possible with certain protective devices; (C) The load I_B
can be as high as I_n and I_z*

273

In the case of semi-enclosed fuses to BS 3036 the long duration operating current, I_2, is equal to $2I_n$. It is therefore necessary to match the cable with a fuse having a rating such that $2I_n < 1.45I_z$, or $I_n < 0.725I_z$.

Since $I_B < I_n$, the above requirement effectively limits the circuit to 72½% of the full thermal rating of the cable. It is convenient, when semi-enclosed fuses are frequently installed, to tabulate these reduced ratings, I_z (as was done in the 14th Edition of the IEE Wiring Regulations for 'coarse protection') so that a direct comparison can be made with values of load current and fuse ratings. If this is done, then the simple relationship $I_B < I_n < I_z$ holds once more.

Short-circuit.   Cables are able to withstand quite high conductor temperatures providing they are of very short duration, and only occur very infrequently. The short-circuit conductor temperatures given in table 18.2, which are based on both experimental evidence and field experience, can be used to determine the combinations of current and time which a cable can carry without a significant reduction in operating life or in insulating capability, see fig. 18.2. (Actually a quantity (I^2t) is used which is proportional to the energy liberated during the fault and hence to the conductor temperature-rise.) A similar relationship can be drawn for the capability of protective conductors to carry earth-fault currents, see fig. 18.3, based on the maximum temperatures that cable insulation or covering materials can tolerate.

Figures 18.2 and 18.3 can be used to check that a conductor has been correctly chosen to meet the requirements of the IEE Regulations for short-circuit and earth-fault protection. Having chosen the size of conductor and calculated the expected value of fault current from the circuit impedance, reference to the characteristic of the protective device gives the expected duration, t sec, of the current. Entry of this duration into figs 18.2 and 18.3 as appropriate gives a maximum current density which, when multiplied by the conductor cross section in square millimetres, should give a permissible current greater than or equal to the expected fault current. If it yields a lower value then a larger conductor must be chosen.

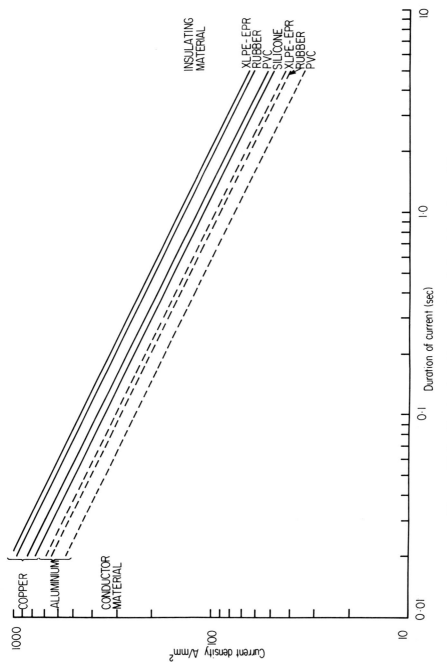

Figure 18.2 Short-circuit current and duration for cables

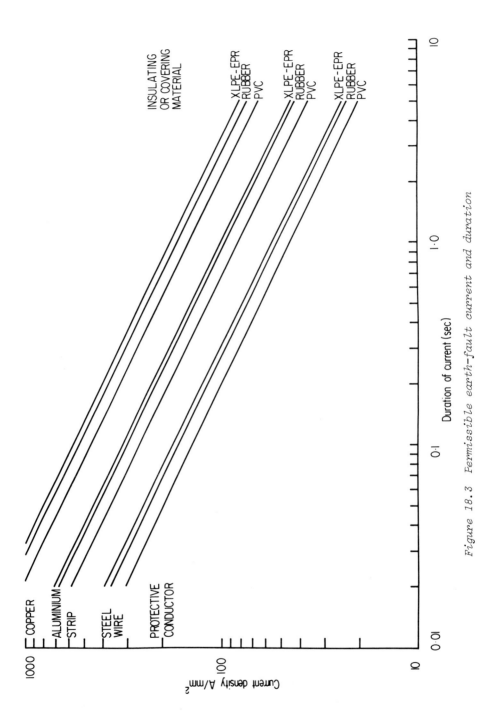

Figure 18.3 Permissible earth-fault current and duration

These figures assume that the cable is installed so that there is no significant crushing pressure on the insulation such as may arise under fixings or over the edges of objects.

Voltage drop

The energy loss involved in distributing electrical power takes the form of a reduction in voltage at the receiving end of each cable run. This reduction is dependent on the impedance of the cable, values of which are given in millivolt/amp/metre (i.e. milli-ohms/metre) in the IEE Regulations or can be calculated. For cable sizes up to about 50 mm^2 the impedance is practically equal to the d.c. resistance of the conductors, but above this size, especially with single-core cables the inductance becomes increasingly important and at the largest sizes is the dominant component. Since the inductance decreases only logarithmically with conductor diameter, it becomes more and more difficult at these large sizes to reduce the voltage drop by increasing the size of conductor and splitting the circuit into two or more independent parallel limbs may be necessary. Circuit inductance increases as conductors are separated so that from the point of view of voltage drop it is best to keep single-core cables as close together as possible.

Although it is general practice to use tabulated values of voltage drop directly without any adjustment, they are in reality vectorial values and in a.c. circuits neglecting the effect of their phase angles amounts to taking the worst case. Actual circuits may have a lower voltage drop than is given by such a simple approach. The effective voltage drop depends on both the power factor of the load and the phase angle of the cable impedance. For large sizes of cable, especially single-core cables, the actual voltage drop for loads with power factors of 0.9 or better can be much less than the tabulated value, and a calculation using the resistance and reactance of the cable could be worthwhile. Similarly, for loads with very low power factors the voltage drop in small cables may be much less than expected.

If materials which either surround or are close to cables (e.g. conduits, trunking, trays, structural items) are magnetic the effect on current ratings is small but the voltage drop can be increased.

Unfortunately the general situation is too complicated to deal with in a simple manner since it is critically dependent on the disposition of the cables in relation to the steel. However, variation in cable disposition in conduits is limited and it is possible to tabulate values of voltage drop figures in rating tables for 'enclosed cables' which are based on experimental data. The impedance of multicore cables and of single-core cables up to and including 25 mm^2 is not affected to any practical extent when they are run in contact with steel.

Where single-core cables are used to feed large discharge lamp loads the neutral conductor carries a considerable third harmonic current which results in a significant voltage drop unless the neutral conductor is laid close to the phase conductors. The loaded neutral must then be taken into account when considering the effect of grouping on the rating of the cables.

CABLE SELECTION

Cable selection is based on a considerable number of factors including regulations in force in the locality concerned, the environment and other matters discussed below.

General

Appendix 10 of the IEE Regulations provides 'Notes on the selection of type of cable and flexible cords for particular uses and environmental influences' and this section is intended to amplify those notes.

The selection of a cable, as of any other part of an electrical installation, must be made on economic grounds. This is not to say that the cable with the cheapest installation cost should always be chosen; it is, however, as bad engineering to select cable the performance of which is in excess of requirements, as it is to select a cable which is inadequate for its task.

The factors to be taken into account in the selection process are environmental conditions, installed costs and circuit design considerations. The placing of these factors in the above order is done advisedly because there is nothing to be gained by choosing a cable which is not capable of withstanding the environmental conditions in which it is to operate.

The relative installed costs of various cables must be known and

278

the cheapest (bearing in mind the environment), chosen. It must then be examined to see whether it is capable of complying with the circuit design parameters imposed by disconnecting times, thermal constraints and voltage drop.

Statutory regulations

Certain statutory regulations limit the range of cables from which the choice may be made, without removing the necessity for taking into account other factors, such as environmental conditions, which may pertain. Such regulations in the UK include the Factories Act, Electricity Special Regulations, 1908 and 1944, which require that all cables operating at a voltage exceeding low voltage (as defined) shall be entirely surrounded by earthed metal, or otherwise so protected as to avoid danger. (This is not the same value as that used in the L.V. Directive which is 1000 V a.c. and 1500 V d.c.) The Quarry Regulations prohibit the use of any cable, the sheath or armour of which does not have at least half the conductivity of the cores. The Cinematograph Regulations insist on the use of conduit in projection rooms.

Environmental conditions

The relationship of the various environmental influences on the selection of cables and cords is given below.

Aesthetics. The aesthetic considerations governing the selection of cables are not really environmental conditions nor are they considered in the IEE Regulations unless it is under the heading of 'Workmanship'. Nevertheless, they are sometimes very important in the choice of a suitable cable, particularly in domestic and some commercial install- ations such as restaurants.

It is obvious that a flush system, i.e. one in which the cables are hidden beneath the plaster or within partitions, presents no difficulty; in situations where additions are to be made and decorat- ions or wall finishes are not to be renewed, the problem is more acute. The choice falls on a cable which is small in diameter (for its current carrying capacity) and which will dress well, i.e. is sufficiently easily bent to be accommodated, where necessary, to curves, etc.

and yet which is stiff enough not to sag between clips. In these
cases MI cable or Pirelli FP 200 or PX are likely choices, with PVCPVC
as a possibility. However, the advantage to be gained from the small
diameter of MI cables may be offset where brass terminations have to
be used.

Temperature.   All cables are suitable for the normal range of
temperatures, i.e. the IEC Classification AA5; it is the extremes of
temperature which cause problems. PVC and to a lesser extent rubber,
becomes brittle at low temperatures and there is a risk of cracking
or shattering. The problem is less serious when no movement is
involved and specially formulated PVCs are available where the additional cost is considered worthwhile. PVC cables should not be
installed in cold conditions; even a shock (such as may be caused by
rough handling of a drum of cable) at low temperatures has been known
to cause damage. It is best to store cables at temperatures above 0°C
for at least 24 hours prior to handling. It can be some time before
heat penetrates thoroughly into the insulation, so that while a cable
may appear externally to have survived handling when cold, it could be
damaged internally. As far as flexibles are concerned, insulation and
sheathing of rubber retain their flexibility to lower temperatures
than those of PVC compounds.

Higher temperatures present different problems; the derating
applicable to all cables when operating at high temperatures is prohibitive, although, when their seals are outside the hot zone, MI
cables can operate at very elevated temperatures. Table 18.1 gives an
indication of suitable cables for higher temperatures; for extreme
temperatures where flexing is minimal, such as in luminaires, glass
fibre insulation is suitable.

Fire, as an environmental condition is not considered by the IEE
Regulations. However, circuits which are required to continue operating during a fire must rely on either MI cable which will continue
to operate up to the melting point of the copper (this does not apply
to the termination) or on Pirelli FP 200. The latter is destroyed by
fire but the insulation is reduced to silica which still provides a
degree of insulation, allowing the circuit to continue operating.

Presence of water.   All rubber and PVC sheathed cables are reasonably
resistant to the presence of water and it is their terminations which
require protection. However, if continued operation in wet conditions
is envisaged, it is necessary to use either unsheathed cables in a
watertight enclosure or MI cable with a PVC oversheath or PVCSWAPVC
cables. Cables with an aluminium content, such as copperclad, or
Pirelli FP 200 or PX are not suitable.

Presence of foreign solid bodies.   Dust and foreign bodies, unless
presenting hazards of corrosion or mechanical damage, do not affect
the choice of a cable.

Presence of corrosive or polluting substances.   There are substances
which have a deleterious effect on steel, aluminium, copper, PVC and
rubber, all of which are used in cable construction. The choice of a
cable must depend upon the nature of the corrosive substance. Water
as a corrosive substance, is resisted by paints or galvanising,
provided that these are continuous and not liable to damage. For more
actively corrosive agents, galvanising may not be adequate and either
black enamel conduit with protective grease tapes, or PVC may be
necessary to provide protection.

The copper sheath of MI cables in damp and mildly corrosive
situations will form a patina and corrosion will not proceed beyond
that point, unless the patina is removed. However, the effect is to
reduce the thickness of the copper sheath and so, if the sheath is
relied upon as a protective conductor the design calculations may be
invalidated.

Besides the more obvious sources of corrosive chemicals in cements
and plastics, care should be taken in the selection of cables to be
fixed to oak and similar woods, some kinds of stone if damp, and to
metals which are dissimilar to the sheath.

Mechanical stresses.

Impact.   Cables should be installed to minimise the possibility of
impact but this is not always possible and so an assessment of the
likelihood of impact must be made. In domestic and office installations, all cables and cable systems provide adequate resistance to

impact, but at points of particular likelihood of damage (at skirting boards for instance) further protection should be provided for PVCPVC cables.

Although MI cables can be shown to continue to operate satisfactorily when hammered flat this characteristic should not be relied upon where damage of this nature is thought likely to occur.

PVCSWAPVC cables provide an adequate degree of protection for most industrial applications, but do not have the same degree of resistance to impact as steel conduit. PVC cables in steel conduit provide a system which is most resistant to impact; any impact of such severity as to damage cables in conduit is likely to destroy the conduit system.

Flexible cables and cords have a very limited resistance to impact and should be so installed as to render impact unlikely; where such a possibility remains, flexible cables and cords with metallic braids are available.

Vibration.   Vibration of the fixed installation of a building is unlikely except at final connections to motors or other equipment. While conduit cables themselves are reasonably resistant to vibration, particularly if stranded, steel conduit is not and is likely to fracture, particularly at box spouts. Patent flexible or semi-flexible conduit systems or PVC conduit do not suffer from this defect.

Copper work-hardens and fractures under vibration; to guard against slight vibration a loop of cable adjacent to the equipment will be adequate but for installations where continuous vibration is experienced, such as gravel processing or asphalt plant, PVCSWAPVC cables are to be preferred. All flexibles except glass fibre types are resistant to vibration.

Animal damage.   Animals, in relation to electrical installations fall into two classes, those which are intended to be present and those which it is feared may be present. The first class occur in agricultural installations and the IEE Regulations (523-34) state categorically that all fixed wiring systems shall be inaccessible to livestock.

The second category, of which rats and mice are the most usual, is vermin. Insects are not known to attack cables in the UK, but may be a problem elsewhere.

Rats have been known to chew lead, copper, PVC and even to attack wire armouring; to be absolutely certain of resisting attack, steel conduit or PVCSWAPVC cables should be selected. It must be said however that there is little or no evidence that rats or mice attack PVC conduit or trunking. This may be because of the different grades of PVC used for conduit and trunking as opposed to that used for cable sheaths.

Solar radiation.   The ultraviolet component of solar radiation can have deleterious effects on PVC. Where cables are to be exposed to sunshine, a metallic sheathed cable, cables in steel conduit or cables with a black PVC oversheath should be used. The reduction in current rating due to the heating effect of solar radiation can be significant.

Utilisation.   Appendix 6 of the IEE Regulations includes utilisation as a class of external influence and lists a number of categories which may influence the choice of cable.

Capability of persons.   This would not seem at first glance to affect the choice of cable, but if extended to the action of persons, part-icularly of children, there is the problem of deliberate damage. No system can totally resist deliberate attack, but in places where it is envisaged that such attack may take place and where a surface install-ation is concerned, there is not doubt that the most resistant system is steel conduit and that PVCPVC sheathed cables are the most vulner-able. MI cables and certain special cables such as Simplex MP (ANTS Certificate No. 79/8) have an increased resistance. The use of flexible cords should be avoided wherever possible. (Note - ANTS, Approval of New Techniques Scheme covers new techniques not envisaged in the IEE Regulations.)   The system is now discontinued.

Contact of persons with earth potential.   All metallic sheathed cables propagate potentials whether earth or higher. The IEE Regulations seek to limit these potentials, particularly by equipoten-tial bonding; in certain situations of high risk, such as bathrooms, extra supplementary bonding is required of all exposed conductive parts and extraneous conductive parts. Since the exposed conductive parts of an installation are primarily sources of raised potentials it seems sensible in bathrooms and similar situations to use either PVC conduit or PVC sheathed cables. PVC sheathed MI and PVCSWAPVC cables require metallic terminating glands, although these can and should be either shrouded or contained within a non-conducting enclosure.

Conditions of evacuation. The only consideration likely to affect the choice of a cable has been dealt with under 'Fire'.

Nature of processed or stored materials. Fire risks arising from the installation of cables in areas where potentially flammable dusts, etc. accumulate arise because either the cable is rated to run with a dangerous surface temperature or because the surface temperature exceeds its rated value due to the insulating qualities of the dust; a combination of these effects is possible and dangerous. Cable selection, as opposed to installation is not affected; MI cables should be rated at 'exposed to touch' values.

Where cables are touching each other, such as when they are clipped to trays, it is advisable to reduce the tendency for dust to collect by mounting the tray on edge, rather than in the horizontal position. Where flammable dust is expected to accumulate the user should be advised to remove such dust at regular intervals.

Explosion risks are dealt with elsewhere than the IEE Regulations; cables suitable for hazardous atmospheres are: cables in suitable metallic conduit systems; MI cables with suitable glands; and PVCSWAPVC cables with suitable glands.

The selection and installation of cable systems in potentially explosive atmospheres are described in BS Code of Practice 5345.

Commercial considerations
Consideration of the environmental influences to which the installation, or any part of the installation may be exposed, may reduce the range of choice of suitable cables, but rarely does it eliminate choice entirely. From the remaining possible cables it is the duty of the designer to select the most economical type. Table 18.3 gives the relative costs per metre installed of various types of cable for a 5 m run of a single-phase 16 A circuit, protected by hbc fuses and run at

normal working height on plaster, in a normal 25°C ambient. It
includes the cost of necessary terminations.

*Table 18.3 Relative cost of 5 m of cable to carry a 16 A single-phase
load, including terminations where necessary*

Type of cable	Relative cost	Notes
1.5 mm^2 PVC twin + CPC*	1	Nailed clips
2 × 1.5 mm^2 singles in steel conduit	8.2	
2 × 2.5 mm^2 singles in steel conduit with two other circuits	3.0	
2 × 1.5 mm^2 singles + 1 mm CPC in PVC conduit	6.5	
Two-core 1 mm^2 light duty MI	5.2	Sheath used as CPC, screw on seals
One pair in a seven-core 2.5 mm^2 heavy duty MI	3.2	Sheath used as CPC, screw on seals
Two-core 1 mm^2 light duty MI/PVC	5.5	Sheath used as CPC, screw on seals
One pair in a seven-core 2.5 mm^2 heavy duty MI/PVC	4.3	Sheath used as CPC, screw on seals
Two-core 1.5 mm^2 PVCSWAPVC	6.8	
Three-core 1.5 mm^2 Pirelli PX	3.1	
Three-core 1.5 mm^2 Pirelli FP 200	3.7	

*CPC = Circuit Protective Conductor.

To arrive at the figures in this table the labour content was
based on published data and the material at trade prices. The labour
cost for Pirelli cables was based on MI costs.

Table 18.3 is not, nor is it intended to be, definitive. It seems
to indicate that for an installation in which the environmental
influences are not severe, the aesthetic considerations low (i.e. the
cable is concealed) and the customer is not prepared to pay for a long
life or rewireability, PVCPVC cables are the only choice, hence the
widespread use in domestic and small offices. It indicates that a
single circuit of cable in steel conduit is marginally more expensive
than a two-core PVCSWAPVC. It also indicates that two circuits of
cable in steel conduit are cheaper than two PVCSWAPVC cables.

The table takes no account of the ability of conduit (and trunking) to span wider gaps than any other system, and its ability (in certain circumstances) to support luminaires. Nor does it take account of the neatness of MI cables or Pirelli cables, of the relatively shallow chases needed (if at all) for MI cable, and of its long life. It does not take account of the ability of PVCSWAPVC to stand a certain amount of vibration and movement. Neither does it take into account the third factor affecting the selection of cable, namely thermal considerations.

Thermal considerations

The choice of a cable to carry a given current is determined from the tables in Appendix 9 of the IEE Regulations applying where necessary the relevant correction factors for grouping and ambient temperature and the presence of thermal insulation. It should be noted that these factors are cumulative only where more than one condition calling for a factor is present; so that if a cable is grouped in one place, is in a high ambient in another and in thermal insulation at yet another, each factor is applied once and the cable is selected to meet the worst condition. For large cables jointing of different sizes of cable may be worthwhile; the cost of jointing must be assessed against savings in cable and installation costs.

A cable protected against overload is also protected against short-circuit, but the size of the protective conductor incorporated in a cable may not be adequate to withstand the thermal effect of the current flowing through it at the time of a fault.

Of the wiring systems under consideration the following form the protective conductors:

PVCPVC cable	Copper protective conductor incorporated
PVC cables in metal conduit	Conduit
PVC cables in PVC conduit	Separate conductor drawn in (size to suit)
MI cable	Sheath
PVCSWAPVC cable	Armouring
Pirelli FP 200 PX cable	Copper protective conductor incorporated
Simplex cable	Copper protective conductor incorporated
Flexible cables and cords	Copper protective conductor incorporated

Tables 18.4A and B indicate that in the range of cable sizes considered, the protective conductor incorporated in a cable, be it a
separate copper conductor, cable sheath or armouring, has a cross-
sectional area which is adequate for the energy let-through demands of
semi-enclosed fuses to BS 3036 which will also protect the circuit
conductors against overload.

Table 18.4A   Cross-sectional area of protective conductor protected
by a BS 88 fuse

Fuse rating (A)	Type of protective conductor*	
	PVC insulated single-core (mm^2)	Protective conductor in PVC two-core + earth cable (mm^2)
5 second disconnecting time		
6	1	1
10	1	1
16	1	1.5
20	1.5	2.5
25	2.5	2.5
32	2.5	2.5
40	4	4
50	4	6
63	6	6
0.4 second disconnecting time		
6	1	1
10	1	1
16	1	1
20	1	1
25	1	1
32	1	1.5
40	1.5	1.5
50	2.5	2.5
63	2.5	4

*The armour of PVCSWAPVC cables and the sheath of heavy duty MI cables
for the above circuits are adequate as protective conductors.

Table 18.4B   Cross-sectional area of protective conductor protected by BS 3036 (semi-enclosed) fuses

Fuse rating (A)	Type of protective conductor[*]	
	PVC insulated single-core (mm^2)	Protective conductor in PVC two-core + earth cable (mm^2)
5 second disconnecting time		
5	1	1
15	1	1
20	1	1.5
30	1.5	2.5
45	2.5	2.5
60	4	4
100	10	10
0.4 second disconnecting time		
5	1	1
15	1	1
20	1	1
30	1	1.5
45	1.5	2.5
60	2.5	4
100	4	6

[*] The armour of PVCSWAPVC cables and the sheath of heavy duty MI cables for the above circuits are adequate as protective conductors.

BS 88 fuses may at first sight appear to marginally fail to protect the protective conductors of PVC twin and earth cables; before rejecting this combination of fuse and cable the actual disconnecting time should be calculated. The circuit impedance is often limited by voltage drop, and a small reduction in impedance could reduce the disconnecting time to a value which enables a BS 88 fuse to protect such protective conductors.

With all fuses, shorter disconnecting times give lower I^2t let-through; in the case of Type 1 and Type 2 mcbs to BS 3871 whose characteristics are given in the IEE Regulations, this is not so; in the case of Type 1 and Type 2 there is no 5 s disconnecting time, the 'knee' in the characteristic occurring at 20 and 7 s respectively. Thereafter the tripping time is anything between the 'knee' time and 0.1 s, so tables similar to those above cannot be prepared and the manufacturers should be consulted concerning the I^2t let-through of their devices.

Steel conduit has an adequate cross-sectional area for the size of fuse which will protect the cables drawn into it; where a separate conductor is drawn in it can be selected accordingly.

Attention is drawn to the minimum sizes required by IEE Regulation 543-1 for protective conductors not enclosed in a wiring system and by Regulation 542-16 for buried earthing conductors.

Voltage drop

After current carrying capacity and cross-sectional area of an incorporated circuit protective conductor the next most limiting characteristic of a cable is the voltage drop, information on which is provided in the regulations in the form of millivolt drop per ampere per metre.

The correct way to select a cable in relation to voltage drop is shown by the following example:

Load current 20 A; circuit length 16 m.
Permitted voltage drop, 2½% of 240 V = 6000 mV.

Maximum mV/amp/metre is: 6000/20 × 16 = 18.75 mV/A/m

The cables listed in table 18.5 would therefore be suitable from the voltage drop point of view.

It is clear that the apparent advantage of the higher current carrying capacities of certain cables is lost under voltage drop considerations. However, voltage drop is not subject to grouping or ambient temperature correction factors and for groups of cables the advantages of higher temperature cables once more become apparent.

Table 18.6 shows the maximum lengths of certain different cables which will give a 2½% voltage drop on a 240 V system with a 20 A load, single-phase, selected on their current carrying capacities. Similar tables can be prepared from the IEE Regulations for other types of load.

It can be seen that voltage drop is in many cases more limiting than current rating and that advantages gained in current rating are lost in voltage drop penalties.

Table 18.5 Voltage drop for different cables

Cable	Size (mm^2)	Voltage drop (mV/A/m)	Current carrying capacity (A)
Single-core PVC	2.5	17	24
PVC two-core and earth	2.5	17	24
PVCSWAPVC two-core	2.5	18	29
Single-core 85°C rubber	4	12	37
Light duty MI twin	2.5	17	29
Pirelli FP 200	2.5	17	29

Notes:
(1) Judged by current carrying capacity only, 1.5 mm^2 PVCSWAPVC or 2.5 mm^2 85°C rubber singles or 1 mm^2 two-core MI would be adequate.

(2) In marginal cases the running of an oversized cable below its rated operated temperature might reduce the voltage drop slightly, allowing a smaller cable to be used than indicated by the above type of calculation. In sub-circuits the relationship between the calculated to the installed length of cable is not usually that accurate.

Table 18.6 Maximum lengths of circuit

Cable	Size (mm^2)	Voltage drop (mV/A/m)	Length in metres for 2½%
PVC single	2.5	17	17.6
PVC two-core and earth	2.5	17	17.6
PVCSWAPVC	1.5	29	10.3
85°C rubber singles	2.5	19	15.8
Light duty MI bare not exposed to touch	1	45	6.7
Pirelli FP 200	1	45	6.7

Earth-loop impedance

For any voltage to earth, fuse and disconnecting time, there is a maximum earth-loop impedance. Some of that impedance is external to the circuit or installation concerned; a typical value for a TN-C-S (PME) service from the public supply network is 0.35 ohm. For a circuit at 240 V to earth a 20 A Type 3 mcb requires a current of 200 A to disconnect either socket-outlet or fixed apparatus circuits so that the maximum earth-loop impedance cannot exceed 1.2 ohms. If the external impedance is 0.35 ohm then the total impedance of the phase and protective conductors in the circuit must not exceed 0.85 ohm. Table 18.7 shows the length of various types of cable to give a phase and circuit protective conductor resistance of 0.85 ohm (assuming a circuit load of 20 A). It is based on the resistance of conductors at 160 °C which is the temperature of the conductor of these cables when the fault is disconnected. Similar tables can be prepared for other cable sizes.

Table 18.7 Lengths of circuit to give a total impedance of 0.85 ohm

Cable	Size (mm^2)	Line + protective conductor (ohm/m)	Length for 0.85 ohm (m)
PVC single, equal circuit and protective conductor	2.5	0.022	39
PVC two-core and earth	2.5	0.030	28
PVCSWAPVC two-core[*]	1.5	0.023	37
85 °C rubber singles	2.5	0.022	39
Light duty MI[†]	1.5	0.014	71
Pirelli FP 200	2.5	0.022	39

[*] Based on BS 6346
[†] Based on BS 6207

INSTALLATION METHODS

Guidance is given in the IEE Regulations on methods of installation including spacing of supports for conduit and trunking and current carrying capacities of cables housed in them.

Conduit and trunking capacities

The cable capacity of conduit is dependent not only on the percentage cross section of the conduit which is occupied by the cables, but on the number of cables which can be pulled in without excessive force.

The length between draw boxes and the number of bends also affects the drawing-in tension required. Excessive force damages the insulation, or in extreme cases stretches the cable and so reduce its cross-sectional area. Hence the IEE Regulations provide two sets of cable and conduit factors, one for short straight runs (less than 3 m) and one for long runs or runs incorporating bends; the total of the cable factors must be less than the conduit factor.

For instance, 20 mm conduit, with a factor of 460 for short straight runs, can accommodate 16×1.5 mm^2 PVC single cables. However, eight circuits must be derated by a group factor to 0.51 times their full rated current, so that 6 mm^2 cables are required to carry 20 A. These need 25 mm conduit. This is still more economical than the alternative of 2.5 mm^2 cables in three separate 20 mm diameter conduits. If a 3 m run with two bends of 20 mm conduit is used, only ten 1.5 mm^2 cables can be accommodated.

There are therefore major economic advantages in maintaining straight runs and in keeping between 3 m distances between draw boxes. This usually can only be a site decision and most drawings do not provide sufficient detail to be certain of the bends or sets required. Factors for trunking installations are also provided and the cable factors are different from those for use with conduit because no pulling in is required. The factors should be strictly adhered to even though it is possible to force a greater number of cables into trunking than the factors allow but at the cost of pressure on the cables. Although the IEE Regulations allow a 45% space factor, care should be taken during installation to ensure that the cables do not press excessively on the trunking, particularly at bends.

Cable supports

Unsheathed plastics and rubber cables need to be enclosed in conduit or trunking. Plastics or metal sheathed cables may be supported on clips or saddles. The spacing of supports for conduit and trunking is based upon the loads and spans that can be supported without undue sag. The requirement for supports within 300 mm of bends acknowledges the additional stresses imposed by thermal expansion. Closer spacing of supports is called for where the installation may be expected to receive mechanical shocks. Fixings may be by way of screws through

the back of boxes. Cables in vertical conduits and trunking must be
supported at intervals to prevent undue pressure on the insulation at
the top.

The internal edges in trunking at bends, etc., must be well
rounded and the use of site constructed adaptations in place of BS
fittings should be avoided unless care is exercised to avoid sharp
edges. The top of vertical runs exceeding 5 m length should be fitted
with a BS bend and not with an elbow or with a box. One of the most
frequent causes of high mechanical pressure on wiring cable is the
treatment it receives when pushed back into a box behind an accessory.
All incoming holes in the box must be properly bushed and good workmanship exercised to arrange the cables as smoothly as possible.

Sheathed cables may be fixed directly to a surface or to tray or
ladder supports. Spacings given in the IEE Regulations are those
which will not impose undue stresses on the cables at the point of
support. Pressure may arise when supporting the weight of a vertical
run of cable; clamps should be distributed uniformly and sharp bends
at the top of the run must be avoided. In order to get satisfactory
dressing of cables, closer fixing centres may be required.

Fixing clips may be metal or plastics; when fixing MI cables,
caution should be exercised if the cables are rated 'not exposed to
touch' as their temperature may be sufficient to distort the clip.

Terminations

Insulation should be stripped back only just far enough to permit
complete insertion of the conductor into an appropriate terminal.
Care must be exercised not to nick or damage the conductor and proper
wire strippers are desirable, sharp knives are not recommended. If a
knife is used then a glancing action, as though sharpening a pencil,
is best.

Where cables enter into terminating boxes or equipment the sheath
is taken through into the box and is stripped off inside. If the box
or cover is made of metal the sheath must be protected from sharp
edges by the use of a grommet, and for surface work or where foreign
substances might enter the box the cable should be mechanically
anchored and the entrance hole properly filled by using a suitably
shaped gland which grips the cable.

If the cable is armoured, the gland must be of a type which provides adequate mechanical anchorage for the wires or strips. Since the armour is often used as a protective conductor the gland must also provide good electrical contact and in turn be reliably connected to the enclosure or other earthed metal work. On installations out of doors or in wet environments the whole gland should be protected against corrosion by a watertight covering which goes well back over the outer sheath.

The ends of MI cables must be completely sealed against the entry of moisture. This is effected by screwing a small brass pot onto the end of the sheath and filling it with a special non-setting water-resistant compound, as shown in fig. 18.4 or by using heat-shrink seals, see BS 6081 and the ANTS Certificate No. 81/1. The conductors, where they emerge from the seal, are covered with insulating sleeving. The materials used for the seal and the sleeving must be selected to suit the expected working temperature of the cable.

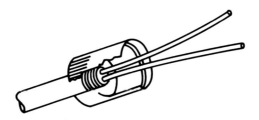

Figure 18.4 MI cable termination (courtesy BICC)

Where MI cable enters terminal boxes and equipment it should be anchored by the use of a gland, which also provides electrical continuity for the copper sheath and, if required, water tightness. Here again it is often appropriate to cover the entire gland with a heat-shrink sleeve which goes well down over the outer PVC covering of the cable.

Terminating the sheath of MI cables calls for the same care to ensure adequate electrical continuity as with the armour of other cables, since both are generally used as protective conductors and must carry the earth-fault current of the circuit. Single-core MI cables involve a further consideration in that a small voltage is induced in them during normal operation which can be much higher during a short-circuit. It is normal practice to avoid danger from these voltages by bonding all the sheaths of each circuit together at each end and earthing them. As a result current circulates continually around the sheath even during normal operation. Providing care has been taken to ensure that bonding connections are sound and adequately robust no harm can arise.

The individual cables or conductors of single-core cables must not be separated by magnetic material; all the glands belonging to each circuit should be mounted on a non-magnetic plate (or an air gap must be formed in the plate) and glands should not be mounted on steel extensions formed by steel sockets or couplers, etc.

Problems

Properly selected and installed cables have few problems but the most common are low insulation resistance and breakdown under overvoltage.

Low insulation resistance in MI cables is usually due to defective seals at terminations and can only be cured by driving the moisture out of the cable with heat and re-sealing. Low insulation resistance can occur because of surface tracking over the insulation at termin-ations due to damp or dust or in the case of braided cables to the trapping of the braid in the connection. This can also affect PVC and rubber-insulated cables and is cured by cleaning the cables. Low resistance also appears to be caused by excessive pressure of PVC cables on earthed metal and is cured by relieving the pressure.

Any cable will break down under overvoltage if the voltage is sufficiently high. In this respect transient voltages in l.v. networks can be as high as 4 kV. This can be withstood by most types of cable, but MI cable can be adversely affected, particularly at sharp bends. Such overvoltages either occur by design (such as lamp ignitor circuits) or result from the rapid collapse of magnetic fields such as those in control equipment coils or fluorescent lighting chokes when the coil circuit is interrupted. This situation is often made worse by chattering contacts.

In the case of ignitor circuits, MI cables should not be used; to do so is wrongly selecting the cable.

In the case of surges from equipment, the first action should be to ensure that there are no intermittent contacts and secondly, to fit surge diverters, available from the manufacturers, either across the terminals of the offending equipment or across the terminals to which the cable is connected. It is often only one length of cable in an installation which is affected.

Chapter 19

Protective Systems

Bryan Dakers, BSc, CEng, MIEE
Denis Robertson, CEng, MIEE
N.E.I. Electronics Ltd, Reyrolle Protection

The term 'Protective systems' refers to the electrical protection of
plant associated with industrial systems and power systems such as
alternators, motors, transformers and cables. Although this chapter
is predominantly concerned with protective systems applicable to
industrial systems and distribution systems up to 11 kV the basic
principles and requirements apply equally to power systems operating
at higher voltages.

A power system is designed to deliver electrical energy without
interruption to the points where it is utilised. By definition,
therefore, a fundamental requirement in the design of a system is
flexibility. If one part of the system becomes faulty it should be
disconnected quickly and ideally without affecting other parts of the
system. Switchgear and protective gear provide this isolation flexibility and thus can be considered in the context of an insurance
against loss of supply. The switchgear must be designed to be capable
of interrupting the current resulting from a fault while the protective
gear must be capable of recognising a fault condition and initiating
the switchgear to disconnect the faulty part of the power system with
minimum disturbance to the rest of the system.

PROTECTIVE SYSTEM REQUIREMENTS
Protective gear is the collective name given to all the components
necessary for recognising, locating and initiating the removal of a
faulty part of the power system. The most important qualities of a
protection scheme are reliability and selectivity, with other important
quantities being speed, stability and sensitivity, none of which

however, is acceptable unless they are provided in such a way that reliability and selectivity are maintained, and the equipment is within reasonable cost.

Although total reliability is impossible, duplicate schemes, alarm supervision circuits and regular maintenance, have resulted in the number of incorrectly cleared faults being less than 5%.

Selectivity, or discrimination as it is more commonly known, may be defined as the quality of a protective system whereby it detects and responds to a fault condition so that only the faulty part of the circuit is disconnected. To improve overall reliability, protective schemes are arranged with back-up and overlapping zones. Because of this, selectivity is of the utmost importance to ensure that only the correct 'zone' is disconnected.

To avoid unnecessary damage to plant, protection must operate quickly, thus, speed of recognition and disconnection of a fault are very important. This is becoming more important with the increased size of plant and the resultant increase in fault current where wide-spread damage to plant can occur much more quickly.

Stability may be defined as the quality of the protective system whereby it remains unaffected by all power system conditions, faulty or otherwise, other than those for which it is designed to operate. The stability limit of a protection can be quoted as the ratio of the maximum through-fault current which may cause mal-operation against the relay setting current. If a protection system is to be completely satisfactory, the relay setting must ensure operation under minimum fault conditions. This, however, is not just a question of setting a relay as low as possible, since the resultant relay burden may cause saturation of the current transformers (CTs) under external fault conditions, resulting in instability of the protection. A compromise must therefore be found between stability and sensitivity.

For the most part, the problems existing can be solved by the application of standard equipment. When considering the choice of a protective system for a particular application, two questions arise: how much protection is required and which type of protection system to use.

In deciding how much protection should be used, a number of facts need to be considered including system fault statistics; type, nature and importance of plant to be protected; and degree of complexity compared with level of maintenance staff and risk of possible mal-operation.

The greatest assistance one can obtain in reaching a final decision on how much protection should be applied is to draw on experience. If experience dictates, for example, that the number of faults on a pilot cable over a few years has been negligible, there is little reason for applying supervisory equipment.

There are a number of possible solutions to known problems and the choice of which system is determined by assessing the required perform-ance, and matching these protection requirements to that of the available protective systems in relation to cost, maintenance and installation.

Having chosen the type of protection system based on the factors above, it must be confirmed that the chosen system is suitable for a particular application. This involves investigating a set of facts which broadly can be divided into two groups: (1) The behaviour of the components of the power system and the limits within which they may be operated, for example, permissible fault clearance time and available fault current during internal and external fault conditions. (2) The characteristics of the protection system and the limits between which the protection system will perform correctly, for example, operating time, fault settings and stability.

UNIT AND NON-UNIT PROTECTION

Protection systems can be broadly defined in two categories, unit and non-unit protection. Economics dictate that protection systems cannot always be fully discriminative and the simpler forms of protection tend to disconnect more of the power system than just the faulted unit. This characterises the fundamental difference between unit protection, which is concerned only with determining whether the fault is within or external to the power system unit it is protecting, and non-unit protection which disconnects the minimum amount of plant by tripping only the circuit-breakers nearest to the fault.

Because power system faults are fairly rare events, the concept of reliability in protection is very much related to stability, (i.e. mechanical or electrical interference must not cause mal-operation).

299

On the other hand, when a fault does occur it is vital that operation
is ensured and protection is always applied with at least one back-up
system. The arrangement of non-unit protection, fig. 19.1, allows
primary protection for a power system unit and back-up protection for
an adjacent unit to be obtained from one set of relay equipment, i.e. a
fault between relays 2 and 1 has relay 2 as primary protection and
relay 3 as back-up protection. Figure 19.2 shows that the fundamental
principles of unit protection dictate that it will not provide back-up
protection for adjacent units so that separate back-up protection must
be provided. Unit protection is not always universally applied throughout a power system so that some power system units rely on the back-up
protection as their primary protection. Busbars are typically in this
category because the low incidence of busbar faults indicates that
this is a reasonable risk. However, the catastrophic nature of a
busbar fault means that the clearance times of back-up protection
should be reviewed as a power system develops so that the rare event
of a busbar fault and its predictable serious effects are constantly
appreciated.

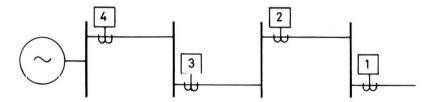

Figure 19.1 Non-unit protection

Discrimination

Discrimination with load current is perhaps the most fundamental
requirement and thus phase-fault settings in simple protection have to
be set above maximum load current which therefore limits the protection
obtainable for phase faults. Fortunately, with earth faults, a residual connection of the CTs, fig. 19.3, can be used which eliminates all
current except earth-fault current from the relay so that low earth-
fault settings are possible and this enables coverage to be given to
power systems which have earth-fault current deliberately limited by
earthing impedances. Settings must always be related to the required
stability level because errors in CTs increase with energisation level

and the out-of-balance currents between CTs having different errors will be fed to residually connected earth-fault relays thus affecting discrimination if the earth-fault relay settings are not above the expected steady state out-of-balance current.

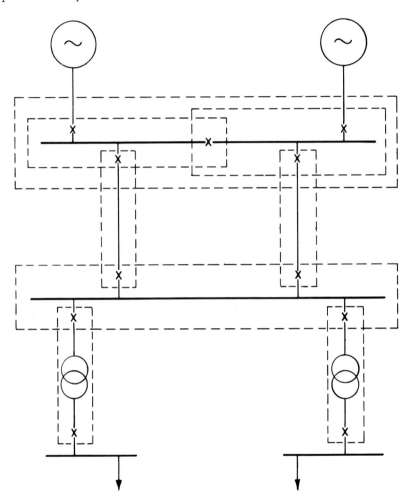

Figure 19.2 Unit protection in overlapped zones

To achieve the requirement that only the minimum of plant is disconnected during a fault, it is necessary that protection schemes discriminate with each other accurately in the presence of fault conditions. Two fundamental types of discrimination exist, first, in the case of non-unit schemes, fig. 19.1, discrimination is obtained by ensuring that the circuit-breaker nearest to the fault operates while those further from the fault remain stable. This is achieved by current or time grading, or more generally, a combination of both. Thus in this case discrimination is dependent upon the intrinsic accuracy of the CTs, the relays and the circuit-breaker clearance times.

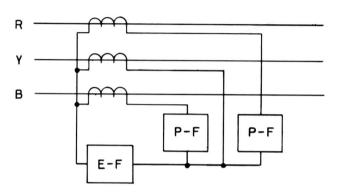

Figure 19.3   Residual connection of earth-fault (E-F) relay with phase-fault (P-F) relays

The second type of discrimination is obtained by the through-fault stability of unit protection. In fig. 19.2, each unit protection involved in a fault must measure end-to-end and decide to trip or stabilise depending on whether the fault is found to be external or internal to the zone bounded by the CTs feeding that protection. With unit protection, the accuracy requirements are therefore to ensure correct comparison and in this case, intrinsic accuracy is not important but comparative accuracy is vital. This has required the establishment of a special category of CTs (BS 3938, Class X) for unit protection where the turns ratio is specified to close limits and the output capability is specified in terms directly related to the requirements of unit protection (i.e. knee point voltage and winding resistance).

In general, protection should be as fast as possible to avoid too much damage and/or disturbance to the power system. However, in non-unit schemes time is often used, at least partially, to provide discrimination so that longer clearance times than may be desirable are involved. Also, it is fundamental to the nature of graded time protection that longer times of operation will be at the source end of radial or ring system, i.e. in fig. 19.1 relay 4 must be the slowest relay, where the fastest time of clearance is preferable and this is the basic objection to simple graded protection schemes.

With unit protection, each unit has the same basic speed of operation so that a fault anywhere within the power system is cleared in the very fast times obtained by unit protection.

Distance protection is perhaps the most complex form of non-unit protection but the most widely used non-unit protection in distribution power systems is graded protection which is used as primary and back-up protection in radial power systems and as back-up to unit protection in interconnected power systems. The relays used to provide graded time protection are generally current-dependent time-lag relays with an inverse definite minimum time-lag characteristic, (idmtl relays).

Inverse time relays

An inverse time characteristic is an attractive feature because high levels of fault are cleared quickly and low levels of fault cleared relatively slowly allowing differentiation between faults and discrimination to be achieved. The relay characteristic has developed with a definite minimum time at high levels where the circuit-breaker operating time dominates the clearance time and if all the relays in a power system are subject to high levels of fault current, discrimination is obtained virtually on a definite time basis.

Some power systems use definite time-lag relays, controlled by overcurrent starting elements, to provide discrimination and this can have advantages because definite-time-lag (dtl) relays can be made much more accurate than idmtl relays. In the general case, however, the advantage of variable time with current level can be exploited because the magnitude of fault current varies with fault position and also with the amount of generation plant connected. Thus the idmtl relay is a combination of the requirement for definite-time-lag discrimination when the circuit-breaker time is dominant and inverse time lag at low levels where fault position can influence the current and hence the time of operation.

The concept of fault position giving different fault levels can be exploited by current grading in a radial system where maximum possible fault current for each relay position is easily calculated. Thus a fast overcurrent relay may be set to operate at high levels and when this is combined with idmtl relays closer grading can be obtained because the high current end of the overall characteristic is current graded and the idmtl curve is only required to ensure discrimination below this level. However, fast overcurrent relays may operate at much lower currents than their setting when an offset transient is present in the energising current. This is referred to as transient overreach because they are operating for a fault current magnitude which is the calculated level for a fault position further away from the source than the relay setting indicates. Specially designed fast overcurrent relays are available which maintain their setting (within declared limits) in the presence of the offset transient; they are referred to as transient free and obviously have wider application technically but are limited in use by economics.

Because continuity of supply is one of the prime requirements in power system design, the radial power system develops naturally into a closed ring type of circuit so that any feeder can be switched out without loss of supply to any busbar. Protection of this type of power system requires that discrimination must be obtained along both paths to the fault. This is achieved by directional control of the idmtl relays so that only the relays nearest to and either side of the fault operate. A typical arrangement is shown in fig. 19.4 where it can be seen that the first circuit-breaker to trip opens the ring which then becomes a radial system allowing the fault to be cleared by the circuit-breaker nearest the fault.

The directional relay determines the direction of the fault current in relation to the voltage at the relay point, and is chosen with a maximum torque angle appropriate to the angle between fault current and energising voltages. In general, the faulted phase voltages are not used but the relay is nevertheless compensated to give correct directional operation at low voltages because all voltages collapse during three-phase faults.

Earth-fault directional relays are fed from residual current and residual voltage.

The directional elements are in effect reverse current relays which are generally arranged to have a maximum torque angle appropriate to the phase angle of the fault current. Overcurrent directional elements

have a relay characteristic angle of 0° or 45° lead and obtain an
overall lagging maximum torque angle by using appropriate phase-to-
phase or phase-to-neutral voltages. Earth-fault directional elements
are generally connected to residual current and residual voltage and
may have a characteristic angle between 0° and about 75° lag.

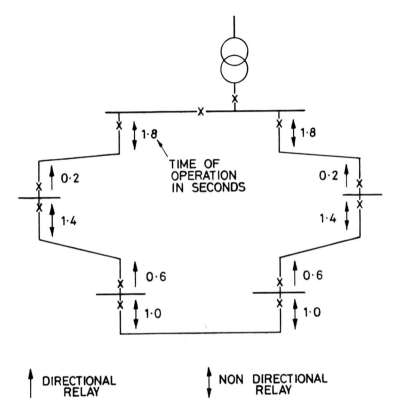

Figure 19.4 Directional overcurrent relays

Directional relays should not be confused with reverse power relays
which are not voltage compensated and are used to detect unusual power
flow conditions subsequent to power system disturbances. The power
relay is not normally required to respond to fault conditions and its
output contacts are therefore time lagged.

Unit protection is characterised by its sensitivity and speed of
operation both of which make it susceptible to transient out-of-balance
between the input and output signals which should theoretically sum

to zero during through-fault conditions. Each type of power system unit has characteristics which affect the design of their unit protection. These are discussed later.

GRADED PROTECTION

In order to apply time-graded protection the relays must be in a radial configuration as shown in fig. 19.1. When a common source feeds several radial feeders it is worthwhile to clearly separate and identify each set of relays and the impedances between them. This will show how the relay at the source must be coordinated to suit the feeder giving the longest times.

Where the source is several identical branches in parallel, a decision must first be made on what basis the grading is to be done, i.e. the minimum number of branches that may be in service. The source impedance is obviously one branch impedance divided by the number of branches in parallel and the CT primary rating can be multiplied by the number of branches to give equivalent relay current.

Figure 19.1 shows how graded protection is characterised by the way in which fault current will be fed to the fault by only one path so that for a particular fault position all relays will be energised by the same primary current and the relay response is therefore easily predicted by choosing appropriate settings. The current in each relay is determined by its CT ratio and the relay response is determined by its current setting (plug setting) and its time setting (time multiplier). Discrimination is ensured by the inverse relationship between current and relay time of operation and the applied specified limits. BS 142 specifies the standard inverse curve for idmtl relays by the check points as illustrated in fig. 19.5. The allowable errors are also specified in BS 142 and these have to be assessed when deciding the time that will be used as the grading step between each adjacent pair of relays.

Effect of impedance

The magnitude of the fault current is determined by the impedances of the power system feeding the fault and in the simplest form can be represented by source impedance (Z_S) and the impedance between the two relays being considered (Z_L) as shown in fig. 19.6. Assuming that Z_S

is much greater than Z_L, the fault current at each relay position will be approximately the same, i.e. $I_F = V/Z_S = V/(Z_S + Z_L)$. If, in addition, the load current and CT ratio are the same for each relay position, discrimination could be obtained by time multiplier setting only.

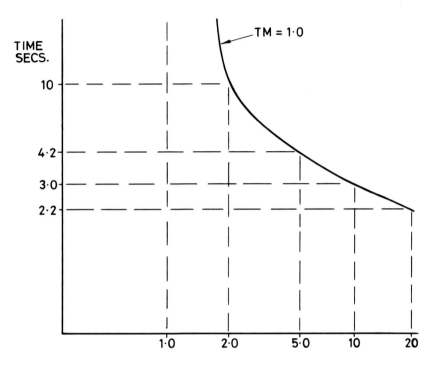

MULTIPLES OF PLUG SETTING

Figure 19.5 Standard idmtl curve

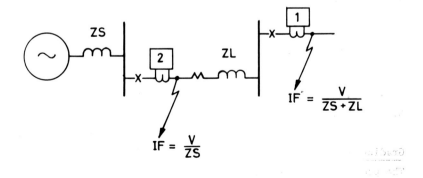

Figure 19.6 Basic circuit for grading

307

The consideration of load current is important because the plug setting of overcurrent relays, which have a plug setting range of typically 50-200% of rating, determine the basic pick-up and reset levels of the relay. Thus for discrimination with load conditions, the relay plug setting must be related to the CT ratio and the maximum possible load current to ensure that the relay resets when clearance of a fault may leave the circuit with increased loading due to an outage.

When Z_L is significant in relation to Z_S, the fault current at the two relay points is different and the plug setting adjustment and/or CT ratio can be used in combination with the time multiplier setting to give discrimination.

In the general case, Z_S is determined by the plant running condition and therefore is variable between minimum and maximum plant limits, hence the reason why idmtl relays are used. At very high levels of fault current the CT output may be limited by steady state saturation of its core material. This limits the effective output of the CT to approximately a current level whose average value is that given by the knee point voltage of the CTs excitation curve divided by the CT winding resistance plus the relay winding resistance. Thus the combined performance of the CT and relay gives the inverse time curve up to the point of CT saturation and a definite time above the current at which the CT saturates. If the standard idmtl curve is used, CT saturation above twenty times the plug setting does not change the overall characteristic. However, very inverse and extremely inverse relay characteristics are modified by CT saturation so that this should be taken into account if high levels of energisation are expected.

The effective burden of relays varies with setting and thus when low settings are used, the possibility of CT saturation is increased. Thus with earth-fault relays and high multiples of setting the guidance on application of CTs as detailed in BS 3938: 1973, Appendix B, Clause B.5.4 should be taken into account.

Grading procedure

The procedure for grading a set of relays is first to establish a common base upon which to compare the curve of each relay with each

adjacent relay. This common base is generally primary current referred
to the base voltage of the power system. Settings have to be chosen
for each relay to maintain the grading step at the highest possible
fault current and to also ensure operation at the lowest possible fault
current. Thus power system data must be available for maximum and
minimum plant condition.

The grading step must take into account maximum circuit-breaker
clearance time, CT errors, relay errors and relay overshoot. Generally,
0.4 of a second has been used as a minimum but lower values are feas-
ible with fast circuit-breakers and accurate relays.

Relay overshoot is related to the inertia of an electromechanical
relay and is the time difference between the operate time for a
specified level of current and the time the relay has to be energised
at this level of current to obtain operation. In other words, the
relay will operate (and its time of operation is unimportant in this
case) if it is energised for a time less than its operate time because
the movement has stored energy which will cause it to continue to move
after the energising current ceases. It is tempting to believe that
because semiconductor designs have no mechanical inertia in their
measuring circuits that static relays will not have any overshoot.
However, trapped charge in smoothing and timing circuits give much the
same effect and although special circuits can obviously be designed to
minimise this, economics may dictate that a static relay has as much
overshoot as an electromechanical relay.

Having established plug settings for each overcurrent relay to
ensure non-operation during maximum load conditions, the current
multiple of the plug setting of the relay furthest from the source
(relay 1 in fig. 19.1) for maximum through-fault conditions will determine the required time multiplier setting for this relay. Often
relay 1 can be set at 0.1 time multiplier because it is known that
other protective systems, fuses, motor protective relays, etc., have
such lower relative current settings that coordination is not required.
Sometimes a minimum time multiplier is specified by the authority controlling the protection in the circuits being fed by relay 1.

If relay 1 has to be coordinated with other protection the time
curve of this protection must be included in the grading exercise.

With the plug settings of each relay set to suit load currents the calculated plug setting multiple for the fault level at each relay is determined. The relay curve is only specified up to twenty times the plug setting and it is possible that CT saturation will affect time of operation at levels higher than this so that the plug setting should be increased if necessary until the fault current is below twenty times the plug setting. If a plug setting above the 200% limit is called for the plug setting multiple and relay burden must be assessed against CT output.

Having decided the setting of relay 1, by one means or another, its time of operation for maximum fault level at its location can be established, this is the point of grading with relay 2. The multiple of relay 2 plug setting for this fault condition and the time of operation of relay 1 plus the grading step give the required time multiplier for relay 2. Figure 19.7 shows grading between two relays illustrating the way in which the two curves obtained from plug settings and time multipliers are drawn to a common base to show the overall protection obtained. The alternative settings for relay 2 which give the same grading step between the two curves show the improved fault coverage obtained for relay 2 if plug settings are held to the lowest value needed to ensure discrimination against maximum load conditions.

High-set relays

If high-set relays are used they must be set so that they can be included in the coordination of the relays. Setting of the high-set relays must take account of the stability requirements for a fault at the next relay point with due allowance made for the 50% overreach of simple high-set elements. If twice the setting requirement for operate current is also introduced, it is often difficult to achieve viable settings for the high-set elements.

Having selected the high-set settings, the operation point of the relays for grading is obtained using the lowest value of current multiple as determined by the high-set setting or the fault current. If the value is less than twice the plug setting the relay current is too low to ensure operation and a change in CT rating should be considered.

The high-set setting of relay 1 or the fault level at relay 1 is

then chosen to determine the grading on the basis of which the lowest
multiple of the plug setting at relay 2 is obtained. With the lowest
multiple of plug setting for relay 2 given by the high-set setting of
relay 1 or a fault at relay 1, the time multiplier of relay 2 is
determined. If a time multiplier setting of greater than 1 is called
for the plug setting must be increased.

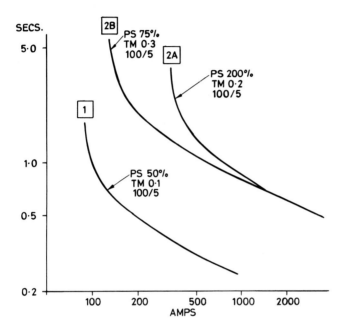

Figure 19.7   Grading between two relays

Grading by computer

The grading of relays is a relatively simple task which can easily be
done by a computer, however, the problem of collecting data and
authenticating the data remains. Often data are only questioned when
engineering judgement indicates that the final result is unusual.
This means that the computer should be used to assist and not replace
the engineer.

UNIT PROTECTION

Unit protection operates for faults which it measures as being within
the protected unit and is stable for faults which it measures as being

external to the protected unit. Differential protection, which forms
the majority of unit protection, can be classified by the means used
to obtain stability. In the current balance system, current is circu-
lated in the secondaries between the sets of CTs at each end of the
protected zone and the relay is fed by the summation of the currents
which is theoretically zero under external fault conditions. The
voltage balance system has voltages derived from and proportional to
the currents which are balanced under external fault conditions, so
that theoretically no current flows in the relays which are connected
in series between ends. The basic arrangement of both systems is
shown in figs 19.8 and 19.9.

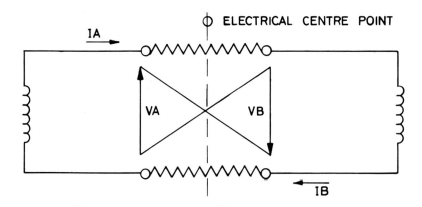

Figure 19.8 Current balance stability

Each type of balance has limitations and the means of overcoming
these limitations characterise relay design. Originally, the use of
distributed air-gap CTs favoured the voltage balance scheme because
this type of CT naturally produced a voltage output proportional to
current. However, as can be seen in fig. 19.9 significant pilot capacitance causes spill current in the relays of a voltage balance pilot
wire differential scheme and thus provision must be made for this in
the relay design. Similarly, in a current balance scheme, fig. 19.8,
the voltage drop due to the circulating current dictates that the
relays must be connected at the electrical centre point.

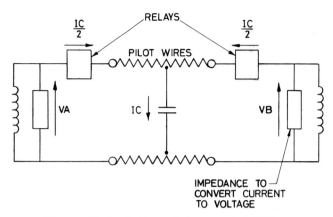

$\dfrac{IC}{2}$ RELAYS $\dfrac{IC}{2}$

PILOT WIRES

VA   IC   VB

IMPEDANCE TO
CONVERT CURRENT
TO VOLTAGE

Figure 19.9 Voltage balance stability

In pilot wire differential schemes it is not practical to connect relays at the electrical centre point because this would be geographically in the centre of the feeder. Thus the design of a feeder protective scheme must arrange for tripping contacts at each end and the relay equipment is therefore duplicated at each end, with both ends and the communication channel between ends forming the measuring circuit.

Steady-state out-of-balance spill currents are overshadowed by the severe out-of-balance during unequal saturation of the CTs caused by the offset transient in the primary current and the remanence left in the CTs from previous fault conditions. Considering that these effects are transient in nature, they are related to the dynamic performance of a protection which must therefore be established in relation to the primary transient and its effect upon the combination of relays, CTs and connections between them which make up the protective scheme.

Low and high impedance schemes

Current balance schemes are classified as low or high impedance by the relative impedance of the relay used. The high impedance differential circulating current scheme allows for transient unbalance more definitely than any other type of protection because it assumes complete saturation of the CTs at one end with the CTs at the other end producing full output. With correct relay design in a high impedance protection system it should be possible to remove the CT at one end and

313

replace it by its winding resistance only and still obtain stability.

Low impedance current balance differential schemes can be considered basically as two CTs feeding an effective short-circuit which is the low impedance relay. Thus assuming the relay has zero impedance, the excitation current of each CT is determined by the through-fault current, the CT winding resistance and the lead burden resistance. The excitation currents are not equal if different CTs or lead burden resistance are used and the difference between the excitation currents flows in the relay giving a tendency to operate during the through-fault condition.

In contrast to the low impedance differential scheme, the high impedance current balance scheme can be regarded as two CTs connected back-to-back so that the current from one secondary is absorbed by the current in the other secondary. Assuming a voltage-operated relay of infinite impedance there is no other path for current to flow and the excitation currents at each end must be equal. Thus, in this case, with unbalanced CTs or lead burdens, the total voltage produced by both CTs has a magnitude determined by the total loop burden of both CT winding resistance and both lead burden resistance and this total voltage is shared between the two CTs in proportion to the appropriate points on their respective excitation curve, with each CT having the same excitation current.

Practical high impedance differential schemes have relays with significant impedance values with respect to the excitation impedance of CTs so that spill current flows in the relay due to unbalance between CTs and this tends to reduce the fundamental voltage unbalance. The steady-state unbalance spill currents must be considered in relation to the sensitivity of the relay which has an operation level of typically 20 mA so that small levels of ratio error in the CTs can be significant, particularly when 5 A CTs are used and the prospective circulating secondary current will therefore be 250 A for a fifty times through fault. Ratio error in CTs introduces additional error to that produced by unequal excitation currents and thus must be minimised by correct choice of CTs. Class X CTs to BS 3938, should be used for differential protection but other classes of protection CTs have been successfully used.

The practice of using class 5P CTs (BS 3938) in differential protection has developed due to the fact that some CT manufacturers make them physically to be the same as class 'X' CTs and thus the only difference is in the specified limits. However, the CT specification allows a broader approach and in general terms the only suitable CTs for differential protection remains the class 'X'. As stated in BS 3938, class 5P CTs may be suitable for differential protection but this depends upon the difference between the CTs at the two ends rather than the protective scheme and the crucial factors are stated in clause B.5.5. of BS 3938. These steady-state considerations must be remembered when settings are being chosen even though the basic stability requirements of high impedance protection are calculated for transient unbalance conditions. Thus steady-state stability requirements may require settings to be higher than transient stability requirements.

High impedance protection is limited to those applications where the lead length between CTs is less than about 1000 m and where CTs can be low reactance and have the same ratio. Pilot wire differential protection and transformer differential protection are therefore based upon low impedance principles.

Differential protection using low impedance relays requires some means to overcome the unbalance between ends during through-faults. Errors in CTs, both steady state and transient, produce differential current which appears to the relay as an internal fault and consequently there is always a limit to the sensitivity that can be used.

Transient unbalance between ends is generally much higher than steady-state unbalance and early low impedance differential schemes used slow relays to withstand these transient conditions. This technique is still used in very sensitive earth-fault protection and in simple differential schemes which may use idmtl relays as measuring elements.

However, speed of operation is one of the basic advantages of differential protection so that some means other than time relay is preferable to allow for transient unbalance and in low impedance differential schemes this has been generally achieved by biasing the relays.

The concept of bias is best understood by observing the change in relay setting with through-fault current in relation to spill current

315

as shown in the idealised composite characteristics of fig. 19.10.

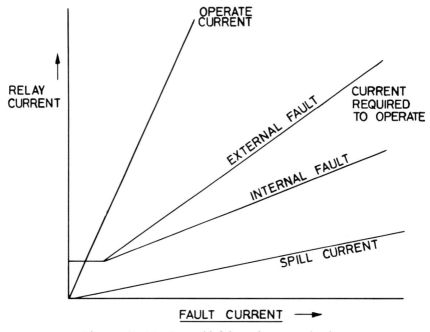

Figure 19.10   Overall bias characteristic

The step in the current required to operate the relay curves is deliberately introduced into the design so that the operate current setting level during internal faults is not affected by the bias current. This gives a reduction in the ratio between spill current and current required to operate causing a potentially unstable condition at a relatively low level of energisation. Hence the requirement to type test low impedance biased schemes stability at levels of through-fault current below maximum. The different slopes of the 'current required to operate' curves for internal and external fault are generally due to only half the bias turns being energised by an internal fault fed from one end.

Power system units take many different forms which dictate the design of the protection that will be applied. Thus each type of unit has unique features related to the particular problems of that type of unit and are each subjects in their own right. However, the salient points are summarised below.

316

<u>Feeder differential protection.</u>   The basic unit protection for
feeders is differential protection using pilot wires between ends to
effect the end-to-end comparison. The limitations imposed by the pilot
wires dictate that sensitive measuring relays are required and the
steady-state and transient unbalance between ends is generally catered
for by biasing the relay.

For economy of pilots, the CT outputs are combined in such a way
that all faults can be measured by comparison across one pair of pilots.
British practice is to use a simple summation transformer to combine
the fault currents but the alternative of sequence networks is used in
some areas.

In common with all circuits which run in parallel with the power
system, the pilot wires are subject to induced voltages when zero
sequence current is flowing in the parallel path. Thus earth-fault
conditions can cause relatively high induced voltages depending upon
the length of common path between the pilots and zero sequence fault
current, the coupling coefficient between the two circuits and the
magnitude of the zero sequence current. Pilot wire protection must
therefore be designed to cater for this induced voltage. Unfortunately,
the simple approach used in telecommunication circuits of by-passing
the induced energy to earth by surge suppressors cannot be used with
pilot wire protection because the pilot wires are required to be active
during the fault condition to stabilise the protection or to enable
tripping. The approach has always been to float the pilots so that
they cannot be affected by the flow of longitudinal zero sequence
current and thus very high voltage withstand levels are required on
the pilot circuits and these have been standardised as 5 kV or 15 kV.
The 5 kV level is applicable to distribution cable networks where the
effective coupling coefficient between pilots and zero sequence current
path is relatively low. The 15 kV level is required where the coupling
coefficient between the two paths is relatively high or at transmission
voltage levels where induced voltages are generally higher.

<u>Solkor R system.</u>   A pilot wire protection is characterised by the
way in which the comparison of the two ends is done and the way in
which the transient unbalance between ends is catered for. A typical
scheme is shown in fig. 19.11. This is Solkor R protection and uses

the principle of current balance to obtain stability during through-fault conditions. The basic current balance scheme requires connection of the relay at the electrical centre point of the pilots. This theoretically ensures that the secondary currents will cancel because the CT excitation currents will be equal. In practice, dissimilar CTs and CT transient saturation mean that the excitation currents can be different during steady-state and considerably different during transient conditions leading to substantial spill currents.

PILOT PADDING RESISTORS

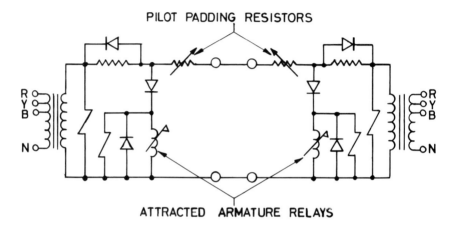

ATTRACTED ARMATURE RELAYS

Figure 19.11 Solkor R pilot wire protection

The physical siting of the relay in the middle of the pilots is not practical and the scheme requires a relay at each end. Diode switching is arranged so that the electrical centre of the pilots is moved end-to-end in response to the polarity of the summation transformer output thus keeping both relays stable.

Although Solkor R is in essence a current balance scheme, a current-to-voltage conversion is made by the summation transformer and pilot voltage limiting non-linear resistance. This voltage is then used to drive current around the pilot circuit which is fixed in ohmic value by having pilot padding resistors. The diodes in this pilot loop ensure that the relays are always at the negative end of the voltage divider created by the fixed resistor and the pilot resistance. By making the fixed resistor 1750 ohms and padding the pilots to 1000 ohms the relays have a negative bias which is effective because they are positively polarised by diodes connected in series with them.

The important factor to note is the absolute and instant application
of the bias. In biased relays generally the smoothing sometimes
required (e.g. when biasing is arranged within magnetic circuits)
causes delay in the establishment of the bias and hence the requirement
to use a relatively slow measuring relay to avoid transient instability.

Transformer differential protection. Transformer differential protection compares the primary and secondary currents of a transformer
and is stable when these indicate that a fault is external to the
transformer. The problem is complicated by the variable ratio of the
power transformer (due to tap change) and the transformer winding
configuration and earthing which can cause different fault current
distribution each side of the transformer. In general, the transformer
winding configuration is allowed for by using star-connected CTs with
power transformer delta windings, and delta-connected CTs with power
transformer star windings. This also excludes zero sequence current
from the differential relay which avoids the problems caused by
different earthing arrangements of the two power systems linked by the
power transformer. Transformer protection is dealt with in detail
later.

Restricted earth-fault protection. Restricted earth-fault protection
uses the high impedance principle which gives extremely good stability
with low settings because the settings are determined by characteristics of the CTs which are not directly related to the characteristics
of the CTs which determine stability, see fig. 19.12. Thus low settings
with high stability levels can be obtained and this gives very good
earth-fault coverage.

The stability criterion of a high impedance system is that the
relay setting voltage is higher than that calculated by assuming that
the maximum current is flowing in the saturated CT and thus producing
a voltage equal to the maximum secondary current times the CT winding
resistance plus lead burden resistance. The setting is determined by
the secondary current required to energise the CTs and the relay at
the relay setting voltage, plus the current taken by a setting resistor
which is generally connected in parallel with the relay in order to
increase the setting to a value reasonably above the steady-state

unbalance that may be expected from the CTs. Details of restricted earth-fault protection are discussed later.

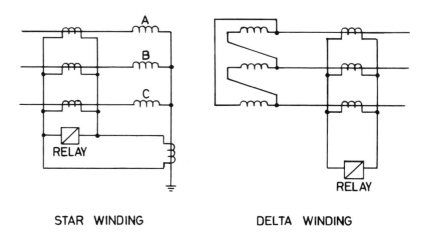

STAR WINDING   DELTA WINDING

Figure 19.12   Restricted earth-fault protection

Busbar zone protection.   The requirements of busbar zone protection are dominated by the stability requirements because the incidence of busbar faults is so low and the incorrect operation of busbar zone protection can have such wide ranging effects.

With fully enclosed metalclad switchgear, simple busbar protection is possible by lightly insulating the switchgear enclosing frame and connecting it to earth through a CT feeding a simple relay. This system of frame-leakage protection only detects earth fault so that the possibility of phase-to-phase faults free from earth is an important factor in deciding whether this scheme is suitable.

With important busbars, the advent of a busbar fault, although an unlikely occurrence, generally causes so much disruption to the power system that high speed differential protection is applied.

The problems of differential busbar protection are: the through-fault current has the same magnitude as internal faults because the busbars have virtually no impedance; the through-fault current may be shared by several circuits feeding into the busbar and leave the busbar by only one circuit thus creating conditions for unbalance in the combination of the CT outputs; and complex busbar arrangements require circuits to be switched from one busbar to another which creates the potentially hazardous requirement of switching CT secondary circuits. This latter problem is overcome by using an overall check zone and applying sensitive alarm relays which detect the unbalance caused by load current when a CT is not connected.

The problem of high through-fault currents coupled with the sharing of the input current is overcome by using the high impedance circulating current differential scheme, i.e. busbar zone protection uses the same basic scheme as that used in restricted earth-fault protection.

Circulating current protection.   There is a tendency to use mesh and breaker and a half substation arrangements and in these the circuits are not switched, so that check zones are not required and the high impedance scheme is used as a plain circulating current scheme. It is used whenever possible because of its good performance and simplicity. Reactors, interconnectors, auto-transformers and generator stators may be protected by high impedance circulating current protection, the only limitation being the capability of the CTs (which must be low reactance type) to support the lead burden.

TRANSFORMER PROTECTION

Protective schemes applied to transformers play a vital role in the economics and operation of a power system. Their percentage cost is extremely small making it totally uneconomic to apply anything less than a complete scheme of protection especially to large transformer units. On smaller transformers where their loss may not be so important to system operation the protection applied must be balanced against economic considerations.

To design a protective scheme for a transformer it is necessary to have a knowledge of faults that have to be detected.

Figure 19.13 shows the types of fault that can be experienced, on a transformer. These are earth-fault on h.v. external connections; phase-to-phase fault on h.v. external connections; internal earth-fault on h.v. windings; internal phase-to-phase fault on h.v. windings; short-circuit between turns h.v. windings; earth-fault on l.v. external connections; phase-to-phase fault on l.v. external connections; internal earth-fault on l.v. windings; internal phase-to-phase fault on l.v. windings; short-circuit between turns l.v. windings;

321

earth-fault on tertiary winding; short-circuit between turns tertiary winding; sustained system earth-fault; and sustained system phase-to-phase fault.

Under fault conditions current in the transformer windings is distributed in different ways and is of varying quantity depending upon the transformer winding connections and, in the case of earth-faults, the method of earthing. An understanding of these is essential for the design of protection schemes, particularly balanced differential schemes, the performance of directional relays and setting of overcurrent and earth-fault relays.

A detailed analysis is outside the scope of this chapter. A full treatise is given in *Fault Calculations* by C.H.W. Lackey, published by Oliver & Boyd Ltd.

Current balance schemes

Most protective schemes applied to transformers are based on the current balance principle of magnitude comparison of currents flowing into and out of the transformer, fig. 19.10. This principle can be used to protect the transformer winding separately or as an overall unit. However, in the latter case certain refinements are necessary.

<u>Separate winding protection.</u>   Relating the current balance principle to each winding of the transformer separately it can be seen, fig. 19.12 that under magnetising, normal load and through-fault conditions the current circulates between the CTs which provided they have similar characteristics, results in no current flowing in the relay. Stability is therefore ensured under all external conditions. If however an earth fault occurs within the zone of the CTs an out-of-balance condition exists whereby current flows through the relay.

The main problem experienced in first applying a current balance scheme was retaining stability on through-faults accompanied by unequal saturation of the CTs during the first few cycles after the fault zero. This was overcome by using a relay of high impedance which has a large value stabilising resistor connected in the relay circuit.

322

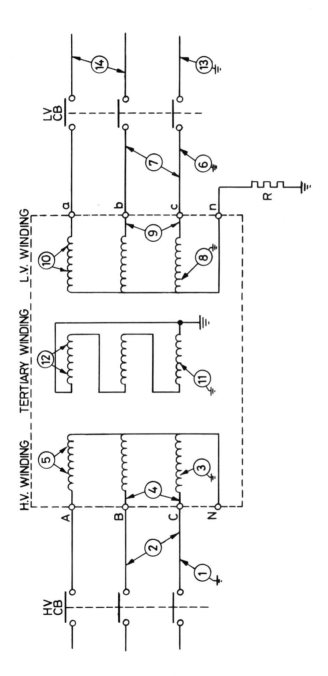

Figure 19.13 Types of transformer fault

This scheme using high impedance relays has now been in use for many years, the simplicity in application being that the performance of the protection on both stability and fault setting can be calculated with certainty. For a given through-fault current (I_a) the maximum voltage that can occur across the relay circuits is given by:

$$V_R = \frac{I_a}{N} (R + X)$$

where V_R = maximum voltage across relay circuit

    R = maximum lead resistance

    X = CT secondary resistance

    N = CT ratio.

This is based on the assumption of the worst condition when one CT completely saturates and ceases to transform any part of the primary fault current, whilst the other CTs continue to transform accurately.

If the setting voltage of the relay is made equal to or greater than this voltage the protection will be stable for currents above the maximum through-fault current level. In practice, the knee point voltage of the CTs is designed to be at least twice this value.

The fault setting of the protection is calculated from:

$$I_{FS} = N (I_R + I_A + I_B)$$

where I_{FS} - fault setting

    I_R = relay circuit current at relay setting voltage

    I_A, I_B = CT magnetising currents at relay setting voltage

    N = CT ratio.

The primary fault setting should be adjusted to the level required by the addition of resistors connected across the relay circuit to increase the relay circuit current I_R.

The circuit of a typical high impedance restricted earth-fault relay is shown in fig. 19.14. The operating element is an attracted-armature relay energised from a full wave rectifier. The capacitor C in conjunction with the resistors form a low pass filter circuit. The function of this is to increase the setting at harmonic frequencies, thus retaining stability when high frequency currents are produced in certain installations during switching.

The links enable the voltage setting to be adjusted and non-linear resistor M1 limits the peak voltage output from the CTs during internal faults and so protects the relay and secondary wiring.

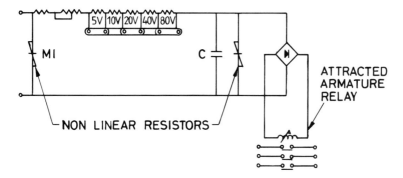

Figure 19.14 High impedance relay

Summarising, separate winding current balance schemes are:

unaffected by load current, external fault or magnetising inrush currents; and unaffected by the ratio of transformer. The complete winding can be protected with solidly earthed neutral but not when resistance earthed, and it will not detect phase faults (three-phase protection), shorted turns or open-circuits.

Overall differential protection.   The current balance principle can also be applied to cover both primary and secondary windings. However an overall scheme is affected by magnetising current, although it remains balanced under normal load or through-faults providing CT ratios are matched; mismatch in CTs causes spill current to flow in the relay circuit. Since most transformers are equipped with tap-changing the design of an overall scheme for three-phase transformers must also take account of this mismatch under through-fault conditions.

Thus the application of an overall scheme to three-phase transformers requires a biased relay with characteristics as illustrated in fig. 19.10 to maintain stability on tap-changing and during magnetising inrush currents.

In both cases the out-of-balance current flowing through the relay circuit may be several times the basic fault setting. A bias winding ensures that the relay remains stable under these conditions, as explained on page 315. Usual practice is to arrange the bias

characteristic with a slope of at least twice the slope of the
expected steady-state spill current characteristic.

During internal faults the whole of the available CT secondary
current passes through the relay operating circuit giving the rapid
rise in operate current.

The second reason, already mentioned, for using a biased relay for
overall transformer protection is that spill current may flow during a
magnetising surge. This spill current contains a large percentage of
second and higher harmonics and it is convenient to convert these
harmonics into bias current, thereby preventing the relay from operating during magnetising inrush conditions.

One thing to be considered with 'harmonic bias' is that harmonics
are also present during internal faults due to CT saturation. To
ensure that the relay will operate under all internal fault conditions
the harmonic bias unit should preferably be designed to use only second
harmonic which predominates in a magnetising surge.

Buchholz relay
On all but the smallest transformers it is usual practice to install a
Buchholz gas relay. This device detects severe faults from the
resultant surge in the oil and low level faults by the measurement of
accumulation of gas. It consists of two pivoted floats carrying
mercury switches contained in a chamber which is connected in the pipe
between the top of the transformer tank and the oil conservator. Under
normal conditions the Buchholz relay is full of oil, the floats are
fully raised and the mercury switches are open.

An electrical fault inside the transformer tank is accompanied by
the generation of gas and, if the fault current is high enough, by a
surge of oil from the tank to the conservator. Gas bubbles due to a
core fault are generated slowly and collect in the top of the relay.
As they collect, the oil level drops and the upper float turns on its
pivot until the mercury switch closes. This generates an alarm.
Similarly, incipient winding insulation faults and interturn faults
which produce gas by decomposition of insulation material and oil will
be detected. Such faults are of very low current magnitude and the
Buchholz relay is the only satisfactory method of detection. Since
these faults are not serious, operation of the relay generates an alarm
but does not trip out the transformer.

Serious electrical faults, such as a flashover between connections inside the main tank generate gas rapidly and produce a surge of oil which forces the lower float to rotate about its pivot, causing the lower mercury switch to close. This is arranged to trip both h.v. and l.v. circuit-breakers. In addition to the above, serious oil leakage is detected initially by the upper float which gives an alarm and finally, by the lower float, which disconnects the transformer before dangerous electrical faults result.

Application to two-winding transformer

It is common practice to apply both overall differential relays and restricted earth-fault relays to transformers over about 5 MVA. The amount of protection must be assessed against the importance to the system and economic considerations. A typical scheme of protection for a star/delta transformer is shown in fig. 19.15. The reason for applying both types of relays is to obtain maximum coverage of earth-faults and phase faults.

Consider a transformer that is resistance-earthed. The current available on an internal earth-fault for operation of a differential form of protection could be inadequate because of the transformer action. This is the reason why a separate form of earth-fault protection is added even when solid earthing is employed.

Some care must also be exercised in choosing the CT ratios and connections. The CT ratio must compensate for the difference in primary and secondary currents of the transformer and their connections must compensate for the phase difference.

The restricted earth-fault relay can be operated from a completely separate set of line CTs or it can be combined as shown in fig. 19.15 with the overall protection by incorporating it into the interposing CT circuit. A CT is required, of course, in the neutral-to-earth connection. The advantage of the restricted earth-fault relay is that it is energised from a CT which 'sees' the whole of the fault current and not just the primary side equivalent of it. Where the system is solidly earthed an overall transformer protection with a setting of about 30% gives complete phase-to-earth fault protection of the delta winding and about 80% of the star winding. In that case additional restricted earth-fault protection is not required for the delta

327

winding, but if it is fitted to the star winding it will detect faults
much nearer to the neutral end of the winding.

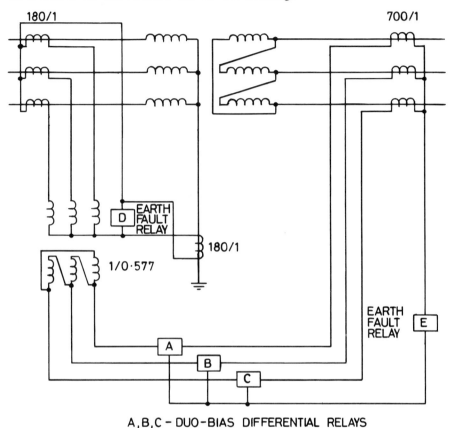

A,B,C - DUO-BIAS DIFFERENTIAL RELAYS

*Figure 19.15 Differential protection with supplementary earth-fault
protection*

In addition to overall protection it is usual practice to protect
all but the smallest transformers against interturn faults using a
Buchholz relay. Back-up protection is normally provided by idmtl
overcurrent relays. In applying restricted earth-fault (REF) protection to distribution networks such as 415 V, three-phase, four-wire
systems care must be taken in the primary connection of the neutral CT,
which is dependent upon the earthing position. Two neutral transformers
may be required in order to detect the total zero sequence current
flowing as a result of a fault.

Table 19.1 gives a general guide as to the protection suitable for
different transformer ratings.

Table 19.1 Transformer protection

	Type of transformer	Type of protection
1.	Distribution Rating < 5 MVA	idmtl o/c ⎱ on each REF ⎰ winding
2.	Distribution Rating > 5 MVA	Overall differential REF each winding
3.	Two winding power transmission	Overall differential REF each winding idmtl o/c back-up SBEF*
4.	Generator/ transformer	Overall differential REF each winding h.v. idmtl o/c l.v. idmtl o/c SBEF*
5.	Auto-transformer	Overall circulating current

*Standby earth fault.

ROTATING PLANT

The operation of rotating machines can be affected by faults within or by external disturbances on the network. The protection of a machine must therefore be designed to be highly discriminative to react efficiently on internal faults and external disturbances.

The number and type of protective relays applied to a machine is a function of the machine characteristics such as size, driving device, single or parallel operation, short-circuit withstand current (and that of the network), and type and protection of network earthing. It is also related to economics such as cost of protection in relation to that of machine and the consequences resulting from a breakdown.

Alternators

On occurrence of a short-circuit at the terminals of an alternator the short-circuit current is initially between five and ten times that of full load of the machine because the initial stator current is limited only by the sub-transient leakage reactance. This is related to the flux set up by the stator m.m.f. which fails to cross the air gap. The increase in stator current causes a demagnetising effect by opposing the air gap flux but it is an appreciable time before a major change in the air gap flux can be effected.

329

The net effect is a gradual decrease in the short-circuit current over a period of seconds to a value which may be considerably below full load current of the machine.

Possible faults on alternators.   An alternator may experience various types of faults the most common being stator faults which consist of earth-faults, phase-to-phase short-circuits, short-circuits between turns, open-circuits in windings and overheating. These failures are usually caused by overvoltage and/or deterioration of the insulation.

Protection against external faults.   This type of alternator fault can be detected by an impedance relay or by an overcurrent relay capable of responding to the fall-off in fault current caused by the impedance change described above, while having under normal operating conditions a pick-up above the nominal current and a time-delay characteristic that will coordinate with other relays.

This is achieved by using the voltage on the machine terminals to determine the time/current characteristics of the relay. Under normal or near normal voltage conditions such as might occur on overload the relay has a long inverse time characteristic. However, under short-circuit conditions when the terminal voltage falls the time/current characteristic is automatically selected to a normal time/current characteristic.

Unbalanced loads.   Alternators can usually only support a small percentage of unbalanced loading permanently and must be disconnected from the system before it reaches too high a level. This condition is detected by a negative phase sequence relay with a time/current characteristic of the form $I_2^2 \cdot t$ where I_2 = negative phase sequence current in terms of full load rating, and t = time.

This form of protection is usually only applied to the higher rated machines.

Overloads.   Overloads causing heating of the stator windings must be eliminated before a temperature dangerous for the machine is reached. Depending on the rating of the machine the overload protection may take the form of an overcurrent relay, a thermal relay or temperature sensors. For small machines, (i.e. hundreds of VA) there are relays which simultaneously provide overload protection by means of low-set elements and external phase-to-phase fault protection by means of high-set elements. For machines above 2 MVA platinum temperature sensors are generally provided. These are embedded in the stator windings and a decision to use these must be made before the machine is manufactured.

Reverse power conditions.   It is usual practice to apply protection against failure of the prime power on back-pressure turbine sets. This usually takes the form of a sensitive reverse power relay, having a setting of 0.5 per cent.

As a general rule all alternators, if they may be operating in parallel with other sources, should also be provided with reverse power protection which, depending on type of machine, may not have to be extremely sensitive, for example, on diesel generators a setting of 5-10% is quite adequate.

Protection against internal faults.   There are a number of different types of internal faults requiring specific protective systems.

Stator sensitive earth-fault protection.   The type of earth-fault protection applied depends on the type of earthing of the machine. There are two forms generally employed - resistor earthing or an earthing transformer.

An earth-fault occurring at the terminals of the alternator with resistor earthing causes full load current to flow. However should the fault occur closer to the neutral point the voltage available to drive fault current is reduced and therefore its magnitude is reduced. Eventually a point in the winding is reached where the voltage is just sufficient to drive current equal to the fault setting of the protection. The remainder of the winding between this point and the neutral is thus not protected against earth-faults. Care must therefore be taken when selecting the value of the neutral resistor and the setting of the relay to ensure that this unprotected section is as small as practical. The protection consists of a current relay fed from a ring CT in the neutral connection to earth.

Where a distribution or earthing transformer is used a voltage
operated relay is connected across the secondary side of the transformer associated with the earthing impedance.

Stator, phase and earth-fault.   The standard scheme of protection
for the stator windings is the simple overall current balance scheme
using a high impedance relay. This employs similar CTs at the line
and neutral end of each phase of the alternator, as explained earlier
in this chapter. It is possible, although not strictly necessary, to
apply an overall biased differential relay for this purpose such as
that described for transformers.

Rotor earth fault.   Modern alternators operate with their field
winding system unearthed but it is still necessary to protect against
breakdown of insulation. A number of schemes are available to provide
this protection the most common being a relay which applies a d.c.
voltage between the rotor circuit and earth to detect any circulating
d.c. current.

A similar scheme using a.c. injection is also available.

Failure of field system.   Protection against loss of field is provided by an impedance relay with an offset circular characteristic
(called 'offset mho'). Care must be taken in the setting of the relay
to ensure that it is not affected by power swings. This protection is
usually only applied to larger turbo-alternators.

Application of protection to alternators.   In considering which of
the foregoing types of protection to apply one must, as already stated,
look at rating, importance and cost.

As a general guide, if considering the protection of a diesel
alternator with rating up to hundreds of VA one would recommend the
following schemes as minimum: overall phase and earth-fault; stator
earth-fault; voltage restrained overcurrent; and reverse power.

For a turbo-alternator rated at tens of MVA all of the schemes
described would be applied.

Motors

Motors, both synchronous and asynchronous, form an important part of
every industrial plant or power system network. The usual faults
experienced by motors are: sustained overloads; single-phasing; and
phase faults and earth-faults on motor windings and connections.

Overloads and single-phasing.   The most generally applied motor
protection relay is a thermal relay. To be effective the relay must
have a setting slightly in excess of the motor full load current but
also remain stable under motor starting conditions which can result,
depending upon method of starting, in currents of many times full load
for several seconds.

Several types of thermal relays are available but generally they
are based either on a bimetallic strip principle or on a static thermal
image principle.

It is usual to have, in the same relay, an unbalanced
load-detecting circuit to prevent operation of the motor under
single-phasing conditions. This is necessary for although a motor will
continue to run on only two phases it may overheat.

Phase and earth-faults.   All motors above 75 kW should be provided
with instantaneous relays to detect the above faults. These relay
elements can also be incorporated in the thermal relay. In addition
an REF system should be provided for earth-faults, using a similar
arrangement to that for transformers.

The use of instantaneous elements depends also on the controlling
circuitry of the motor. If a motor is controlled by a contactor which
incorporates fuses then it is normal practice not to include instantaneous elements, allowing the fuses to cover multi-phase faults.
However some form of earth-fault protection is still recommended.

As far as relays performing other functions are concerned no
definite rule can be given to decide above what rating they should be
applied. Economic considerations, principally the cost of protection
including the necessary CTs, must be compared with the cost of the
motor as well as the importance of the motor in the operation of an
industrial process, and the consequences of its being out of service.

The use of a starting device incorporating either resistors, an auto-transformer or inductance in the stator circuit does not modify the protection requirements. However, the relay characteristics and settings must be defined in relation to the starting current and time corresponding to the use of the starting device.

Other forms of essential protection which may be used depending upon the type of motor, in addition to those described are: undervoltage; loss of field; negative sequence; locked rotor; and undercurrent.

The use of static components has made a big impact on the protection of machines. It is now possible to incorporate many of the protective relays described into an overall protection module using the international 483 mm rack mounted principle.

COMMISSIONING TESTS

Commissioning tests are required to check that the relays are correctly connected to the appropriate instrument transformers and that their operation is within reasonable limits. Generally, commissioning tests are limited by the need to transport the necessary equipment to site and the site conditions which may include temporary power supplies; thus the commissioning test instructions have to take this into account.

In preparing a test instruction, there is a dilemma in deciding the level of basic knowledge of the engineer receiving it. In general, information more appropriate to national standards and text books is not included in a particular test instruction, because these are available to supplement the manufacturer's test instructions. Because protective relays are generally measuring current, the concept of the current source is very important. A voltage source is characterised by the fact that a load applied to it does not cause the voltage to change in any way. Conversely, a current source is characterised by the fact that a load introduced into the current circuit does not change the current in any way. The character of a CT fed by a power system dictates that protective relays in service are energised by very good current sources.

Test equipment based upon mains supply is obviously fundamentally more a voltage source than a current source, so unless precautions are taken, the in-service condition is not correctly represented by simple test arrangements and incorrect results will be obtained.

For example, when timing an overcurrent relay, the inductance and resistance of the coil dictate the time constant of current build-up within the coil if it is fed from a voltage source. Thus a slower time of operation can be obtained to the true in-service condition where with the current source of power system feeding a CT, the current is established in the coil at full magnitude without any delay.

However, the most common problem with using a poor current source is due to the non-linear nature of relay impedance. An induction disc idmtl relay obtains its current/time characteristic by saturation of the core material of the induction disc motor. This means that at an energising level above the point at which the definite minimum time is obtained (twenty times the plug setting) the relay impedance is virtually the winding resistance of the coil whereas at lower levels the inductance of the coil has significant value. Typically, a 5 A relay impedance varies from 0.12 to 0.5 ohms and a 1 A relay from 3.2 to 1.5 ohms at 100% tap over its working range. Other taps give higher or lower impedance and generally at the higher percentage taps the variation between impedance at low currents and high currents is not so marked. Of course, the impedance of the relay varies with instantaneous values of current so that the impedances quoted are somewhat fictitious because they represent a combination of a sinusoidal current and a non-linear voltage. Also, the voltage is processed by an instrument giving a value appropriate to the type of instrument and its calibration, generally the rms equivalent of the average value, i.e. a moving coil type of a.c. instrument.

Once the non-linearity of the relay impedance is understood the requirement for a suitable current source is evident. Obviously it is not practical to produce a perfect current source and it is therefore necessary to establish the rules for determining the suitability of the various degrees of perfection in a current source. In the laboratory, it is possible to establish very good current sources by the use of heavy current rigs feeding CTs. The next level below this is to use phase-to-phase mains voltage with resistance to limit the current and below that to use phase-to-neutral mains voltage with resistance to limit the current. Tests on site are generally done with a fixed resistor fed by a constantly variable auto-transformer which is used for fine control. If the same value of resistor has to be used for all

335

currents, the auto-transformer may be at a very low voltage for some current levels which immediately questions the suitability of the current source. The first check on the suitability of a current source is to observe the ammeter feeding the relay from the current source while short-circuiting the relay. Obviously with a perfect current source the ammeter should show no change whether the relay is in circuit or not. If significant change is detected in the current, then the linearity of the relay impedance should be checked before settings and timings obtained with that particular test rig are argued.

The requirement for fundamental accuracy in non-unit protection leads to a necessity to prove that the current source is suitable to determine the true setting or timing of a relay. This can be achieved by repeating the test with an improved current source until no change is apparent in the result between say, maximum resistance fed by phase-to-neutral voltage and the equivalent maximum resistance fed by phase-to-phase voltage. In some cases, or when absolute assurance is required, the heavy current rig is the only recourse but, even in this case, care must be taken that saturation of the various current limiting reactors or impedance changing transformers does not distort the current feeding the primary of the CT. This is particularly important in high impedance schemes where, for an internal fault, the CT is virtually unloaded and thus the impedance reflected into the primary, although extremely small, may still be significant if the heavy current machine is not carefully matched to the CT and the relay combination. It should also be appreciated that with a distorted waveshape the ammeter is unlikely to have the same relative response as the relay, so that the only true measurement is when the current is completely sinusoidal because relay and ammeter are both calibrated using sine-wave current.

In some critical relays, the harmonic content in the driving voltage can cause incorrect measurement and this must then be reduced by using inductance to provide a current source simulating the power system conditions more accurately than the more commonly used resistance current limiting.

Another common problem is the determination of direction of current. This is important in a relative sense for establishing the residual connection of CTs and in a fundamental sense, for setting up the operate direction of directional relays.

336

In a REF arrangement, using four CTs, each phase CT may be connected to give minimum spill current with the neutral CT as shown in
fig. 19.16 but with only three CTs the phasing-out must be done by
phase-to-phase primary injection as shown in fig. 19.17 and observat-
ion of the out-of-balance current obtained between each pair of CTs.
In each case, ammeters should be available as shown for the energised
CTs so that the CT ratios can be checked co-incidentally.

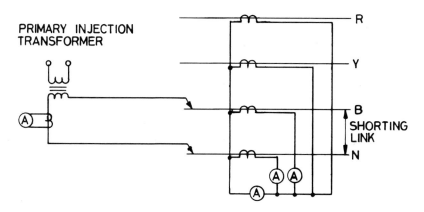

Figure 19.16 Ratio and directional tests with neutral CT

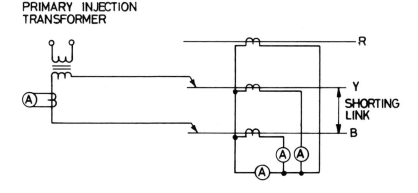

Figure 19.17 Ratio and directional tests without neutral CT

Because conventions are not universally standardised for windings,
it is not possible to be precise whether connecting start to start and
finish to finish will give a reversal of polarity or not. Thus the

direction of a directional element should be confirmed in relation to
an independent quantity. This quantity is generally load current, for
which the direction, in relation to the power system, is clearly known.
In some cases the load may have a low power factor and thus the phase
angle between load current and voltage at the relay terminals may not
be decisive in defining the direction. If the relay has a variable
characteristic angle, study of the vectors may allow direction to be
checked at a different relay angle before finally setting the relay
back to the setting required for fault current conditions.

Directional earth-fault relays are particularly difficult to check
for polarity because they are fed from residual voltage which gives a
reversal of the effective voltage signal which can be confusing.
Again, load current gives the best overall check on direction and a
red phase-to-earth fault is represented by disconnecting and short-
circuiting the yellow and blue CTs to provide only red load current as
a residual current to the relay, and disconnecting the red phase winding of the VT to represent the total collapse of the red phase voltage
which occurs due to a close-up red earth-fault. The red phase main
secondary winding should be short-circuited to provide the correct in-
fault loading on the directional element. This is in line with the
note in 'Additional requirements for directional relays' of
BS 142: 1966, page 57.

An important aspect in all testing is to take account of the heat
generated in a relay when subject to relatively long energisation
times at currents in excess of rating. Apart from the possibility of
damage to the relay by excessive heat, lower levels of heat could
affect the performance if the relay is susceptible to self-heating.

Finally, it is worthwhile considering the accuracy of basic test
equipment and simple cross-checks that can be done if some doubt exists
with results. With multi-range meters it is simple to change their
role or cross-check them against each other. Fundamental instrument
accuracy (which is related to full scale) can be of the same order as
relay accuracy, so that some thought is necessary in establishing the
true accuracy of settings even when supplies, wave-shape, temperature,
frequency are within reference conditions. British protective relays
are generally made to BS 142 which prescribes the reference conditions
for which the various aspects of relay performance shall be declared.

Chapter 20

Power Factor Correction and Tariffs

T. Longland, CEng, MIEE, AMEME
Chief Engineer
Johnson & Phillips (Capacitors) Ltd

Power capacitors have been employed in many and varied ways in industry over the past 40 years, but their increasing use is often limited by the apparent lack of practical information on their application. This chapter provides information and guidance on the selection, and use, of capacitors for power factor correction.

With increasing electricity charges, and the need to save energy, it is of paramount importance to both industrial and commercial users of electricity to ensure that their plant operates at maximum efficiency. This implies that the plant power factor must be at an economic level.

IMPORTANCE OF POWER FACTOR

Most a.c. electrical machines draw from the supply apparent power in terms of kilovolt amperes (kVA) which is in excess of the useful power, measured in kilowatts (kW), required by the machine. The ratio of these quantities is known as the power factor of the load, and is dependent upon the type of machine in use. Assuming a constant supply voltage this implies that more current is drawn from the electricity authority than is actually required.

$$\text{Power factor} = \frac{\text{true power}}{\text{apparent power}} = \frac{\text{kW}}{\text{kVA}}$$

A large proportion of the electrical machinery used in industry has an inherently low power factor, which means that the supply authorities have to generate much more current than is theoretically required. This excess current flows through generators, cables, and transformers in the same manner as the useful current. It is understood that these are resistive loads such as lighting and heating but these are generally outweighed by the motive power requirements.

If steps are not taken to improve the power factor of the load all the equipment from the power station to the factory sub-circuit wiring, has to be larger than necessary. This results in increased capital expenditure and higher transmission and distribution losses throughout the whole supply network.

To overcome this problem, and at the same time ensure that generators and cables are not overloaded with wattless current (as this excess current is termed), the supply authorities often offer reduced terms to consumers whose power factor is high, or impose penalties for those with low power factor.

THEORY OF POWER FACTOR CORRECTION

The kVA in an a.c. circuit can be resolved into two components, the in-phase component which supplies the useful power (kW), and the watt-less component (kvar) which does no useful work. The phasor sum of the two is the kVA drawn from the supply. The cosine of the phase angle ϕ_1 between the kVA and the kW components represents the power factor of the load.

The phasor diagram for this is shown in fig. 20.1. The load current is in phase with the kVA so that it lags the supply voltage by the same phase angle.

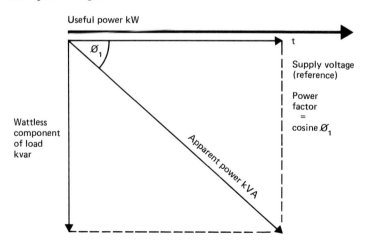

Figure 20.1   Phasor diagram of plant operating at a lagging power factor

To improve the power factor, equipment drawing kvar of approximately the same magnitude as the load kvar, but in phase opposition (leading) is connected in parallel with the load. The resultant kVA is now smaller and the new power factor, cosine ϕ_2 is increased. Thus any value of cosine ϕ_2 can be obtained by controlling the magnitude of the leading kvar added. This is shown in fig. 20.2.

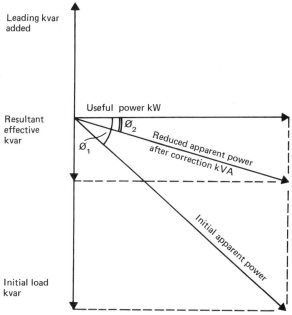

Figure 20.2   Power factor improvement by adding leading kvar to a lagging power factor load

POWER FACTOR IMPROVEMENT

In practice two types of equipment are available to produce leading kvar:

(a) Rotary equipment. Phase advancers, synchronous motors and synchronous condensers. Where auto-synchronous motors are employed the power factor correction may be a secondary function.

(b) Static equipment. Capacitors.

When installing equipment, the following points are normally considered; reliability of the equipment to be installed; probable life of such equipment; capital cost; maintenance cost; running costs and space required; and ease of installation.

341

Generally, the capital cost of rotating machinery, both synchronous and phase advancing, makes its use uneconomical, except where one is using rotating plant for a dual function-drive and power factor correction. In addition the wear and tear inherent in all rotary machines involves additional expense for upkeep and maintenance.

Capacitors have none of these disadvantages. Compared with other forms of correction, the initial cost is very low, upkeep costs are minimal and they can be used with the same high efficiency on all sizes of installation. They are compact, reliable, highly efficient, convenient to install and lend themselves to individual, group or automatic methods of correction. These facts, indicate that generally speaking, power factor correction by means of capacitors is the most satisfactory and economical method.

The static capacitor, owing to its low losses, simplicity and high efficiency, is now used almost universally for power factor correction.

ECONOMIC CONSIDERATIONS

When considering the economics of power factor correction it is important to remember that any plant used for this purpose does, in general, compensate for losses and lower the loadings on supply equipment such as cables, transformers, switchgear and generators.

The rating of the capacitor required to improve the power factor and the saving achieved depend largely on the electricity tariff. Charges can be related to kVAh, kvarh, or to md kVA, all of which can be reduced by installing power factor correction capacitors.

In the United Kingdom there are fourteen area electricity boards, all of which have a different tariff structure. Figure 20.3 shows how the country is divided up. Tariffs based on power factor are as follows:

(a) kVA maximum demand (kVA md) charge plus a unit charge dependent on this maximum demand. Each charge has a sliding tariff scale for the different ranges of kVA md, and number of units per kVA md respectively. Such tariffs are levied by the following area boards: Southern Electricity Board (SEB); Eastern Electricity Board (EEB); East Midlands Electricity Board (EMEB); Midlands Electricity Board (MEB): Yorkshire Electricity Board (YEB); and the South of Scotland Electricity Board (SSEB).

Figure 20.3 Electricity board areas in the United Kingdom

(b) kW maximum demand charge plus a unit charge dependent on this md, the demand charge being related to the power factor. Both charges have sliding scales. Such tariffs are further subdivided, into two types, depending upon the basis of the 'Demand charge'.

   (i) Demand charge increased according to the amount of average lagging power factor below a set base value. Such tariffs are found in the following area boards: North Western Electricity Board (NORWEB); South Western Electricity Board (SWEB); and North Eastern Electricity Board (NEEB).

   (ii) Demand charges varied according to the ratio of base power factor to the average power factor, or when the power factor is outside set limits. Such tariffs are found in the following area boards: South Eastern Electricity Board (SEEB); London Electricity Board (LEB); South Wales Electricity Board (SWAEB); Merseyside and North Wales Electricity Board (MANWEB); and North of Scotland Hydro-Electric Board (NSHEB).

Commercial tariffs also include penalty clauses for low power factor and the most economic power factor is assessed on the same basis as for industrial tariffs. Domestic tariffs are not affected because the power factor is of the order of unity.

Power factor correction should always be regarded as an investment with two opposing considerations. First, the expenditure incurred in the overheads charged against the capacitor installation, and, second, the income brought about by the saving in the cost of electricity, together with the reduction of losses in the electrical system. The main capacitor overheads are depreciation, interest on capital, electrical losses and maintenance costs. The last two items, in most cases, are covered by the savings on the losses in the electrical system.

The efficiency of a capacitor installation remains almost constant throughout the 10-12 year life of the capacitor. It is, therefore, usually estimated that an overhead allowance of approximately 8% to 10% of the installed cost of the equipment be used.

Where tariffs are based upon a standing charge per kVA, plus a charge for each unit (kWh) supplied, the most economical degree of correction is found when the final power factor is approximately 0.97/0.98. It is never economic to attempt to improve the power factor to unity, since the nearer the approach to unity the more is the kvar that must be installed for a given improvement. This can be seen from fig. 20.4.

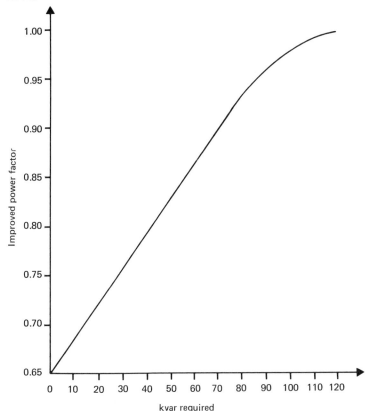

Figure 20.4   Graph showing how the kvar to be connected varies with the power factor to be achieved.   The curve is based on an initial load of 100 kW at a power factor of 0.65

In the average power factor tariff, where there is a bonus or penalty clause if the power factor is above, or below, some datum figure, the most economic power factor is the datum one.

Table 20.1 indicates how the most economic power factor depends on the type of tariff. The table has been confined to tariffs applied by the United Kingdom electricity boards.

Three worked examples of savings to be made are shown in table 20.2.

Table 20.1 The most economic power factor required by the various United Kingdom electricity boards

Electricity board	Maximum demand charge based on	Power factor should be improved to	Type of power factor penalised
Eastern	kVA	0.97/0.98	Maximum demand
East Midlands	kVA	0.97/0.98	Maximum demand
London	kW	0.90	Average
Merseyside and North Wales	kW	0.93	Maximum demand
Midlands	kVA	0.97/0.98	Maximum demand
North Eastern	kW	0.90	Average
North of Scotland Hydro	kW	0.90	Average
North Western	kW	0.90	Average
South Eastern	kW	0.85	Average
Southern	kVA	0.97/0.98	Maximum demand
South of Scotland	kVA	0.97/0.98	Average
South Wales	kW	0.95	Average
South Western	kW	0.90	Average
Yorkshire	kVA	0.97/0.98	Maximum demand

Table 20.2 Examples of savings to be made by power factor improvement

Example 1	£
Initial load conditions: 300 kVA, 0.67 power factor, 201 kW	
Tariff. Maximum demand charge each month based on:	
Each kVA of the first 200 kVA of maximum demand	0.86
Each kVA of the next 300 kVA of maximum demand	0.83
Total charges, before correction:	
200 kVA per month, at the above rate	172.00
100 kVA per month, at the above rate	83.00
Total charge, per month	255.00
Total charge, per annum	3060.00
Correction: 182 kvar of capacitors is required to improve the power factor to a level of 0.98, at an approximate cost of:	940.00
Improved load conditions: 205 kVA, 0.98 power factor, 201 kW	
New total charge per annum after correction	2113.80
Savings in electricity charges per annum	946.20
Note: Cost of the capacitors is recovered in 12 months.	

Example 2   £
Initial load conditions: 85 kVA, 0.60 power factor, 51 kW

Tariff. Maximum demand charge each month based on:

The first 10 kW of maximum demand	12.75
Each kW of the next 10 kW of maximum demand	1.27
F⁊ch kW of the remaining kW of maximum demand	1.17

In addition, if the power factor in the month is less 0.9 the
demand charge, for that month, is increased by 1% for each 1%
by which the power factor is below that figure

Total charges, before correction:

51 kW per month, at the above rate	61.72
Power factor penalty clause, 30% of the above	18.52
Total charge, per month	80.24
Total charge, per annum	962.88

Correction: 51 kvar improves the power factor to a level of
0.95, thus allowing for future load increased, at a cost of: 280.00

Improved load conditions: 53.6 kVA, 0.95 power factor, 51 kW

New total charge per annum, after correction   740.64

Savings in electricity charges per annum   222.24

Note: Cost of the capacitors recovered in 15 months.

Example 3
Initial load conditions: 517 kVA, 0.58 power factor, 300 kW

Tariff. Maximum demand charge each month based on:

Each kW of the first 200 kW of maximum demand	1.25
Each kW of the remaining kW of maximum demand	1.22

In addition, if the power factor is lagging, the kW of maximum
demand recorded is increased by dividing it by the average
lagging power factor and then multiplying the figure so
obtained by 0.95.

Total charges, before correction:

The chargeable kW of maximum demand is increased in line with
the power factor penalty clause, as follows:

$$\text{Chargeable demand} = \frac{300}{0.58} \times 0.95 = 490 \text{ kW}$$

490 kW per month, at the above rate	603.80
Charge per annum	7245.60

Correction: 330 kvar of capacitors is required to improve the
power factor to a level of 0.95, at an approximate cost of: 2010.00

Improved load conditions: 316 kVA, 0.95 power factor, 300 kW
New total charge:

$$\text{Chargeable demand} = \frac{300}{0.95} \times 0.95 = 300 \text{ kW}$$

Total charge per annum	4464.00
Savings in electricity charges per annum	2781.60

Note: Cost of the capacitors is recovered in 12 months.

CALCULATION OF CAPACITOR SIZE

There are a number of methods of calculating the capacitor size required. Figures 20.5 and 20.6 together with table 20.3 have been prepared with the object of providing speedy and simple methods of ascertaining if any benefit can be derived from improving the power factor of an industrial or commercial a.c. load.

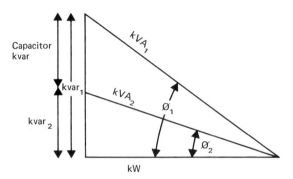

Initial conditions:

$$\text{Power factor} = \cos\phi_1 = \frac{kW}{kVA_1}$$

$$\tan\phi_1 = \frac{kvar_1}{kW}$$

$$kvar_1 = kW \times \tan\phi_1$$

Improved conditions:

$$\text{Power factor} = \cos\phi_2 = \frac{kW}{kVA_2}$$

$$\tan\phi_2 = \frac{kvar_2}{kW}$$

$$kvar_2 = kW \times \tan\phi_2$$

Capacitor kvar required to improve power factor from $\cos\phi_1$ to $\cos\phi_2$

$$= (kvar_1 - kvar_2)$$
$$= kW(\tan\phi_1 - \tan\phi_2)$$

This value of capacitor kvar can be determined either by drawing the vector diagram to scale, or by calculation using values from trigonometrical tables.

Figure 20.5 Reduction of kVA loading for constant kW loading by improvement of power factor

348

Instructions.   Place a rule to join the value of the initial power
factor (Column 1) to that of the improved power factor required
(Column 3) and read the multiplying factor at the point where the rule
intersects Column 2.

Example.   Given 100 kW load to be improved from 0.65 to 0.85 power
factor.   From chart:

       multiplying factor = 0.55
∴   capacitor (kvar)   = 100 kW × 0.55 = 55 kvar

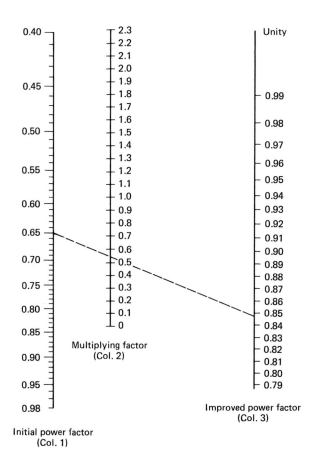

*Figure 20.6   Nomogram for determining size of capacitor for power
factor improvement*

Table 20.3 Table of factors for calculating size of capacitor for power factor improvement

Initial power factor	Factor for improving power factor to:								
	Unity	0.99	0.98	0.97	0.96	0.95	0.90	0.85	0.80
0.40	2.291	2.148	2.088	2.040	1.999	1.962	1.807	1.617	1.541
0.41	2.225	2.082	2.022	1.974	1.933	1.896	1.741	1.605	1.475
0.42	2.161	2.018	1.958	1.910	1.869	1.832	1.677	1.541	1.411
0.43	2.100	1.957	1.897	1.849	1.808	1.771	1.616	1.480	1.350
0.44	2.041	1.898	1.838	1.790	1.749	1.712	1.557	1.421	1.291
0.45	1.984	1.841	1.781	1.733	1.692	1.655	1.500	1.364	1.234
0.46	1.930	1.787	1.727	1.679	1.638	1.601	1.446	1.310	1.180
0.47	1.878	1.735	1.675	1.627	1.586	1.549	1.394	1.258	1.128
0.48	1.828	1.685	1.625	1.577	1.536	1.499	1.344	1.208	1.078
0.49	1.779	1.636	1.576	1.528	1.487	1.450	1.295	1.159	1.029
0.50	1.732	1.589	1.529	1.481	1.440	1.403	1.248	1.112	0.982
0.51	1.686	1.543	1.483	1.435	1.394	1.357	1.202	1.066	0.936
0.52	1.643	1.500	1.440	1.392	1.351	1.314	1.159	1.023	0.893
0.53	1.600	1.457	1.397	1.349	1.308	1.271	1.116	0.980	0.850
0.54	1.559	1.416	1.356	1.303	1.267	1.230	1.075	0.939	0.809
0.55	1.519	1.376	1.316	1.268	1.227	1.190	1.035	0.899	0.769
0.56	1.480	1.337	1.277	1.229	1.188	1.151	0.996	0.860	0.730
0.57	1.442	1.299	1.239	1.191	1.150	1.113	0.958	0.822	0.692
0.58	1.405	1.262	1.202	1.154	1.113	1.076	0.921	0.785	0.655
0.59	1.369	1.226	1.166	1.118	1.077	1.040	0.885	0.749	0.619
0.60	1.333	1.190	1.130	1.082	1.041	1.004	0.849	0.713	0.583
0.61	1.229	1.156	1.096	1.048	1.007	0.970	0.815	0.679	0.549
0.62	1.265	1.122	1.062	1.014	0.973	0.936	0.781	0.645	0.515
0.63	1.233	1.090	1.030	0.982	0.941	0.904	0.749	0.613	0.483
0.64	1.201	1.058	0.998	0.950	0.909	0.872	0.717	0.581	0.451

PF									
0.65	0.419	0.549	0.685	0.840	0.877	0.918	0.966	1.026	1.169
0.66	0.388	0.518	0.654	0.809	0.846	0.887	0.935	0.995	1.138
0.67	0.358	0.488	0.624	0.779	0.816	0.857	0.905	0.965	1.108
0.68	0.328	0.458	0.594	0.749	0.786	0.827	0.875	0.935	1.078
0.69	0.299	0.429	0.565	0.720	0.757	0.798	0.846	0.906	1.049
0.70	0.270	0.400	0.536	0.691	0.728	0.769	0.817	0.877	1.020
0.71	0.242	0.372	0.508	0.663	0.700	0.741	0.789	0.849	0.992
0.72	0.214	0.344	0.480	0.635	0.672	0.713	0.761	0.821	0.964
0.73	0.186	0.316	0.452	0.607	0.644	0.685	0.733	0.793	0.936
0.74	0.159	0.289	0.425	0.580	0.617	0.658	0.706	0.766	0.909
0.75	0.132	0.262	0.398	0.553	0.590	0.631	0.679	0.739	0.882
0.76	0.105	0.235	0.371	0.526	0.563	0.604	0.652	0.712	0.855
0.77	0.079	0.209	0.345	0.500	0.537	0.578	0.626	0.686	0.829
0.78	0.052	0.182	0.318	0.473	0.510	0.551	0.599	0.659	0.802
0.79	0.026	0.156	0.292	0.447	0.484	0.525	0.573	0.633	0.776
0.80	—	0.130	0.266	0.421	0.458	0.499	0.547	0.607	0.750
0.81	—	0.104	0.240	0.395	0.432	0.473	0.521	0.581	0.724
0.82	—	0.078	0.214	0.369	0.406	0.447	0.495	0.555	0.698
0.83	—	0.052	0.188	0.343	0.380	0.421	0.469	0.529	0.672
0.84	—	0.026	0.162	0.317	0.354	0.395	0.443	0.503	0.646
0.85	—	—	0.136	0.291	0.328	0.369	0.417	0.477	0.620
0.86	—	—	0.109	0.264	0.301	0.342	0.390	0.450	0.593
0.87	—	—	0.083	0.238	0.275	0.316	0.364	0.424	0.567
0.88	—	—	0.056	0.211	0.248	0.289	0.337	0.397	0.540
0.89	—	—	0.028	0.183	0.220	0.261	0.309	0.369	0.512
0.90	—	—	—	0.155	0.192	0.233	0.281	0.341	0.484
0.91	—	—	—	0.127	0.164	0.205	0.253	0.313	0.456
0.92	—	—	—	0.097	0.134	0.175	0.223	0.283	0.426
0.93	—	—	—	0.066	0.103	0.144	0.192	0.252	0.395
0.94	—	—	—	0.034	0.071	0.112	0.160	0.220	0.363

Table 20.3 (contd)

Initial power factor	Factor for improving power factor to:								
	Unity	0.99	0.98	0.97	0.96	0.95	0.90	0.85	0.80
0.95	0.329	0.186	0.126	0.078	0.037	–	–	–	–
0.96	0.292	0.149	0.089	0.041	–	–	–	–	–
0.97	0.251	0.108	0.048	–	–	–	–	–	–
0.98	0.203	0.060	–	–	–	–	–	–	–
0.99	0.143	–	–	–	–	–	–	–	–

This table gives values of $\tan\phi$ for various values of power factor, $\cos\phi$, and therefore provides a simple method of calculating values of kvar, and the size of capacitor required to improve the power factor.

Example: Given 100 kW load to be improved from 0.77 to 0.95 power factor. Factor from table is 0.5.

Capacitor (kvar) = load (kW) × factor to improve from existing to proposed power factor

= 100 × 0.5 = 50 kvar

PRACTICAL POWER FACTOR IMPROVEMENT

Figures 20.5 and 20.6 and table 20.3 enable the capacitor requirements
to be calculated knowing the initial power factor. In practice the
problem is to determine this initial power factor.

The type of tariff that a consumer is charged not only determines
the level of correction, but also the method by which the capacitor
size is determined.

Maximum demand tariffs

Under an md tariff the md value is recorded on an appropriate meter
which measures it either in kW or kVA. This meter usually measures
twice the largest number of kVA (or kW) of md supplied during any half
hour period, in any month.

With these tariffs, therefore, it is only necessary to ensure that
the capacitors are in circuit at the time the md is being reached, if
the prime function of the capacitor installation is to save money by
reduced md charges.

Average power factor tariffs

Average power factor tariffs incorporate a power factor penalty clause
based on the average power factor determined from the kWh and kVAh
recorded in any metering period.

With this type of tariff, therefore, it is necessary to reduce the
number of kvar hours recorded during the metering period. To do this
the capacitor must be in circuit whenever reactive units are being
recorded.

A refinement on this type of tariff, usually found on the contin-
ent, penalises all reactive units, be they leading or lagging. With
this type of tariff small steps of capacitors are required to ensure
that there is no reactive power recorded at any loading condition.

CAPACITOR SIZE RELATED TO TARIFF

A different calculation is necessary for ascertaining the correct
capacitor rating depending on the particular tariff applicable.

Maximum demand tariff

The first step is to obtain past md records over a period of several

years if possible. These normally indicate either md kVA, or md kVA
and kW. In large systems recorders as well as instruments and meters
are usually installed close to the point of metering, thus simplifying
the calculations. If the meter records indicate both kVA and kW it is
easy to obtain the md power factor from the relationship between kVA
and kW outlined earlier. If, however, the md records only indicate
kVA it is then necessary to estimate a power factor.

Prior to this, however, the md records should be studied to see if
there is any pattern to the demands, or if there is any marked variation in demand from month to month. If such a pattern, or variation,
is found the reason for it should be established.

If only the kVA demand is known the power factor has to be obtained
from site measurements. The kWh and kVAh meters are read at the
beginning, and end, of a known time period. The difference between the
readings at the start and end of the period enables the relevant kW,
kVA, and kvar components of the load during the test period to be calculated.

Ideally these tests should be performed at the same time as the md
occurs, although in practice this very rarely happens. It is necessary,
therefore, to determine what plant is in use at periods of md which was
not in use during the test period and make allowance for this in the
calculations.

Example.   A study of a consumer's electricity bill indicated an
average md of 288 kVA. A test carried out at the plant provided the
following load figures: 240 kVA, 168 kW, 0.7 power factor, 171 kvar.

It was noted, however, that at the time of the test there was 20 kW
of resistive load not in circuit, together with some 31 kW of fluorescent lighting. Both items could be in use at times of md. The md
power factor can be calculated as shown in table 20.4.

Utilising the tables already referred to it will be seen that to
improve the md power factor of 0.76 to an economic level of 0.97
requires 132 kvar of capacitor correction equipment.

Table 20.4   Calculations of md from known operating conditions

	kVA	kW	Power factor	kvar
Test load	240	168	0.7	171
Resistive load		20	1.0	0
Lighting load		31	0.9	15
Calculated maximum demand	288	219	0.76	186

Average power factor tariff

The following information is required to enable a capacitor size to be arrived at: md records; kWh consumed during the month; kvarh consumed during the month; and working hours of the plant during the month.

The example below shows how this information is used to calculate a capacitor size.

Example.   A consumer is charged on a tariff which imposes a penalty charge when the average lagging power factor falls below 0.9.   From a study of the electricity accounts, and a knowledge of the plant the following information was obtained: kWh consumed during the month 48000; kvarh used during the month 56000; average power factor (calculated from the above) 0.65; working hours 160 per month.

To improve the average lagging power factor from a level of 0.65 to an economic level of 0.90 some 33300 kvarh must be removed from circuit by means of capacitors.   Therefore

capacitor size required = 33300/160 = 206 kvar.

In practice this capacitor size would probably be increased by 5 or 10% to ensure that the average power factor was kept above 0.90. The capacitor size arrived at in the above example is the minimum possible size.   It does not necessarily follow that the installation of this capacitor would, in fact, give the required value of average power factor, as a number of other factors have to be considered.   If load variations occur so that the capacitor gives a leading power at times, then the full kvar rating of the capacitor is not available for the reduction of kvarh during these periods.   It will prevent, during such periods, the recording of any kvarh units, so that the difference between the reactive component of the uncorrected load and the capacitor kvar is lost.   This is based on the assumption that the kvarh

355

meters are fitted with devices to prevent 'unwinding' under leading
power factor conditions. It, therefore, follows that the actual capacity required must be increased over and above the minimum value to
allow for this.

During periods when the factory is not in production, kWh, and
kvarh, may still be recorded due to small items of plant that run continuously, or to transformer magnetising currents (this fact is
discussed later). It may, therefore, be necessary to provide for a
portion of the total capacity to be left in circuit during light load
periods. It is reasonable to assume that the supply authority will
object to the whole capacity being in circuit 24 hours a day.

DETERMINATION OF LOAD CONDITIONS
The first step in designing any practical power factor correction
scheme must be to obtain accurate details of the load conditions with
values of kW, kVA and power factor at light, average and full load,
together with type and details of the loads.

This may be achieved in one of the following ways: measurement of
kW and kvar; measurement of voltage, current and kW; measurement of
kVA and kvar; or use of a power factor indicating instrument, voltmeter
and ammeter.

Use of tariff metering
In many instances it is possible to use the supply authority's meter
to arrive at a plant loading condition. On the disc of the meter will
be found a small mark, usually a red or black band, which can be
watched. Count the number of revolutions of the disc for about one
minute, note the number of revolutions made, and the time in seconds
to make the revolutions, then:

$$X = 3600 \ N/R \cdot t$$

where X = instantaneous reading in kWh (kvarh)

     N = number of revolutions of the disc in t seconds

     t = time in seconds for N revolutions

     R = meter constant in revolutions per kWh (kvarh).

The meter constant is stamped on the rating plate of the meter and
is in revolutions per kWh or kvarh.

Where the meter constant is shown as units per revolution (U), then the formula becomes:

X = 3600 N•U/1000 t

The meter constant in this case is in either Wh or var per revolution.

It should be appreciated that the readings obtained by this method are instantaneous so that they should be taken when load conditions are normal.

METHODS OF CORRECTION

Each power factor correction scheme requires individual consideration and, as the successful operation of a scheme depends largely on the correct positioning of the capacitors in the network, the importance of studying all relevant factors is emphasised. The relevant factors are: tariff in force; metering point; details of light, average, and full load kVA, kW and power factor; position of motors, welding equipment, transformers or other large plant causing bad power factor; and supply system problems such as harmonics.

Capacitors themselves do not generate harmonics, but they can either reduce or increase them, depending upon particular circumstances. The major sources of harmonics are such things as thyristors, rectifiers and arc furnaces.

The siting of the capacitors, does, to some extent, depend on whether each piece of equipment, e.g. a motor, or a transformer, is being individually corrected or the plant as a whole, or part, is being corrected as a block (generally known as bulk or group correction). In the first case the capacitor and motor, or capacitor and transformer, are as close together as possible, in the second case the capacitor is located at some convenient point in the system, such as a substation.

On small installations individual correction can be applied to motors which are constantly in operation or, in the case of kVA md tariffs, on certain motors known to be in operation at the time of md. This method reduces the current loading on the distribution system with consequent improvement in voltage regulation, and generally speaking, is more economic. No additional switchgear is required as the

357

capacitor is connected directly to the piece of equipment it is corr-
ecting, and can, therefore, be switched with that piece of plant.

Where a capacitor is connected to a motor it is connected directly
across the motor terminals, and is switched with the motor starter,
resulting in complete automatic control. The balance of the correction
required, can then be connected to the main busbars of the supply
system, and controlled by a fuse-switch. It should be noted, however,
that some supply authorities stipulate the maximum amount of kvar which
may be switched in this manner.

Automatic switching of capacitors is recognised as an ideal method
of obtaining the full electrical and financial benefits from a capacitor installation, the resulting economics and convenience far
outweighing the initial cost. Optimum power factor is achieved under
all conditions and there is no possibility of the equipment being
inadvertently left out of commission. A bank of capacitors with the
required total capacitor kvar controlled in equal stages by a multi-
step relay and air break contactors connected to the main busbars is
used in many applications.

Large industrial sites involving different kinds of manufacturing
processes often require a combination of bulk and individual correction
to provide the most economic means of power factor correction.

In providing for power factor correction it should be remembered
that distribution boards and circuits can carry a greater useful load
if the capacitors are installed as near as possible to the source of
low power factor. For this reason either bulk or individual correction,
rather than correction at the intake point, can almost invariably be
justified.

Individual correction of motors

The practice of connecting a capacitor across the starter of an
induction motor, and switching the motor and capacitor as one unit, is
now universally established, and is to be recommended where there are
no objections on technical and economic grounds. One size of capacitor
gives an almost constant value of power factor over the normal load
range since variations in motor kvar are comparatively small.

Care should be taken in deciding the kvar rating of the capacitor
in relation to the magnetising kVA of the machine. If the rating is

too high damage may result to both motor and capacitor, because the motor, while still revolving after disconnection from the supply, may act as a generator by self-excitation and produce a voltage higher than the supply voltage. If the motor is switched on again before the speed has fallen to about 80% of the normal running speed, the high voltage will again be superimposed on the supply circuit and there may be a risk of damage to other types of equipment. As a general rule the correct size of capacitor for individual correction of a motor should have a kvar rating not exceeding 90% of the no-load magnetising kVA of the machine.

Connecting a capacitor direct to a motor results in a lower load current under all load conditions and, therefore, the overload settings on the starter must be reduced in order to obtain the same degree of protection.

Correction of individual motors is to be recommended where they are used for group drives, or where they are used continuously during maximum load conditions, but it should not be applied where the motors are used for haulage, cranes, colliery winders, or where 'inching' or 'plugging' and direct reversal takes place. Individual correction of tandem, or two-speed motors should be avoided. If correction of a two-speed machine is necessary the capacitor should never be connected directly to the low speed component but a contactor arrangement installed using one capacitor for both windings. Care should also be taken when offering capacitors for direct connection to motors whose braking system is intended to be operated by loss of voltage, as the voltage remaining across the capacitor, when the main supply is removed, may be such as to prevent operation of the braking system.

Where capacitors are connected direct to motors it is not usual to provide the capacitor with any protection or isolating gear other than that afforded by the control gear of the machine. Separate protection of the capacitor is usually only provided when the drive is of such importance that it is undesirable for a failure of the capacitor to put the motor out of service. For the individual correction of h.v. motors, hbc fuses should be placed in the circuit between the motor and the capacitor.

Where star-delta starting is used a standard three-terminal delta-connected capacitor should be employed, which gives maximum power factor correction at the start when the power factor of the motor is low. The capacitor is connected as shown in fig. 20.7.

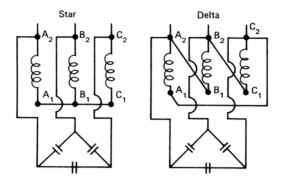

Figure 20.7 Use of a three-terminal capacitor with a motor fitted with a star-delta starter

Individual correction of transformers

In any electrical distribution system the one item of plant in circuit continuously is the transformer. It is often convenient, therefore, to connect a capacitor directly across the transformer terminals. The benefit of this to a consumer charged on an average power factor tariff is that the size of capacitor required to correct all the other plant can be reduced considerably. Where a tariff penalises lagging kVA, transformer correction is a necessity. If the site has numerous transformers, and a high diversity of l.v. load, improving the power factor of the transformers often dispenses with the need for a central automatically controlled bank of capacitors.

The size of capacitor to be connected to the transformer depends on its no-load kVA. As a general rule up to 10% of the transformer rating, in kVA, is acceptable for the capacitor rating, e.g. the maximum size of capacitor for use with a 1000 kVA transformer is 100 kvar.

Bulk power factor correction

It is sometimes impossible to connect capacitors in the desired location owing to high temperature, restricted space, or the presence of explosive gases. Alternatively, it may not be economic to correct individually each piece of electrical equipment because they are small items in terms of electrical load. For these reasons, or when an installation operates with a high diversity factor, bulk correction may be employed.

Capacitors used for bulk power factor correction may be controlled manually or automatically. The manual type of scheme utilises fuse-switches, circuit-breakers or other switching devices to control the capacitors.

Manually controlled capacitors are normally employed for factory loads which are too small to warrant splitting the total capacitance required, or where high diversity of motor load makes individual correction uneconomic. Manual control can only be justified technically for continuous process work where minimum switching is required and where there is sufficient reactive kVA available in the circuit continuously to warrant the capacitor being connected all the time.

In the United Kingdom manual control of capacitors is limited to capacitors less than 40 kvar.

Automatic power factor correction

In larger installations, automatic power factor correction is being increasingly recognised as the ideal method of obtaining the full electrical and financial benefits from a capacitor installation; the resulting economies and convenience far outweigh the initial cost. Optimum power factor is achieved under all conditions and there is no possibility of the equipment being inadvertently left out of commission.

The equipment normally consists of a capacitor bank sub-divided into a number of equal steps, each step being controlled by a contactor. The contactors, in turn, are controlled by a relay responding to reactive kVA, of which there are several reliable makes available. The relay consists of a voltage coil connected across two phases of the load supply system, and the current coil, normally rated at 5 A, connected, through a current transformer, to the remaining phase.

The number of stages installed is usually a compromise between the technical requirements and cost. The aim of the automatic system is to have each contactor switching its maximum rated capacitance and, at the same time, have the capacitor bank divided into the most economic sub-sections, so that all meaningful variations in load can be corrected.

LOCATION OF CAPACITORS

Mention has, so far, only been made of the point of connection of the capacitor to the system to achieve the required, corrected power factor. In addition care must be taken as to the physical location of the capacitor to avoid problems that could lead to malfunction of the equipment.

Since the maximum working temperature of capacitors is lower than that of other electrical equipment any conditions which give rise to unacceptable overloads must be avoided. This, therefore, stipulates ambient temperature, maximum voltage and overload current.

Care should be taken in choosing a site for the capacitor to minimise the ambient temperature. If the site is outdoors, the direct rays of the sun should be avoided, especially in tropical climates. Rooms housing capacitor assemblies must be adequately ventilated.

If there are harmonic producers on site, such as thyristor-controlled machines, then the capacitors need to be located well away from the source of such harmonics, or designed to cope with any overloads produced in the capacitor by harmonic currents or voltages.

Because the ambient temperature is an important consideration in the life of any capacitor installation it is important that it is correctly specified by the purchaser to the supplier. Three temperature categories are available, as will be seen from table 20.5. This table is taken from BS 1650: 1971 'Capacitors for connection to power frequency systems'.

Table 20.5 Limits of ambient temperature for capacitor installations

Temperature category	Maximum permissible ambient temperatures (°C)		
	mean over 1 hour	mean over 24 hours	mean over 1 year
Temperate	40	30	20
Tropical	45	40	30
Super-tropical	50	45	35

Capacitors can be supplied for either indoor or outdoor use. It should be appreciated, however, that whilst an outdoor capacitor can be installed indoors, the reverse is not true.

362

INSTALLATION OF CAPACITORS

Installation and maintenance of capacitors should be carried out generally as specified in British Standard Code of Practice CP 321 102: 1950, 'Installation and maintenance of electrical machines, transformers, rectifiers, capacitors and associated equipment', and BS 1650: 1971.

The cable supplying either an automatic capacitor bank, or a permanently connected capacitor should be fitted with some form of protection such as hbc fuses for capacitors up to 660 V, and thermal overloads and earth-fault protection for capacitors up to 11 kV and a means of isolating both capacitor and supply cable.

In selecting suitable switchgear, or fusegear, for capacitor duty it must be appreciated that the duty imposed on such equipment is more onerous then when used with other equipment of equivalent kVA loadings.

The reasons for this can be summarised as follows:

(a) At the instant of switching a large transient current flows.
(b) High overvoltage transients can occur when capacitors are disconnected by switching devices which allow restriking of the arc.
(c) The switchgear has to carry continuously the full rated current of the capacitor whenever it is in circuit, i.e. there is no allowance for diversity.
(d) At light loads, when the voltage may be higher than normal, the capacitor current is increased.
(e) If harmonics are present in the supply voltage the capacitor current is increased.

In view of these factors the following limitations are imposed on the capacitor by the manufacturer:

(a) The capacitor must be suitable for operation under abnormal conditions to an overvoltage of 1.1 times rated voltage.
(b) The capacitor must be suitable for continuous operation with a current of 1.3 times normal current.

In addition to these factors the capacitor manufacturer is permitted a manufacturing tolerance on output of -0 + 10%.

In view of these conditions it is normal practice to derate switchgear and fuses used with capacitors. Tables 20.6 and 20.7 give recommended hbc fuse and switch sizes, together with cable sizes for

low voltage capacitor applications. For systems not covered by the
tables the advice of the capacitor manufacturer should be sought.
This is specially important in the case of capacitors used above 660 V
where large derating factors are required. At voltages of 3.3 kV and
11 kV it is not unusual to find fuses rated at three or four times
capacitor current. With such large fuses it becomes important to
ensure that the energy required for current operation of the fuse is
considerably less than the energy required to cause the capacitor tank
to burst. It is also important to ensure that there is adequate discrimination between fuses used for capacitor protection and fuses
further back in the system.

*Table 20.6   Recommended sizes of fuses and cables
for use with capacitors*

Nominal capacitor current (A)	HBC fuse rating (A)	Copper conductors	
		PVC armoured three-core (mm^2)	PVC non-armoured single core (mm^2)
19.5	32	10	2.5
33	50	16	6
40	63	25	10
67	100	50	25
100	160	70	50
139	200	120	70
208	300	240	150
278	400	300	240
347	500	2 × 150	300
417	600	2 × 240	400
556	800	2 × 300	630

Note - The table assumes an ambient of 30°C with
cables clipped to a surface and unenclosed.

In addition to precautions when connecting the capacitor bank it
is also necessary, in the case of automatic equipment, to supply a
current and voltage signal to the reactive relay.

In the past reactive sensing relays were supplied as separate items
and it was, therefore, necessary to provide both voltage and current
signals. Modern practice, however, is to mount the relay within the
automatic capacitor bank, thus only a current signal has to be provided.
This is normally obtained by means of a current transformer having a

5 A secondary current. It is important, however, to ensure that the
CT monitors the total load, including the capacitors, if the equipment
is to work correctly. It is also important to note that there has to
be a phase displacement between voltage and current signals to the
relay.

*Table 20.7 Recommended fuse-switch ratings for use with capacitors
at various voltages*

Fuse switch rating (A)	Nominal capacitor ratings (A)	Nominal capacitor kvar ratings at various voltages (V)				
		380	400	415	440	500
30	19.5	13	13.5	14	15	17
60	33	21.5	23	24	25	28.5
60	40	26	27.5	28.5	30	34.5
100	67	43	46	48	50	57
200	100	65	69	72	76	86
200	139	91	96	100	105	120
300	208	136	144	150	157	180
400	278	182	192	200	210	240
600	347	227	240	250	262	300
600	417	273	288	300	315	360
800	556	364	384	400	420	480
1000	695	455	480	500	525	600

After completing a capacitor installation the insulation resistance should be tested. This is done by shorting together all the
capacitor terminals and applying a voltage between terminals and container. The value of this voltage, which must be maintained for 10
seconds is given in table 20.8 which is taken from BS 1650: 1971.

*Table 20.8 Routine test voltages between
capacitor terminals and
container*

Rated insulation level (kV rms)	Test voltage (kV rms)
0.6	3
1.2	6
2.4	11
3.6	16
7.2	22
12	28

It is important to note that such a test cannot be made between capacitor terminals as this will only result in the capacitor being charged and not give an indication of insulation resistance.

CAPACITOR MAINTENANCE

Capacitors, being static apparatus, do not need the same attention as rotating machinery, but, nevertheless, require regular maintenance. Normally a power factor correction capacitor should be inspected at least every twelve months and preferably every six months. The time interval between inspections is, however, governed mainly by the conditions on site. Where capacitors are installed in a humid atmosphere, or are subjected to chemical fumes, or exposed to dirt and dust, more frequent attention should be given.

Before any examination always ensure that the capacitor has been disconnected from the supply, and then wait for at least one minute (capacitors up to 660 V) or five minutes (capacitors operative at voltages higher than 660 V) and then ensure discharge is complete by measuring the voltage between terminals. Finally, short all terminals together before testing. Shorting the terminals to earth is not effective for adequate discharge.

The following points should be observed when carrying out any capacitor maintenance.

Physical examination
(a) Examine externally that there is no damage or leakage of impregnant.
(b) Check that all cables are securely fixed and that all earth bonds are tight.
(c) Measure, if possible, the running temperature of the capacitor.

Testing
(a) Examine all insulators for signs of tracking, clean terminals and check for tightness.
(b) Ensure that discharge resistors, where fitted, are in order.
(c) Check all connections for tightness.
(d) Measure insulation resistance of the terminals to case.
(e) If a capacitance bridge is available measure the capacitance prior to energising. If such a device is not available the capacitor

should be energised and the line current measured by means of a 'clip-on' ammeter. The current measured should be compared with the current obtained from the following equation.

$$I = kVA/\sqrt{3}\ V$$

where V is line-to-line voltage.

In considering the question of maintenance it is important to know that most capacitors lose output during the course of their life. Some capacitors fail completely after a number of years of operation. The failure mode of most capacitors is a gradual loss of output without any noticeable signs of defect. Some capacitors, however, especially of the bulk oil filled variety, can fail with disastrous consequences.

Many capacitors, manufactured between the early 1950s and the late 1970s, are filled with a liquid whose chemical name is polychlorinated biphenyl generally called askarel. It has a variety of trade names, such as, Aroclor, Biclor, Pyraclor, etc. The use and disposal of this fluid is covered by stringent regulations, including the 'Disposal of Poisonous Wastes Act'.

It is important, therefore, both from an economic point of view, and in order to comply with the Health and Safety at Work Act, that capacitor installations are checked periodically.

Index